Seattle Audubon  ...ue Series

A Field Guide to the Common
Wetland Plants of
Western Washington
& Northwestern Oregon

Sarah Spear Cooke, Editor

Seattle Audubon Society
Washington Native Plant Society

A Field Guide to the Common Wetland Plants
of Western Washington and Northwestern Oregon
Copyright © 1997

ISBN 0-914516-11-6

Published by Seattle Audubon Society
Graphic Design by Nancy Pascoe, Sarah Spear Cooke and Mary-Ellen Voss.
Illustrations by Jeanne R. Janish by permission of University of Washington Press
Printed in Hong Kong by Mantec Production Company

Sponsored by:
U.S. Environmental Protection Agency
Washington Native Plant Society
Seattle Audubon Society

To obtain additional copies of this book call or write:
Seattle Audubon Society   (206) 523-4483
8028 35th Avenue NE
Seattle, Washington, 98115

First Printing
May 1997

Acknowledgements

The wetland flora project began in 1991 as a result of the desperate need for a wetland-specific flora that was less technical than Hitchcock's *Flora of the Pacific Northwest,* but was none-the-less as accurate and technically complete, and emphasized the field characteristics. More than 55 people have volunteered their time and energy on the project since that time. Many of those who have helped cannot be formally acknowledged here. Thanks also go to the Seattle Audubon Society and the Washington Native Plant Society for their support.

My thanks to all the authors who wrote the original species treatments for the book. My additional thanks for the cooperation of each author in the editing process. The diversity of writing styles made achieving consistency difficult without considerable editing and the cooperation of the authors. Joe Arnett, Ron Vanbianchi and Tom Dubendorfer reviewed the final manuscript and helped with the index. Many thanks to all the photographers for the use of their photographs in this publication.

Funding for the project has been limited to a starter grant from the U. S. Environmental Protection Agency (EPA), some editing funds from the Washington Native Plant Society, and printing costs from Seattle Audubon Society. Many people have donated their time and others worked for a very small stipend. The project has mostly proceeded through the generosity, sheer determination, and the love of the wetland flora on the part of many people.

There are four people without whom this book would not have been a reality. First is Dr. Fred Weinmann, the initiator of the project and the grant administrator for the EPA. Fred was also a contributing author, photographer, and reviewed the book. Second is Nancy Pascoe who has stuck it out from the very beginning despite more delays than anyone could have imagined. She is responsible for the clean and attractive format, and the consistency of information and format throughout the book (despite so many authors). Susan Libonati-Barnes and Joe Arnette reviewed the book as a whole and helped clean it up when the rest of us could no longer see errors. Mary-Ellen Voss is responsible for taking the book the last step and making it worthy to be a member of the Audubon Trailside Series.

Many thanks to all involved!

Sarah Spear Cooke, Editor and Senior Author
Seattle, June 1997

Authors

Cyd Brower	Richard Robohm
Ken Brunner	Kathleen Sayce
Marty Chaney	Dyanne Sheldon
Catherine Conolly	Priscilla Stanford
Sarah Spear Cooke	Scot Sundberg
Scott Claypoole	Jon Titus
Tom Dubendorfer	Sharon Walton
Mary Fries	Fred Weinmann
Scott Moore	Stacey Wenger
Laura Potash	Ron Vanbianchi
Sharon Rodman	Peter Zika

Editors

Sarah Spear Cooke, Editor
Nancy Pascoe, Copyeditor
Susan Libonati-Barnes, Assistant Copyeditor
Joe Arnette, Technical Proofreader

Editorial Board

Clayton Antieau	John Malek
Joe Arnett	Ken Pritchard
Ken Brunner	Priscilla Stanford
John Christy	Scot Sundberg
Catherine Conolly	John Titus
Tom Dubendorfer	Ron Vanbianchi
Kittie Ford	Fred Weinmann
Bob Frenkel	

Layout/ Graphics

Nancy Pascoe
Sarah Spear Cooke
Mary-Ellen Voss
Rick Pratt

Photography

Clayton Antieau	Ken Pritchard
Marc Boule	Ruth Schaefer
Sarah Spear Cooke	Dyanne Sheldon
Kittie Ford	Fred Weinmann
Frederick Huston	Jim Wiggins
Kathy Kunz	Vic Yoshino
Alisa Pearson	

Contents

Publishers Preface

The mission of the Seattle Audubon Society (S.A.S.) is to assist its members and the public in the enjoyment and preservation of the birds, plants and animals of the Pacific Northwest and the natural environment in which they occur. Preserving and restoring marshes, bogs, and other wetlands are at the core of this mission, as wetlands shelter and feed much of our wildlife. Healthy wetlands are critical to the functioning of the different ecosystems within our region. Wetlands help mitigate shoreline erosion, store flood waters and protect property, filter sediments, nutrients, and toxic chemicals. They also provide us with unique open space and recreational opportunities.

Beginning in 1991, Seattle Audubon Society's Washington Wetlands network, WETNET, now includes over one thousand individuals and over 350 organizations. It has trained and provided technical assistance to many citizens and policy-makers in eight Puget Sound counties.

The S.A.S. Trailside Series of guides has been in existence for over twenty years. Important features of these guides are the clearly laid-out text, keys, maps, and good quality color or black and white illustrations. They are intended for use by schools, colleges, wildlife biologists, and consultants, as well as the general public.

This plant guide is the product of some years of disciplined effort by Sarah Spear Cooke, and our Society owes her a great debt. We should also like to thank the many members of the Washington Native Plant Society and our own society for donating their valuable time. This important work has been has been financed entirely by funds provided by S.A.S and the Environmental Protection Agency. It would not have been published without the long-term support of Dr. Fred Weinmann of that agency and we thank him. The high quality work of Nancy Pascoe and Mary-Ellen Voss is also appreciated.

David Hutchinson
Publications Chair
Seattle Audubon Society (A Washington Non-Profit Corporation)

Guides available in The Trailside Series:
Amphibians of Washington and Oregon
Birding in Seattle and King County
Mammals of the Northwest
Reptiles of Washington and Oregon
Field Guide to the Common Wetland Plant Species of Western Washington
and Northwestern Oregon

Forthcoming Titles in The Trailside Series:
Butterflies of Cascadia

Introduction

The Pacific Northwest is home to many wetlands that were created by both glaciers and a wet climate. As a result, there are many plants common to this area that are wetland-adapted, or wetland-associated. This field guide has been written to help the interested public identify plants that are associated with lowland wetland habitats, both freshwater and coastal, in the Puget Basin in western Washington from the Pacific Ocean to the foothills (800 meters in elevation) of the Cascade Mountains, through to the Willamette Valley in Oregon. Many of the species discussed in this guide also extend into British Columbia, Alaska, and Southern Oregon, as well as eastern Washington, eastern Oregon, and Idaho. Occurrences and community associations, as well as functional value and ethnobotanical uses of more than 325 of the most common wetland and wetland-associated species are included here. Native, naturalized, and exotic invasive species are discussed. Trees, shrubs, herbs, sedges, rushes, grasses, ferns, and horsetails are covered, but mosses have been omitted in this edition.

In order for this guide to be useful for the general public, technical terminology has been kept to a minimum, only to the extent that the accuracy or utility of the book is not put at risk. However, it is necessary when discussing certain groups such as the willows, grasses, sedges, rushes, and ferns to include some technical terms. A picture glossary has been included at the end of this guide for reference. Characteristics easily identified in the field that are clearly visible either with the naked eye or with a hand lens are emphasized.

Wetlands can take on many sizes, shapes, and characteristics. They can include lakes, rivers and streams, all of which are bounded by dry land. Not all wetlands are obvious however, and it is often difficult to determine where the wetland ends and the dry land begins. The wetland boundary is defined by the soils, plants, and presence of surface water or saturated soil.

A detailed wetland classification system has been developed by the United States Fish and Wildlife Service (FWS). The FWS classification system is used in this guide to describe wetland habitats where various species are likely to occur. The wetland types found in western Pacific Northwest are as follows:

- Forested
- Scrub-shrub
- Emergent
- Aquatic bed
- Open water

Open water systems have very little associated vegetation and so are not wetland types for the purposes of this guide. All these wetland types are found in fresh water systems and emergent wetland types are found in estuarine (coastal saltwater-influenced) systems.

Geology, Age of the Region, Soils, and Climate

The Olympic Peninsula to the Pacific Coast, and Coast Ranges of Washington and Oregon form the western boundary of the region, and the Cascade Mountains the eastern boundary. The trough between these ranges forms the Puget Basin. Much of the Puget Basin in Washington was glaciated during the last ice sheet advance 10,000 to 15,000 years ago. Thick glacial deposits extend from the northern extent of the Puget Basin in the San Juan Islands down to Thurston County. Very porous gravels, sands, and some hard till (including clay and silt) are common in the basin causing extensive wetland pockets. The soils in the northern Puget Basin are formed in glacial deposits under conifer forests. The soils south of the glacial deposits are highly weathered and dominated by basalt flows and breccia with a small amount of non-marine sedimentary rock. Sandstones and mudstones dominate from southern Washington through Oregon's Coast Ranges, with occasional basaltic headlands. The Cascade Mountains from

Steven's Pass south to Oregon are dominated by volcanic deposits, some of which are recent. The soils of the foothills which are derived from these deposits are richer in nutrients than those which have developed from the glacial material. The wetlands in the glaciated areas are therefore younger than some found south of Thurston County.

A subtropical high pressure system located between Hawaii and the west coast of North America creates clear weather along the west coast of our area during most of the summer. A high pressure system moves southward during the winter causing heavy rains in the coastal lowlands and snow higher in the Cascade Mountains. The Cascades act as a barrier keeping the moist maritime air from reaching eastern Washington and Oregon. These mild, rainy fall-winter-spring seasons and warm summers created the large tracks of coniferous forest that dominated the Puget Basin before Europeans came into the area.

Overall Format

This guide is divided into chapters for trees, shrubs, herbs, rushes, sedges, grasses, and ferns and horsetails. Each new chapter is marked with the group name at the page margin so that different sections are easily located. The genera and species are arranged alphabetically within each group. Color plates are located at the end of each chapter. Genera with many species represented are introduced with an explanation of the characteristics and terminology of the group, as well as a taxonomic key. The groups which fall into this category include: willows, rushes, *Carex* sedges, *Scirpus* sedges, grasses, ferns, and horsetails.

Page Format of the Species Descriptions

Plant names
The species proper scientific name, synonyms, and misapplied scientific names are listed at the top of the page. Common names are listed below. The plant family and plant wetland indicator status is located beneath the names.

The scientific name consists of two words, the first indicating the genus and the second, the species. More than one name is often listed in the proper category. The first name is the most correct name for the species according to Kartesz (1993) and Hickman (1993). The second name comes from Reed et al. (1993), and Reed, P. (1988). The third name (if there is one) comes from Hitchcock, C., and Cronquist A. (1973). Some of the species are represented by either, or both, native and non-native varieties.

If there are multiple varieties and only one is named in the book, then the variety that is common is included. If there are multiple varieties and more than one is common, then no varieties are mentioned. For most purposes, it is only important to mention the species name when discussing the plant.

Family names are listed for each species for those botanists who know plant taxonomy based on family characteristics.

Plant Indicator Status
The wetland indicator status is included in each species description for those users who need information salient to delineating wetlands. Common to all wetland identification methods is an assessment of three parameters: soils, vegetation, and hydrology. With respect to vegetation, wetland delineation methods require consideration of whether an area is dominated by plants that are hydrophytes. In general, hydrophytes are those species of plants which are adapted for growth, either physiologically, morphologi-

cally, or reproductively, in water or soils which are at least periodically deficient in oxygen as a result of high water content.

The US Fish and Wildlife Service, in cooperation with other United States federal agencies, has published a list of hydrophytes for various regions of the United States, to assist in determining which plants are officially considered wetland-adapted species. These lists categorize plant species based on their estimated fidelity to wetland environments. The following categories are used.

Code	Designation	Wetlands Probability*
OBL	Obligate wetland species	>99
FACW	Facultative wet wetland species	67 to 99
FAC	Facultative wetland species	34 to 66
FACU	Facultative upland species	1 to 33
UPL	Obligate upland species	<1
NI	No indicator status	

*percent occurrence of plant in a wetland

Species indicator status included here in caps are from the following publications: *National List of Plant Species that Occur in Wetlands:NW Region 9* Reed (1988); and *Addendum to the National List of Plant Species that Occur in Wetlands: Northwest (Region 9)* Reed (1993). Where no indicator status has been published, an indicator status, marked in lower case letters, has been included based on local field experience.

The indicator status is determined from a consensus of input from plant ecologists, based on their field experience. It is not the result of quantitative sampling of individual species. The wetland indicator status should not be equated to the degree of wetness – many obligate wetland species occur in permanently or semi-permanently flooded wetlands, but a number of obligates also occur in wetlands which are flooded during only a small portion of the year. Also, the wetland indicator status is intended to reflect a plant's occurrence in wetlands across the entire region and may not reflect occurrence on a sub-regional basis.

It should be understood that a plant's presence in a wetland is mostly dependent on the water regime of the wetland. The water regime is defined by the depth, frequency, and duration of inundation or soil saturation (which can vary enormously on a daily, seasonal, and annual basis).

Species Description

Species are described individually or a few similar species of the same genus may be discussed together. The first paragraph gives a broad description of a species or genus, with the most distinctive features listed below in bulleted format. For all species of a particular group the same characteristics are covered in the bullets so that comparisons can be made quickly. For the most part, descriptions follow those found in the *Vascular Plants of the Pacific Northwest* (Hitchcock et al. 1969) with much additional information contributed from *The Jepson Manual* (Hickman 1993) and *Plants of the Pacific Northwest Coast* (Pojar and Mackinnon 1994). Field characteristics not necessarily mentioned in these texts were also generated after examination of herbarium specimens and from personal observations made by field biologists.

Characteristics emphasized are: root type (tap root vs. branched root; presence of rhizomes (below ground runners) or stolons (above ground runners); height of the plant; stem characters (round, square, stipules, thorns); leaf arrangement (opposite, alternate, whorled); leaf shape (lance-shaped, elliptical, oblong); leaf length and width; hairs or waxy coatings on the leaves; inflorescence (flowering stalk) type, size; flower characters (number of petals, petal color, sepal characters, ovary position, number of stamens); and fruit and seed characteristics. Winter identification characteristics of bark, twigs, and buds are included for all woody species.

Illustrations
Species illustrations were provided with the permission of the University of Washington Press. They originate from Jeanne R. Janish's work in the five volume set of *Vascular Plants of the Pacific Northwest* (C.L. Hitchcock, A. Cronquist, M. Ownbey, and J. W. Thompson. 1969. University of Washington Press).

Habitat Description
The habitat preferences of the each species is described. This information generally comes from field experience and Hitchcock et al. (1969). The water regime preference and sun or shade tolerance of the species is described. If the species occurs at higher elevations, this is indicated. Commonly associated plants are listed if they are important.

Range
The range of the plant, apart from its presence in specific counties in the area covered by this guide, is also discussed. A shaded distribution map is included to show where the plant is found. If the plant is found in all counties covered in the book, a map is not included but the last line in the range section says "found in all counties in our area."

Similar Species
Any species that appear similar to the species being described, or are commonly confused for that species, are described in the "Similar Species" section. Characteristics that differentiate the two species are identified and described. Characters are both vegetative (leaves, presence of hairs or waxy coatings on leaves and stems, color, size, presence of rhizomes and stolons, etc.) and reproductive (flower color, size, petal shape and numbers, capsule shape and size, seed characters, etc.).

This section includes a few species that are not covered elsewhere in the book. These species are not included because they are either not common in the region, or are ordinarily exclusively upland species. Similar species may be in the same genus, in other genera, or sometimes, in other families.

Functional Value
Characteristic attributes of a wetland, including vegetation (species composition and canopy structure), water (hydrology and water quality), soils (nutrient regime and organic content), and wildlife, are functionally interconnected. For example, wetland vegetation is integral in supporting food chains, creating habitats for a variety of animal species, removing sediments and toxic compounds from stormwater, stabilizing river and stream banks and generally providing erosion control. Most of the plants discussed in this manual provide these functions to varying degrees and are therefore useful for wetland and buffer restoration, creation, and enhancement. Species that are particularly useful for certain functions are identified.

Ethnobotanical Information
An ethnobotanical section has been added to the book to describe human uses of each species for: shelter, basketry, food, medicine, horticulture, agriculture, and any other use that may be known. CAUTION should be taken when considering the edibility or use of the plant for medicinal purposes. Similar-looking plants may not be edible, and may in fact be poisonous. There is a potential for allergic reactions with any of the species when they are used for food or medicine, or used as a mashed topical poultice. Any plant may aggravate hay fever, cause dermatitis, or affect humans in some way. When several species of the same genus have been combined, similar species and ethnobotanical information is discussed at the end of that genus.

Wetland Type Descriptions

General habitat information is displayed as an icon. These different habitats types are displayed below with a brief description.

Forested wetlands contain woody vegetation that is over 6 meters (m) tall (such as alder, cedar, hemlock, black cottonwood, and some species of willows, etc.) and covers at least 30 percent of the area. In mature forested systems the deciduous trees are more than 60 years old, and coniferous trees are more than 80 years old.

Scrub-shrub wetlands contain woody vegetation that is less than 6 m tall (such as most willows, hardhack spirea, dogwood, salmonberry, etc.) and covers at least 30 percent of the area. The woody plants can be either true shrubs or small trees.

Emergent wetlands contain non woody vegetation (such as cattails, grasses, sedges, rushes, and herbs etc.) cover at least 30 percent of the area. Emergent wetlands can have deep water (60 cm), or shallow water that may even drain such that the soils are only moist during the latter part of the growing season.

Aquatic bed wetlands consist of any area of open water that contains rooted aquatic plants (such as water lilies, pond weed, etc.) Aquatic vegetation does not have to reach the water surface. The leaves can either be floating or submerged.

Distribution Maps

The distribution of species has been carefully researched by examining the previously described distributions of Hitchcock, and modifying those by examining herbarium material at the University of Washington in Seattle and the University of Oregon in Corvalis. Additionally, some personal observations from field biologists have been added if available and verifiable.

The area covered by the book is shown on the map. When a species is found in a county, the entire county is shaded although it should be noted that the plant may only be found in a limited portion of that county. Plants may also be found in areas not reported here. The editor requests that new sightings that expand on the distributions described here be reported so that subsequent printings can reflect the more current information.

Index

The index includes all family names, current scientific names (and alternatives), common names (and alternatives) in a single alphabetical listing.

Measurements

All measurements are given in metric units. A metric scale is given on the inside back cover of the book.

10 mm (millimeter) = 1 cm (centimeter)
1 cm = 0.394 inches
10 cm = 3.94 inches
1 m (meter) = 100 cm = 39.4 inches or slightly longer than 1 yard

Identification of Plants with Taxonomic Keys

A taxonomic key is a tool for identifying plants. The keys in this guide are either in tabular form, where specific characteristics are listed for many species and comparisons can be made visually; or written as a series of paired, mutually exclusive statements which divide the available species into smaller subsets until all possibilities but one have been dismissed. The keys in this guide are for either selecting both the genus and species (grasses, ferns), or separating individual species (sedges, rushes, willows).

An attempt has been made to accentuate the most obvious characteristics for the keys; most of which relate to the physical appearance of the plant, but a few concern species distribution (estuarine vs. fresh water). The keys only include the species covered in the guide and will be of little use if the species being considered is not included. If identification accuracy is important, final verifications of species identifications should be done by comparing a specimen with a plant that has been identified by a qualified botanist. Herbariums are the repository of voucher plant specimens that are accurately identified. Herbariums are found at the major universities in Washington, Oregon, and British Columbia. These facilities are usually open to the public.

References

The first Pacific Northwest wetland flora entitled *Wetland Plants of the Pacific Northwest* (Fred Weinmann, et al., 1984) was published by the Army Corps of Engineers and is no longer available. This valuable guide and teaching tool included only a small number of the wetland species found in the Puget Basin and was mostly estuarine-oriented. There are two books currently available that include information on a limited number of Puget Basin wetland species. Guard's book (1995) *Wetland Plants of Washington and Oregon* discusses the flora of the Willamette Valley in Oregon, with about a third of the species also found in Washington and northern Oregon. Pojar and Mackinnon's book (1994) *Plants of the Pacific Northwest Coast* emphasizes upland species and is oriented more towards British Columbia, but does include many common wetland plants found in Washington and Oregon. Most of the species covered in this guide are found in Hitchcock and Cronquist's book (1973) *Flora of the Pacific Northwest*. This plant guide is highly technical in nature and includes upland species; the wetland plants are a small portion of the manual. A complete reference list is located on page 387.

Acer macrophyllum
big-leaf maple
Family: Aceraceae
Status: FACU
Color photos page 14

Big-leaf maple is a common deciduous tree in our area. It can reach 30 m and the crown may be as wide as it is tall. This species has single or multiple stems. Twigs are stout, round, smooth, and red-brown to brown-green during the first season, turning dark red during winter. Leaf buds are terminal and large. The large leaves are borne on stalks 25-30 cm long. The inflorescence is a thick, drooping raceme, 10-15 cm long. Each raceme bears 10-50 flowers some of which are male and some of which have both male and female organs. Blooms March to June.

- bark brownish or grayish, deeply furrowed into narrow, vertical ridges in older specimens, often thickly covered with moss
- leaf buds twice as thick as stem, covered with thin, papery, red sheaths
- leaves 20-35+ cm wide and long, opposite, shiny green above and pale underneath, deeply and unequally palmately 5-lobed, with the terminal lobe sometimes 3-lobed
- flowers greenish yellow, fragrant, about 0.5 cm long, with both petals and sepals
- fruits propeller-like, paired, winged samaras in V-shape; wings about 3.5 cm long, 1.25 cm wide

Leaf and inflorescence of big-leaf maple with details of an individual flower and propeller-like samaras.

Habitat: Wide variety of upland sites and in the transition zone between wetland and upland. From sea level to 1000 m. Licorice fern *(Polypodium glycyrrhiza)* grows in branch notches of big-leaf maples. Sword fern *(Polystichum munitum)*, and upland species such as ocean-spray *(Holodiscus discolor)* and Douglas-fir *(Pseudotsuga menziesii)*, are common associates.

Range: In addition to occurring throughout our area, big-leaf maple may be found along some water courses in eastern Washington.

Similar Species: The large size of big-leaf maple distinguishes it from the several opposite-leaved shrubs found in similar habitats. Vine maple *(Acer circinatum)* has palmate leaves with 7-9 lobes and toothed margins, and flower clusters of fewer than 10 flowers.

Functional Value: The spreading nature and dense canopy of big-leaf maple limbs make them a valuable habitat for nesting birds, and an important substrate for epiphytes such as licorice fern and mosses. The flowers are a desirable source of nectar for honeybees. Douglas' squirrels, finches, and evening grosbeaks eat the samaras in winter. Big-leaf maple is a valuable species for restoring riparian and upland sites.

Ethnobotanical Uses: Native Americans made paddles, bowls, and utensils from the wood. Pioneers used saplings for wagon construction and prized the wood for gun stocks. The wood is currently a raw material for furniture, veneer, and flooring. Sugar can be made from the sap. It makes excellent firewood when seasoned.

Alnus rubra
red alder
Family: Betulaceae
Status: FAC
Color photos page 14

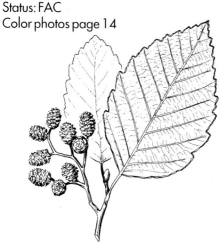

Leaves and woody female "cones" of red alder.

Red alder is often a pioneer in newly disturbed wetland areas. It grows from seeds, which are abundant, or by sprouting from stumps. Heights of 25-30 m are common in drier conditions; growth may be stunted when occurring in soils that are saturated for long periods. Twigs are gray to brown, hairy towards the tips, and often angled. Club-shaped buds are borne on short stalks. Leaves are deciduous, 5-15 cm long, and half as wide. Male catkins are produced as early as November of the year preceding their maturity, and will impart a reddish glow to hillsides during February and March. This feature and the red coloration of newly cut wood are the basis for its name.

- bark smooth, gray to nearly whitish, with horizontal sap blisters, often mottled with splotches of lichens; branch scars oval
- leaves alternate, oval, variable in size, heavily veined, smooth-surfaced, deep green above and gray-green below, with single-toothed, turned-under margins
- separate male and female catkins; male 5 mm in diameter, 2-5 cm long, drooping; female roundish to 2.5 cm long, cone-like, green when new but deep brown when mature, texture woody, remain on trees throughout winter

Habitat: Very common in the Pacific Northwest at lower elevations (below 300 m) in both wetland and nonwetland situations. It is typical of river bottomlands west of the Cascades where there is normally flooding for short periods one or more times per year and the soil remains saturated near the surface for much of the growing season. Although it often dominates habitats in floodplains, it is salt-intolerant and will not reach into estuaries. It is shade-intolerant. Salmonberry *(Rubus spectabilis)*, lady fern *(Athyrium filix-femina)*, and skunk-cabbage *(Lysichiton americanum)* are common understory associates.

Range: Southern Alaska to Santa Cruz, California, on west side of Cascades and coastal ranges. Occurs in all counties in our area.

Similar Species: Seedlings and saplings of slide alder *(Alnus sinuata)* are similar, but slide alder is a multistemmed shrub with leaf margins that are not turned under and winter buds are sharply pointed. Leaves and male catkins of beaked hazelnut *(Corylus cornuta)* are similar, but hazelnut leaves are rounder, irregularly shaped, lighter green, and hairy; the male catkins are longer and thinner. Bark and leaves of cascara *(Rhamnus purshiana)* are similar, but cascara trunks are narrow and spindly and seldom covered with lichen; leaf margins are smooth-margined and rounded at the tip.

Functional Value: Red alder has nitrogen-fixing bacteria that enriches the soil. Modern forestry practitioners have learned that leaving a few alders in second growth forests can reduce fertilization costs. Alder also has been known to decrease or prevent the growth of conifers. It is an important structural component of extensive floodplain wetlands. Its abundant leaf litter contributes to the organic layer on the forest floor. It provides habitat for numerous birds, including cavity nesters and small, cavity-dwelling mammals.

Ethnobotanical Uses: Alder is widely used for preparing traditional alder-smoked fish (salmon) and meat. It is a commonly used firewood for Northwest fireplaces. It is also a choice hardwood for furniture and is often sold as "western maple." The bark can be used for a natural red-brown dye.

Fraxinus latifolia
Oregon ash
Family: Oleaceae
Status: FACW
Color photos pages 14 and 15

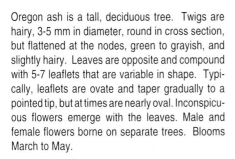

Oregon ash is a tall, deciduous tree. Twigs are hairy, 3-5 mm in diameter, round in cross section, but flattened at the nodes, green to grayish, and slightly hairy. Leaves are opposite and compound with 5-7 leaflets that are variable in shape. Typically, leaflets are ovate and taper gradually to a pointed tip, but at times are nearly oval. Inconspicuous flowers emerge with the leaves. Male and female flowers borne on separate trees. Blooms March to May.

- 10-20 m tall, to 1 m in diameter
- bark grayish brown, deeply vertical-ridged in mature trees; young twigs hairy
- leaflets opposite, with no stalks, to 15 cm long, light green above, paler below, with mostly smooth margins
- fruits (samaras) in crowded, drooping panicles, 3-5 cm long

Female flowers.   *Male flowers.*

Compound leaves and samaras of Oregon ash.

Habitat: Largely restricted to wetland habitats. Typically a component of wooded wetlands adjacent to lakes and lowland streams, it prefers saturated, highly organic soils. Frequent associates include red alder *(Alnus rubra)*, cascara *(Rhamnus purshiana)*, redstem dogwood *(Cornus sericea)*, Pacific ninebark *(Physocarpus capitatus)*, and willows *(Salix* species).

Range: Along the coast and inland to the foothills from British Columbia to south of San Francisco. Occurs in all counties in our area, but is found mostly south of Snohomish County.

Similar Species: Sapling leaves of Oregon ash may be confused with those of red elderberry *(Sambucus racemosa)*, but elderberry leaflets are narrow and linear with sharp-toothed margins. Mountain ashes *(Sorbus* species) are shrubs and have alternate leaflets that are small with highly sharp-toothed margins.

Functional Value: Provides nesting sites for birds, including cavity nesters. It is a major provider of structure in certain wetlands, e.g., ash swales of Oregon.

Ethnobotanical Uses: Folklore maintains that poisonous snakes are unknown where this ash grows, and rattlesnakes will not crawl over a branch or stick from the tree. Oregon ash is the only western ash with commercially important wood. It is used for furniture, flooring, boxes, and fuel.

Picea sitchensis
Sitka spruce

Family: Pinaceae
Status: FAC
Color photos page 15

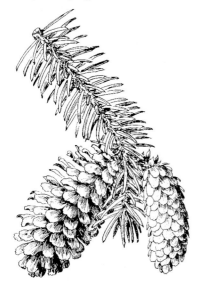

Sitka spruce branch with mature cone on left and young cone on right.

Sitka spruce is a needle-leaved evergreen that often becomes a massive tree to 70 m tall with a trunk up to 5 m in diameter. The tree may have limbs nearly to the ground. Mature trunks are straight, round, and untapering, though often buttressed. The needles, which project from all sides of the twig, are whitened by two bands of stomata on the upper surface. Male cones are red and occur at ends of the drooping lateral branches. Seeds are about 3 mm long, pale reddish brown, with slender oblique wings 1 cm long.

- bark thin (less than 2 cm thick), grayish brown to reddish brown, smooth and gray on young trees, broken into large, loose, thick scales on mature trees.
- needles 4-sided, somewhat flattened, bluish green, 1.5-2.5 cm long, stiff, very sharp-tipped
- needles attached at the base to persistent woody pegs (1-2 cm long), which can be seen on twigs that have lost their needles
- female cones drooping, 5-10 cm long, with tan, papery scales that are toothed at the tip

Habitat: A major constituent of the coastal temperate rain forests within the north Pacific fog belt where annual rainfall is 1.5-5 m and temperatures are moderate. It is abundant near the ocean, but is also common in riparian zones, in forested freshwater wetlands, at the edges of bogs, and in sandy soils.

Range: This large forest tree grows along nearly 3300 kilometers of the Pacific Coast from northern California to Kodiak Island. In Washington, Sitka spruce extends from the coast up the major river valleys into the Olympics and Cascades. In Oregon, it is restricted to within a few miles of the coast.

Similar Species: Spruces are distinguished from other conifers by their stiff, sharp needles arranged singly on raised pegs on the twig, and by the cones with gray-brown papery scales. Sitka spruce has somewhat flattened needles, whereas the other spruces have needles that are square in cross section.

Functional Value: Provides an important habitat for numerous wildlife species. Bald eagles and other predatory birds use the trees as roosts to survey the shore for prey. Columbian black-tailed deer and Roosevelt elk consume the succulent new shoots.

Ethnobotanical Uses: Native Americans inhabiting coastal areas used the long, tough, and fibrous roots as material for making baskets, twine, and rope, including whaling lines. Harpoon tips and canoes were caulked with spruce pitch. The pitch was chewed for its initially fragrant and spicy sweet flavor that soon turns bitter.

Sitka spruce limbs are dense and resinous and thus burn well. The bole wood is light, strong, and resilient, and is used for shelving, ladders, etc. The resonant qualities of the wood make flawless logs in demand for musical instruments. Because of the high strength-to-weight ratio of the wood, it was used for making airplanes during WWI and WWII.

Pinus contorta var. *contorta*
coast pine; shore pine; beach pine; sand pine; knotty pine

Family: Pinaceae
Status: FAC
Color photos page 15

Male cone of coast pine.

Branch of coast pine
with female cone.

Coast pine, a needle-leaved evergreen, is commonly a small, twisted tree in exposed coastal bogs and dunes. In more sheltered sites, it develops a large, rounded crown and has limbs to the ground. Young branches are at first orange and then turn a dark brownish black. Male cones grow at the branch tips, often in groups. Female cones form near branch tips but may be very persistent on the tree after opening, sometimes hanging on for decades.

- bark orange-brown, thin, arranged in purple-tinged, flattened plates when young; dark brown to blackish, thick and furrowed with age
- needles in bundles of 2, dark green or yellow-green, often curved and twisted, 3-6 cm long
- female cones small, brown, lopsided, 2-6 cm in length, with spine-tipped cone scales
- male cones brown in crowded spikes, 3-5 cm long, woody scales stiff with a sharp prickle at the tip

Habitat: Widespread in the coastal wetlands of the Puget Sound area. Coast pine inhabits peat bogs in coastal British Columbia (occasionally in Washington), and coastal sand dunes and cliffs in Oregon.

Range: Alaska to northern California. North of Puget Sound intermediate varieties between coast pine and lodgepole pine *(Pinus contorta* var. *latifolia)* may occur in the Cascade foothills, but south of Puget Sound the var. *latifolia* and var. *contorta* are widely separated.

Similar Species: Coast pine can be distinguished from other pines by the short needles in bundles of 2 and the lopsided cones that are covered with spines. Lodgepole pine only rarely inhabits wetlands within our range. Western white pine *(Pinus monticola)*, a more common wetland species, has 5 long (5-10 cm) needles per bundle.

Functional Value: It is an important habitat for the parasite dwarf mistletoe *(Arceuthobium americanum)*. Porcupine depend upon shore pine for winter forage.

Ethnobotanical Uses: Native Americans inhabiting coastal areas placed the pitch on open sores and chewed the buds to relieve sore throats.

Pinus monticola
western white pine

Family: Pinaceae
Status: FACU- (facw)

Female cone.

Branch showing the long needles of western white pine.

Western white pine, a needle-leaved evergreen, has a long, smooth trunk and a slender crown. The trunk may grow larger than 1 m in diameter and the entire tree may reach 75 m tall, but more commonly is 30-40 m tall. Needles have a slightly frosty appearance as a result of the rows of white stomata found on all sides.

- young bark greenish gray with resin blisters; mature bark dark gray with cinnamon interior, checkered by narrow furrows that form small, regular, oblong, scaly plates
- twigs with fine, reddish, down-like hairs that turn red-brown at maturity
- needles blue-green, 5-10 cm long, delicate, in bundles of 5
- male cones small, in clusters of 6-7 on the lower branches
- female cones 15-25 cm long, slender, curved, sticky with sap; borne on branch tips in upper part of tree; green when new, turning reddish brown at maturity; scales thin, without spines

Habitat: Most common in nutrient-poor soils and on gravelly sites where it competes successfully with Douglas fir *(Pseudotsuga menziesii)* and other

conifers. This species grows in sphagnum bogs in the Olympics, and in King, Kitsap, Mason, Island, Skagit, Snohomish, and Whatcom counties. Also found in low subalpine forests.

Range: Between sea level and 1750 m in southwestern British Columbia and western Washington. In Oregon, and through the eastern Cascades into the Rockies of Idaho and Montana, it may grow at higher elevations.

Similar Species: The long smooth trunk and slender crown are distinctive from a distance. The slender, flexible needles in bundles of 5 distinguish western white pine from other conifers. Coast pine *(Pinus contorta)*, the other wetland-associated pine, has only 2 needles per bundle.

Functional Value: The seeds are a favorite food of squirrels.

Ethnobotanical Uses: The wood of western white pine is light in color and weight, but strong. The grain is especially straight and takes nails without splitting. Uses include windows, door frames, and moldings. It is also the prime material for matches and toothpicks. It is a favorite with whittlers.

Note: Western white pine used to be much more widespread until it was stricken by white pine blister rust. The rust was introduced in 1910 in a shipment of eastern white pine. Infected trees are quickly killed; however, some white pines have a degree of natural resistance. White pine blister rust has five separate stages and requires currant *(Ribes* species) as an alternative host.

Populus balsamifera ssp. *trichocarpa*
black cottonwood; balsam poplar

Family: Salicaceae
Status: FAC

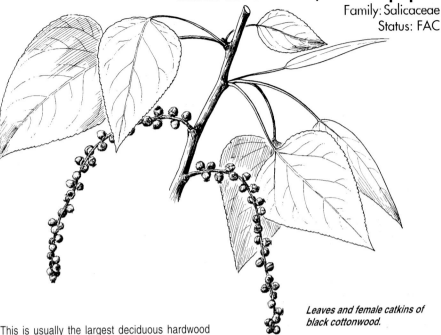

Leaves and female catkins of black cottonwood.

This is usually the largest deciduous hardwood tree in our region, often reaching more than 50 m tall and 3 m in diameter. Twigs vary from slender to quite thick. Bud scales are 2 cm long, 0.5 cm wide, heavily resinous, and very fragrant in spring. Leaves are thick, leathery, 7-15 cm long, and 5-10 cm broad. In a strong wind the pale undersides of the leaves are unmistakable in contrast to the darker green upper surface. Male catkins are dense, long, with many light purple stamens; female catkins are loose. The cottony fruits fill the air from late May to June.

- bark yellowish green, smooth on young stems, thick, deeply furrowed with gray, rounded ridges on mature trees; branch scars oval, mouth-shaped
- leaves roughly triangular-shaped, rounded to heart-shaped at base and sharp-pointed at tip, dark green above, white to pale yellowish green beneath, with prominent orange veins
- fruits cottony, 3-valved capsules, 1 cm long, in loose-hanging, long, stringy clusters

Habitat: Common along streams and lakeshores throughout our region. May form pure stands on bottomlands, moist flats or any moist, usually sandy, soils. May also grow in well-drained soils.

Range: From Alaska to Baja and west through the Rocky Mountains. Occurs in all counties in our area.

Similar Species: Quaking aspen *(Populus tremuloides)* has flattened leaf stalks, round leaves, and greenish white bark with black blotches and black fissures at the base of the trunk. Very large Pacific willow *(Salix lucida)* leaves resemble those of young black cottonwood saplings; however, Pacific willow has winged leaf stalks at the base of the leaves, and yellow, shiny bark on young branches.

Functional Value: Important in freshwater shoreline stabilization. Bees collect the bud resin which functions as an antiseptic.

Ethnobotanical Uses: The white, light, and soft wood makes good crates, veneer, and pulp. The bud resin has been used as an ingredient in antibiotic ointments for numerous ailments, as a glue, and for waterproofing. Native Americans ate the inner bark in the spring. The bark was stripped off trees to make buckets; roots were twisted into rope.

Populus tremuloides
quaking aspen; aspen
Family: Salicaceae
Status: FAC+

Leaves of quaking aspen.

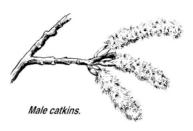

Male catkins.

Quaking aspen is a short (12-20 m), slender, deciduous tree. Large, horizontal roots send up suckers that often develop into trees. A chalky substance can be rubbed off the white bark. Male and female catkins occur on separate trees. Blooms April to May.

- bark smooth, greenish white, thin with black markings; becomes black, thickened, fissured at base in mature trees
- leaf stalks flat, allowing leaves to quiver in slightest breeze
- leaves alternate, nearly round with pointed tip, finely toothed, bright green above, silvery beneath, to 7 cm long
- fruits small capsules

Habitat: Thrives in mineral soils and on exposed sites; often grows in dense stands in logged or burned areas. Common in riparian corridors and disturbed wetlands. Often found associated with red alder *(Alnus rubra)*, Douglas spirea *(Spiraea douglasii)*, and willows *(Salix* species).

Range: Alaska to Labrador south to the mountains of northern Mexico, the elevation increasing with decreasing latitude. This is one of the most widespread trees of North America. Occurs sporadically in all counties in our area.

Similar Species: Black cottonwood *(Populus balsamifera)* has leaves with rounded stalks which therefore do not quiver, and young bark that is green, smooth, shiny, and without markings.

Functional Value: Many animals such as snowshoe hare, moose, black bear, cottontail rabbit, porcupine, grouse, elk, mountain beaver, and deer eat the buds and bark. This is an important species for beaver because the cuttings, when present, can constitute much of their winter food supply and logs are often used for making dams. Aspen is often used as a wind break and for erosion control along riparian corridors.

Ethnobotanical Uses: The wood, although weak, has a wide variety of uses: log cabins, furniture, utensils, barn floors, and horse stalls. When shredded, the wood makes a good packing material. The tree is now gaining importance as a source of pulp. It is used as an ornamental.

Prunus emarginata var. *mollis*
bitter cherry
Family: Rosaceae
Status: FACU
Color photo page 16

Bitter cherry is a small shrub or tree to 15 m tall and 30 cm in diameter. Twigs are round, 2 mm or greater in diameter. The bark of young twigs is smooth and slightly shiny; bark of mature trunks and branches peels horizontally. Small, fragrant, white flowers are borne in round clusters near branch tips at the same time as the leaves emerge, in April to June.

- bark shiny red-brown, with scattered grayish raised areas to 5 cm long
- leaves oval, 2.5-8 cm long, alternate, with a pair of knob-like glands attached at the base, margins toothed, undersides somewhat hairy
- flowers in clumps of 5-8, stamens about 20 per flower
- fruits small, 1 cm in diameter, bright red to black

Habitat: Establishes easily in moist, disturbed areas. Bitter cherry prefers open sandy or gravelly sites and stream banks. It is shade-intolerant and as a result is frequently crowded out by red alder *(Alnus rubra)*.

Range: Widespread and common throughout southern British Columbia and Vancouver Island, Washington, Oregon, the mountains of California and east throughout the Rocky Mountains. In Washington and Oregon it occurs from sea level to 1300 m. Bitter cherry is found in all counties in our area.

Similar Species: Ornamental cherries *(Prunus* species) also have knob-like glands on the leaf stalk, but have pointed leaf tips, longer and denser clusters of showy flowers, and fruits that are larger, rounder, dark purple, and somewhat less bitter. Western crabapple *(Malus fusca)* has black, nonshiny bark, and mitten-shaped leaves.

A branch of bitter cherry showing leaves, flowers, and fruits.

Functional Value: The fruits are an important food source for many birds, which act as dispersal agents for the seeds. The bark of dead trunks is more decay resistant than the wood, therefore downed logs have intact bark with rotting wood on the inside, providing a habitat for insects, amphibians, and small mammals. Fragrant flowers attract honeybees and other pollinators.

Ethnobotanical Uses: The bitter fruits are edible, though disagreeable in flavor, and are best used in jams. Bark has been woven into decorative baskets.

Rhamnus purshiana
cascara; buckthorn cascara
Family: Rhamnaceae
Status: FAC-
Color photo page 16

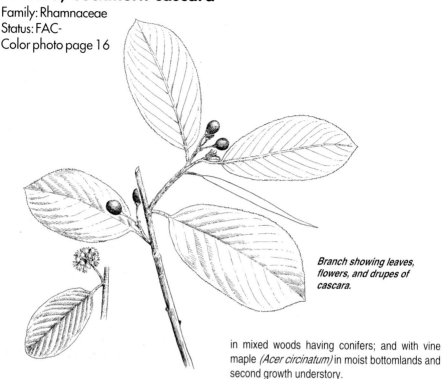

Branch showing leaves, flowers, and drupes of cascara.

Cascara is a small, deciduous tree with a narrow, straight trunk, and few branches. It seldom exceeds 10 m tall. Twigs are round, 4 mm in diameter, deep red-brown, and short-hairy near the tips. Winter buds lack bud scales. Leaves are oblong, alternate, but closely spaced and sometimes appearing opposite. Blooms April to June.

- bark thin, usually smooth, gray to dark brown, may be tinged with red
- leaves yellow-green, round-tipped with finely toothed to smooth margins
- leaf veins numerous, readily apparent below, parallel, with yellow hairs
- flowers tiny, 5-petaled, in small umbels at the base of the leaves
- drupes small (less than 1 cm), round, black, several per umbel

Habitat: Occurs in dry to wet, often shady, sites. Commonly associated with red alder *(Alnus rubra)* in mixed woods having conifers; and with vine maple *(Acer circinatum)* in moist bottomlands and second growth understory.

Range: Lower elevations (to 750 m) west of the Cascades from northern California to British Columbia. Also found in moist canyons in eastern Washington, Idaho, and Montana.

Similar Species: The bark of red alder has branch scars and horizontal sap blisters, and leaves that are deep green, lack hairs, pointed at the tip, and coarsely toothed.

Functional Value: Though attractive, cascara is seldom used as an ornamental as it is prone to aphid attack and is not very pollution-tolerant. The fruit is a valuable food source for a variety of wildlife.

Ethnobotanical Uses: The bitter bark has been collected for many years for its powerful laxative properties.

Taxus brevifolia
Pacific yew
Family: Taxaceae
Status: NI (fac-)
Color photo page 16

Pacific yew is an evergreen shrub to small tree 5-10 m tall. Instead of a female cone, this species bears a red fleshy berry that surrounds a large bare seed. Male cones are less distinct and found in the leaf axils as small clusters of 6-14 stamens. Branches are long and droop heavily, and the trunk is often twisted and irregular. Flowers from April to June, berries ripen September to October.

- bark reddish to purplish when freshly shred, light red-brown when older, thin, papery, fibrous; readily peels off in scales, rather than long strips
- needles flat, yellow-green, pale below, sharply pointed, attached spirally to the twigs by short-ridged stalks in two rows forming flat sprays
- fruits a fleshy berry surrounding a naked seed, attached on lower side of branches

Habitat: Grows best in moist forests along stream corridors and slopes with seeps, especially at low elevations.

Range: Along Pacific Coast from southern Alaska through British Columbia, western Washington and Oregon, reaching northwest California. Occurs in all counties in our area.

Similar Species: The foliage looks similar to all the flat-needled conifers, except the needles attach to the twig by a twisted stalk, are stiff, and have a pointed tip. There are no other conifers that have red berries and flaky, purplish red bark.

Functional Value: Pacific yew snags are a valuable habitat for cavity nesting birds. Many birds eat

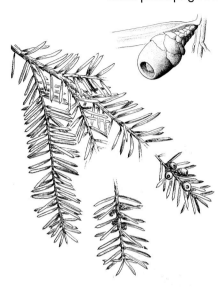

Needles of Pacific yew are flat and attached spirally to the twigs. Fruits are a fleshy berry.

the fleshy berries, and the rotting foliage is good winter browse for moose.

Ethnobotanical Uses: The wood of pacific yew, highly prized by the west coast Native Americans, is strong and dense and makes excellent bows and other tools; in addition, it is attractive and takes a high polish, making it desirable for carving. The berries are poisonous to humans and the foliage is poisonous to horses and cattle. Taxol, a compound found in the bark, is helpful in combating certain forms of cancer.

Thuja plicata
western red-cedar, red cedar

Family: Cupressaceae
Status: FAC
Color photos page 17

A branch showing male cones of western red-cedar on the tips of the foliage. A female cone is shown above to the left.

Western red-cedar has a conical trunk, tapering rapidly from a sometimes heavily buttressed base. These are long-lived evergreen trees with broad crowns of spreading, drooping branches that turn up at the tips. The small female cones are composed of 3 opposite pairs of seed-bearing scales. Male and female cones occur on separate branches.

- bark dull red, thin, vertically stringy, fibrous; readily peels off in long narrow strips
- foliage drooping, flat, branchlets covered with tiny scale-like leaves about 2 mm long
- crushed foliage with sweet, aromatic smell
- female cones oval, thin-woody brown, 1 cm long, borne above foliage

Habitat: Grows best in moist habitats in areas of maritime climate with high rainfall. In drier areas, western red-cedar becomes abundant only on wet

sites such as in ravines, seeps, along streams, or in poorly drained bottomlands. It thrives on soils rich in organic material. It is shade-tolerant and will germinate and grow under an intact canopy. This species seldom dominates the forest except at very wet sites where other conifers do poorly.

Range: Along Pacific Coast from southeast Alaska through British Columbia, western Washington and Oregon, reaching into coastal redwood forest of northern California. Western red-cedar grows from sea level to 1250 m in Washington, and up to 2500 m in southwestern Oregon. It also occurs at moist sites in the Rocky Mountains, in northeastern Washington, Idaho, and northwestern Montana. Found in all counties in our area.

Similar Species: Yellow cedar *(Chamaecyparis nootkatensis)* has similar scale-like leaves and stringy bark, but an extremely drooping habit and globose female cones. The scale-like leaves, small thin-woody cones, and stringy red bark distinguish western red-cedar from other conifers.

Functional Value: Western red-cedar often provides the canopy for a luxuriant undergrowth of ferns, skunk-cabbage *(Lysichiton americanum)*, or devil's club *(Oplopanax horridus)*. Snags are a valuable habitat for cavity nesting birds. The hollow stumps provide shelter for bears, raccoons, skunks, and other animals.

Ethnobotanical Uses: Western red-cedar was the most valuable tree to Native Americans inhabiting the Pacific Northwest coast, providing materials for shelter, clothing, canoes, and nets. The soft fiber of the inner layer of the bark was used for diapers, cradle padding, clothing, and blankets. Bark fiber was woven into baskets, fishing nets, and sails for canoes. The wood is easy to carve and work and was used for totem poles and dugout canoes.

The wood is highly prized today for shingles, shakes, and boards for untreated exterior siding. The straight grain allows it to be split easily into shakes. The wood is light, soft, weak, and brittle but is decay-resistant due to a natural fungicide — western red-cedar roof shingles will last 100 years. Wood provides reliable kindling. Western red-cedar is commonly used as an ornamental.

Tsuga heterophylla
western hemlock
Family: Pinaceae
Status: FACU-
Color photos page 17

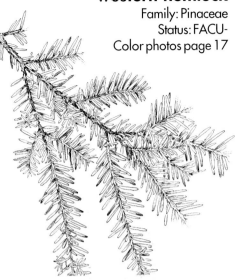

Western hemlock trees grow to 60 m tall in lowland forests. The small foliage and branching arrangement give the boughs a delicate spray-like appearance, especially when viewed from below the tree. Short needles, 0.5-1 cm long, grow from the upper part of the twig and longer needles, 1-2 cm, grow from the lower surface.

- bark 2-4 cm thick, deeply seamed into broad flat ridges covered with thin cinnamon-brown scales; bark on young trees and branches smooth, gray with a hint of red
- branch tips and top leader droop
- needles vary in length, round-tipped, flat, green, grooved above, with 2 white rows of stomata underneath
- cones small, 2-2.5 cm long, light brown, somewhat papery, borne in large quantities on the branchlets

Branch of western hemlock.

Small male cones and larger female cones.

Habitat: Dominates most of the western Washington and Oregon lowland forests, occupying all but the wettest and driest of sites. Seedlings often germinate on rotten logs, humus-rich soil, or moss, and are able to grow in dense shade. When western hemlock occurs in sphagum bogs, growth is stunted. Western hemlock forests may harbor a luxuriant undergrowth of vine maple *(Acer circinatum)*, Rhododendron, salal *(Gaultheria shallon)*, blueberries, and sword fern *(Polystichum munitum)*. However, many sites are rather lacking in understory species because of the dense canopy.

Range: Western hemlock is the potential dominant tree at sea level, abundant to 1100 m, and may occur to 1600 m in western Washington, on Vancouver Island, and in western British Columbia. It is also common throughout much of western Oregon and grows in wet areas of the northern Rocky Mountains in Idaho and Montana. It occurs on the seaward slopes and islands of southeastern Alaska from sea level to 900 m. Grows in all counties in our area.

Similar Species: The short needles of unequal length and drooping leader distinguish western hemlock from other conifers. Douglas-fir *(Pseudotsuga menziesii)* has bark that is more deeply grooved. Western red-cedar *(Thuja plicata)* has reddish stringy bark and scale-like needles.

Functional Value: Western hemlock forests are an important habitat for a diverse community of fungal and animal species.

Ethnobotanical Uses: The wood is pale yellow-brown, light yet hard and tough, fine-textured, straight-grained, free of pitch, saws without splintering, and holds nails well. It is good for building and hardens and darkens with age. It is well suited for a wide range of uses, such as flooring, interior paneling, furniture, etc. The wood makes fine pulp for paper production, and serves as the principal source for fiber used in the manufacture of rayon, cellophane, and many plastics. The bark is rich in tannin used in making leather.

Acer macrophyllum (big-leaf maple)
Photo by Fred Weinmann

Acer macrophyllum (big-leaf maple)
Photo by Fred Weinmann

Alnus rubra (red alder)
Photo by Sarah Spear Cooke

Alnus rubra (red alder)
Photo by Fred Weinmann

Fraxinus latifolia (Oregon ash)
Photo by Sarah Spear Cooke

Fraxinus latifolia (Oregon ash)
Photo by Fred Weinmann

Fraxinus latifolia (Oregon ash)
Photo by Sarah Spear Cooke

Picea sitchensis (Sitka spruce)
Photo by Fred Weinmann

Picea sitchensis (Sitka spruce)
Photo by Sarah Spear Cooke

Pinus contorta (coast pine)
Photo by Al Hanners

Prunus emarginata (bitter cherry)
Photo by Fred Weinmann

Rhamnus purshiana (cascara)
Photo by Al Hanners

Rhamnus purshiana (cascara)
Photo by Fred Weinmann

Taxus brevifolia (Pacific yew)
Photo by Fred Weinmann

Thuja plicata (western red-cedar)
Photo by Clayton Antieau

Thuja plicata (western red cedar)
Photo by Sarah Spear Cooke

Tsuga heterophylla (western hemlock)
Photo by Clayton Antieau

Tsuga heterophylla (western hemlock)
Photo by Fred Weinmann

Acer circinatum
vine maple
Family: Aceraceae
Status: FAC-
Color photo page 75

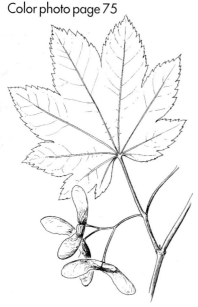

*Leaf and propeller-like samaras of
vine maple.*

Vine maple is an erect, tall, deciduous shrub with
either multiple tangled trunks or, when growing in
full sunlight, a single trunk. Twigs and leaf buds are
slender, reddish, sticky, 1-3 mm in diameter, and
round to oval in cross section. Leaves are bright
green, opposite, to 10 cm across, and borne on
bright red stalks 4-9 cm long. Blooms in late spring
after big-leaf maple *(Acer macrophyllum)*.

- woody shrub to 8 m tall, with smooth, bright-
  green-tinged bark turning brown with age
- leaves small, to 10 cm wide, palmately veined,
  shallowly 5- to 9-lobed
- flowers small, 6-9 mm wide, few, creamy
  white with purple-red sepals
- fruits propeller-like, 2-seeded samaras; wings
  reddish, point away from each other on the
  same horizontal plane

Habitat: Clearings or openings within forested
communities adjacent to wetlands in the transition
zone between wetland and upland, where soils are
moist, but not saturated for long durations. Common along stream banks where it can establish in
dense, nearly impenetrable, tangles. Occurs in
nitrogen-rich soils. Often associated with sword
fern *(Polystichum munitum)* and trailing blackberry
(Rubus ursinus).

Range: From Alaska south to northern California,
primarily on the west side of the Cascades, mostly
below 1,000 m in elevation. Uncommon within the
San Juan Island archipelago, probably as a result of
the relatively dry conditions. Occurs in all counties
in our area.

Similar Species: Douglas' maple *(Acer glabrum)*
is far less frequent west of the Cascades, does not
sprawl, has 3- to 5-lobed leaves, and fruits with
wings that tend to form a "v". Winter twigs of vine
maple may be confused with those of red huckleberry *(Vaccinium parvifolium)* because both are
green, but the huckleberry twigs are much finer and
ridged in cross section, and leaves are alternate.
Pacific ninebark *(Physocarpus capitatus)* also has
palmately lobed leaves, but has light tan to dark
reddish brown bark that sheds, and the leaves are
alternate. Saplings of big-leaf maple have leaves
20-35 cm wide and buds that are 1.5-2 cm long and
deep purple-red.

Functional Value: Constitutes an effective buffer
preventing human and/or domestic animal intrusion into a wetland. Vine maples provide nesting
locations for small birds. Twigs, buds, and seeds
are consumed by a variety of wildlife: deer and elk,
squirrels and ground squirrels, and birds including
grouse. The dense root masses are important for
bank stabilization within stream bank habitats.

Ethnobotanical Uses: Vine maple was widely
used by Native Americans for making open-weave
baskets for clams and fish. Wood was used for
bows and as fuel for smoking fish or fowl. Vine
maple is often used as an ornamental because of
the intensity of fall leaf coloration.

Amelanchier alnifolia
western serviceberry; Saskatoon serviceberry

Family: Rosaceae
Status: FACU
Color photo page 75

Color photo page 75

Western serviceberry forms low-spreading shrubs to erect, small trees, 1-7 m tall. Twigs are slender, green to brown, occasionally reddish, with short-hairy tips. Mature branches are gray-barked. Leaves are deciduous, bright green, oval to elliptic, 2-4 cm long, and are borne on stalks. Flowers are 2-3 cm across with 20 stamens and are arranged in drooping clusters. Petals are white, long, and loosely twisted. Blooms from May to June.

- young branches and buds reddish brown, smooth
- leaves smooth-margined at the base, usually sharply toothed across the tip
- flowers plentiful, fragrant, visible from a distance as showy white clusters
- fruits globose, fleshy, red at first, ripening to dark purple, blueberry-like, with several seeds

Habitat: Open woods, canyons, and hillsides from sea level to subalpine, especially in rocky soils. Common in transition zone between wetland and upland, and in disturbed sites. Often associated with red alder *(Alnus rubra)*.

Range: Southern Alaska, south to California, east to Alberta.

Similar Species: The cherries *(Prunus species)* form much more substantial trees in which the bark, when mature, is burgundy-purple with distinctive light stripes, has an iridescent sheen, and peels off in thin strips. Indian plum *(Oemleria cerasiformis)* also has oval to elliptical leaves, but with tips that are not toothed, and bark has round, gray pores.

Functional Value: Fruits are eaten by many wildlife species including upland game birds, mammals, and various songbirds; twigs and leaves are used for browse.

Branch of western serviceberry showing flower clusters with detail of flower above.

Ethnobotanical Uses: Berries are edible and sweet, either fresh or dried, and are high in iron and copper. Berry juice can be used as a dye. Native Americans mixed the berries with meat and fat to make a form of dried travel food. The wood was used to make arrows, spears, and crosspieces for canoes. Used as an ornamental.

SHRUBS

Andromeda polifolia
bog rosemary
Family: Ericaceae
Status: OBL

Leaves and bell-shaped flowers of bog rosemary.

Bog rosemary is one of the low-growing, evergreen shrubs with dark green leaves that grows within coastal bog communities. Generally it is less than 0.5 m tall and 1-6 m wide. Blooms May through September.

- leaves alternate, rather long and narrow, leathery, 3-4 cm long, without leaf stalk
- top surface of leaves dull green with sunken veins, margins curl under, undersides have white, waxy, powdery surface
- flowers white to pinkish, bell-shaped, 5-8 mm wide, single or in clusters of 2-5
- fruits woody, globose, 4-5 mm, 5-chambered with many tiny seeds

Habitat: Within coastal bog communities in Oregon and Washington on the surface of the sphagnum peat mat. Conditions may range from seasonal saturation, though rarely inundated, to completely dry surface conditions in late summer. Bog rosemary is shade-intolerant.

Range: Circumboreal within sphagnum bog communities, reported within the southern coastal portion of Washington south to California; also Alaska, Yukon, British Columbia. East of coastal states across northern Canada, and in Nevada and Colorado.

Similar Species: Smooth Labrador-tea *(Rhododendron neoglandulosum)* and bog laurel *(Kalmia microphylla)* both tend to be larger in general form and leaf size. Smooth Labrador-tea has dense, rust-colored hairs on leaf undersides and a pungent odor when the leaves or stems are crushed. Bog laurel has a white stripe along the top of much wider (5-15 mm) leaves, which have gray hairs on the undersides, and large, bright pink, saucer-shaped flowers.

Ethnobotanical Uses: Bog rosemary is toxic if ingested. Although challenging to maintain in urban landscapes, it may be used as an ornamental.

Betula glandulosa var. hallii
bog birch; dwarf tundra birch

Family: Betulaceae
Status: OBL
Color photo page 75

This spreading or erect, small-branched shrub grows to 3 m, but is most often less than 2 m tall. Leaves are deciduous, somewhat leathery, and shaped typically of birches. Plants in our area belong to variety *hallii* and have patches of short soft hairs. Blooms late April to July.

- bark becomes reddish brown at maturity
- young branches with numerous round, wart-like, sticky glands and hairs
- leaves alternate, bright green, smooth-surfaced, round to oval, small, 1-4 cm long, with blunt single-toothed margins
- female catkins 1-2.5 cm long, 3-5 mm thick; male catkins tiny, inconspicuous, not drooping

Habitat: Most commonly grows along the margins of bogs in the Puget Basin. May occur in emergent wetlands along streams, lakes, and marshes.

Range: Alaska south to California. In our area bog birch is found mostly south of King County. Scattered occurrence throughout much of the remainder of the United States.

Similar Species: Horticultural varieties of birch are found as escaped in similar habitats and are not easily distinguishable in seedling stage; when mature they are usually more tree-like and have larger leaves than bog birch. White birch *(Betula papyrifera)* has copper-colored bark, which peels more easily than that of bog birch.

Functional Value: Important structural component of the shrub layer. Provides habitat for many birds and refuge for small mammals. Browse for deer and elk.

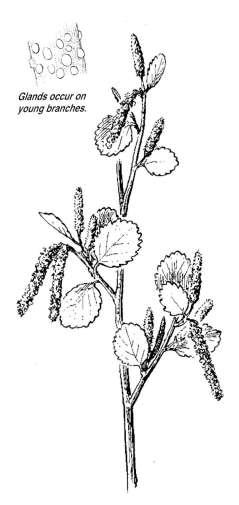

Glands occur on young branches.

Leaves and male catkins of bog birch.

Cornus sericea ssp. sericea
(Cornus stolonifera)
redstem dogwood; red-osier dogwood; creek dogwood

Family: Cornaceae
Status: FACW
Color photo page 76

Flower and fruits.

Leaves and flat-topped flower cluster of redstem dogwood.

Redstem dogwood is a woody deciduous shrub with many thin stems. A leaf carefully split in half width-wise will disclose the wispy, connective tissues associated with the veins. Flowers are creamy white to green, 2-4 mm long, and lack showy petals. Flowers are borne in flat-topped clusters. Fruits are white, 6-9 mm long, and root easily. Blooms May to July.

- bark and twigs red from autumn to late spring; bark, twigs and leaves bright green in spring through summer
- round pores common on older, gray-tinged bark
- leaves opposite, dark green above, hairy and lighter below, with smooth margins, rounded bases, pointed tips, and falsely parallel veins

Habitat: Occurs in soils that are saturated for at least a portion of the growing season. Common on the edges of lakes, ponds, within wetlands, and along streams. Not as tolerant of long-term root saturation as some other shrubs, redstem dogwood seems to prefer wetland margins where soils are nitrogen-rich, saturated, and shallowly inundated in the spring, and may be completely dry by late summer. It is tolerant of fluctuating water tables. Associates include black cottonwood *(Populus balsamifera)* and red alder *(Alnus rubra)* stands, especially in open, nitrogen-rich, alluvial floodplain forests; also commonly found in willow scrub-shrub wetlands.

Range: Alaska to southern California, east to Idaho and Nevada. Common in mid- to lower elevation shrubby wetlands and stream courses of the Pacific Northwest. Occurs in all counties in our area.

Similar Species: The deep to bright red stems on the late winter/early spring growth of redstem dogwood are very distinctive. Willows *(Salix* species) have alternate leaves and some species have reddish twigs in the winter and spring. Pacific dogwood *(Cornus nuttallii)*, a native dogwood common to upland habitats, has similar leaves, but brown bark and twigs, and flowers that are surrounded by large, showy, pink-white bracts.

Functional Value: Wildlife browse the twigs, foliage, and fruits. The shrubs provide excellent nesting habitat for songbirds.

Ethnobotanical Uses: Native Americans used the inner bark in tobacco mixtures and teas, and for tanning or drying animal hides. Some tribes ate the white, sour berries, while others used the branches for arrow-making, stakes, or other tools. Often used as an ornamental.

Corylus cornuta var. *californica*
beaked hazelnut

Family: Betulaceae
Status: FACU
Color photo page 76

Beaked hazelnut is a finely-branched, densely clumped, upland deciduous shrub that grows 3-4 m tall. Twigs are round and 3 mm in diameter. Leaves are alternate with doubly toothed margins. Buds are rounded with short-hairy, brown scales. Separate male and female flowers appear on the same plant. Male flowers are borne in hanging catkins, 4-7 cm long. The bright red female flowers are small, feathery, and attached directly to the ends of short branches. Male catkins bloom March to April before leaves appear.

- bark gray-brown, hairy when young, smooth with age
- young twigs glandular and white-hairy when young, with zigzag growth pattern
- leaves hairy, soft, slightly asymmetrical, oval, heart-shaped at the base, 4-10 cm long
- fruits hard-shelled nuts, surrounded by long tubular, leafy sheath with beak-like appendage on the tip

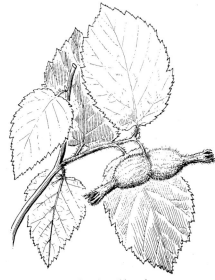

Leaves and female catkins of beaked hazelnut.

Male catkins and bud scales.

Habitat: Common in deciduous or mixed-canopy upland forests. Grows only in upland zones adjacent to wetlands. Not found within wetlands, unless on a well-drained hummock within a recently flooded area. Prefers calcium or nitrogen-rich soils.

Range: Throughout the United States and lower Canadian provinces at lower elevations on well-drained soils. Occurs in all counties in our area.

Similar Species: The hairy appearance of the young twig makes this species relatively distinct during any season and the very soft texture of the asymmetrical leaves is quite unique. Red alder *(Alnus rubra)* has leaves that appear similar, but they taper at the base and are symmetrical, and male catkins are longer (5-12 cm).

Functional Value: Nuts are eaten by wildlife, particularly squirrels. Twigs and leaves are browsed by deer and elk, and grouse feed on the catkins. The low-spreading nature of the shrub make it attractive for some low-nesting songbirds.

Ethnobotanical Uses: Nuts are edible and can be roasted or ground into flour. The roots and inner bark produce a blue dye when steeped in water.

Crataegus douglasii
black hawthorn; Douglas' hawthorn

Family: Rosaceae

Status: FAC

Color photo page 76

Spiny twigs, leaves, flower, and fruits of black hawthorn.

Black hawthorn is a deciduous shrub or small tree rarely taller than 8 m. Twigs are brown, to 4 mm in diameter, with thorns that emerge at right angles to the stem. Leaves are dark green above, paler underneath, and 3-7 cm long. White flowers with 5 petals and 10-12 stamens are borne in apple-like clusters. Blooms May to June. Fruits mature in August.

- thorns short, thick, single, 2 cm long, present on large twigs and main stems
- stems often grow in zigzag pattern
- leaves alternate, leathery, nearly smooth to shallowly lobed, with pointed base, oval tip, and close set teeth along margin nearly to the base
- fruits small, 1 cm, black, often persisting into winter

Habitat: Prefers moist nitrogen-rich soils in open areas; often grows on the edges of shrub swamps and streams. In the northern portion of the Puget Basin, hawthorn is common in wet, grazed pastures and along roadsides with various rose species.

Range: At low elevations from Alaska south to California, and east to Alberta and the Dakotas. In our area black hawthorn occurs mostly in southern Washington and Oregon.

Similar Species: There are many escaped and naturalized ornamental species of hawthorn present in our region. However, they all have red, persistent fruit, and leaves that are deeply and many lobed. Western crabapple *(Malus fusca)* grows in similar habitats and has nonpointed spurs that may be confused for thorns, but generally tends to be taller with denser twigs.

Functional Value: Dense thickets are a preferred nesting sites for birds throughout the region. The apple-like fruit is not as commonly used by wildlife as might be expected; however, it is eaten by fox, sparrows, and cedar waxwings. Grazers use the twigs for browse, but use is limited by the presence of the spines. Dense hedgerows and thickets of black hawthorn provide impenetrable cover and escape habitat, as well as a good buffer around some wetland communities.

Ethnobotanical Uses: The fruits and flowers contain flavonoids and ascorbic acid, and are an excellent heart tonic. The wood can be used for handles of small tools. The native species are rarely used as ornamentals.

Gaultheria shallon
salal

Family: Ericaceae
Status: FACU
Color photo page 76

Salal, a low-growing shrub, is generally less than 1 m tall but will sometimes grow to 5 m. In forests, it has thick, freely branching stems and can form impenetrable thickets. Leaves are evergreen and to 8 cm long. New growth is very pale, almost yellow-pink, with distinctive dark red hairs. Blooms April to July.

- leaves alternate, leathery, waxy, dark green and shiny above, lighter underneath, oval at base with short-tipped apex, very finely toothed, on short stalks
- flowers urn-shaped, white to pink, 7-10 mm long, in racemes of up to 15 flowers
- fruit a capsule surrounded by a reddish blue-black, fleshy, expanded calyx, 6-10 mm wide, with stiff, sticky, short-hairy glands

Fruits.

Leaves and urn-shaped flowers of salal.

Habitat: Lower elevations within moist to dry woods. Often the dominant shrub in upland conifer forests. Found in forested wetlands on raised hummocks or topographic features (logs) that allow the roots to remain out of saturated zones. Common throughout low to midelevation forests and on exposed coastal bluffs of our region. Associates include Oregon grape *(Mahonia nervosa)* and sword fern *(Polystichum munitum)*.

Range: From British Columbia south to California, from the eastern slope of the Cascades to the coast. Occurs in all counties in our area.

Similar Species: Oregon grape is often found in conditions similar to salal, but has pinnately compound leaves that are sharply toothed and yellow flowers that are held in a terminal spike.

Functional Value: Fruits are consumed by wildlife and humans. Important for upland game birds such as grouse. Leaves, buds, and twigs are browsed by deer and elk.

Ethnobotanical Uses: Native Americans dried the fruits and mixed them with dried meat and fat to form a dried travel food that would not spoil. Fruits are edible and taste something like huckleberries marinated in a dilute extract of fir needles. They can be eaten from the bush, or made into pies or jams. The hairy texture of the fruit dissuades some consumers. The dark green, waxy foliage is often used by florists as an ornamental.

Ilex aquifolium
holly

Family: Aquifoliaceae
Status: FACU
Color photo page 76

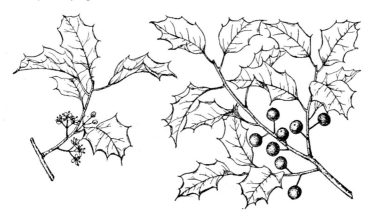

Branches of holly showing leaves and flowers on left and leaves and berries on right.

Holly is an evergreen, upland exotic shrub usually with a single stem that can grow to a tall tree. Both stem and twigs are smooth and green. Leaves are generally long (6-9 cm), dark glossy green above, and paler underneath. Flowers are small, nondescript, and creamy white. Male and female flowers are borne on separate plants.

• leaves very stiff with sharp spines on the tips of the spiny lobes
• leaves leathery, decomposing slowly and remaining sharp
• fruits on female plants bright red, similar in size and shape to blueberry

Habitat: Commonly grows within upland forests and wetland edges. Can be found as a single individual in the middle of a forest quite some distance from human habitation. This exotic species can invade undisturbed old growth forests, although it is more common in disturbed areas. Fruits are dispersed by birds.

Range: Escaped ornamental throughout western United States. Occurs in all counties in our area.

Similar Species: Oregon grape *(Mahonia nervosa)* and tall Oregon grape *(Mahonia aquifolia)* are somewhat similar, but have brown twigs, compound leaves that are light green, yellow flowers that grow in a cluster on a terminal spike, and dark purple fruits.

Functional Value: Birds eat the fruits.

Ethnobotanical Uses: Planted for ornamental and commercial purposes. Used as a holiday season green decoration. Red berries may be toxic to humans.

Kalmia microphylla ssp. occidentalis
(Kalmia occidentalis = Kalmia polifolia var. microphylla)
bog laurel; swamp laurel; western swamp laurel

Family: Ericaceae
Status: FACW+
Color photo page 77

This small, evergreen shrub is found in bogs where it may form intertangled mats. It is generally less than 50 cm tall but can grow up to 1 m. Leaves are to 4 cm long and 5-15 mm wide. Blooms June to September.

- leaves erect, dark green, with white midstripe above; light green, waxy, smooth, or with fine, gray hairs underneath
- leaf margins slightly turned under
- flowers large, bright pink, saucer-shaped, approximately 2 cm across, with 10 stamens
- fruits woody, spherical capsules, 2-3 mm

Habitat: Generally grows in sphagnum bogs at low elevations. Most common on the open bog mat because it is shade-intolerant. Associates include bog Labrador-tea *(Rhododendron groenlandicum)*, smooth Labrador-tea *(Rhododendron neoglandulosum)*, and wild cranberry *(Vaccinium oxycoccus)*.

Range: Southern Alaska south to northwest Oregon, across North America. West of the Cascades in our region.

Similar Species: Most easily confused with bog rosemary *(Andromeda polifolia)*, which only occurs in coastal sites, has leaves that are more linear, with a dull green upper surface having silvery veins and a powdery white wax underneath, and flowers that are small, white to pinkish, and bell-shaped. Smooth Labrador-tea *(Rhododendron neoglandulosum)* has generally broader, horizontal, or hanging leaves; new leaves can have a pure white (not gray), waxy coating or fine hairs on the undersides. Leaf margins of both smooth Labrador-tea and bog rosemary curl under to reduce water loss through transpiration.

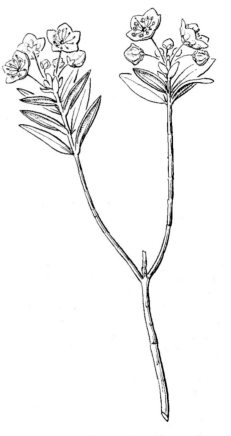

Leaves and saucer-shaped flowers of bog laurel.

Functional Value: Provides cover and nesting for various small birds.

Ethnobotanical Uses: Toxic if ingested. Native Americans boiled bog laurel and used it as an antibiotic solution to clean and aid the healing of skin eruptions.

Lonicera involucrata
black twinberry; twinberry honeysuckle; bearberry honeysuckle

Family: Caprifoliaceae
Status: FAC+
Color photos page 76

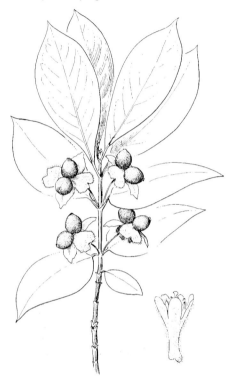

Leaves and paired fruits of black twinberry with detail of tubular flower.

Black twinberry is a deciduous shrub less than 2 m tall. It has elliptical, opposite, shiny yellow-green leaves that are 5-8 cm long. Blooms April to August.

- young twigs green, very fine, thin, with distinctive lengthwise ridges and long, hairy tips; turn reddish brown in the fall
- older bark yellow-silver-tan, peels in strips
- flowers yellow, tubular, 5-lobed, paired on terminal, small stalks, closely underlain by a single, 2-lobed, purple-red bract
- fruits paired, black when ripe, with red-purple bracts

Habitat: Moist woods to wet forest and shrub communities, especially on the edges of lakes and streams.

Range: Alaska panhandle to southern California, east to Montana and New Mexico. Occurs in all counties in our area.

Similar Species: Indian plum *(Oemleria cerasiformis)* has bark that is reddish brown and smooth (even on young twigs), alternate leaves, and lacks the red bract beneath the flowers. Common snowberry *(Symphoricarpos albus)* also has yellow-silver bark, but has thin (0.2 cm), silvery gray, and opposite stems that branch at right angles, small pink flowers, and white, globose fruit. Rusty menziesia *(Menziesia ferruginea)* is similar when plants are young, but the leaves are bright green and more rounded, and the bark is dull, smooth, and medium-brown.

Functional Value: Deer browse twigs and leaves, and bear and grouse eat the berries. The bark is peeled by birds and small mammals and used as nesting material.

Ethnobotanical Uses: Native Americans used the berries in ceremonies, and the leaves to cause vomiting. They are bitter and rumored to be poisonous. The bark has been used in a variety of medicines.

Mahonia nervosa
(Berberis nervosa)
Oregon grape; dwarf Oregon grape

Family: Berberidaceae
Status: FACU

Oregon grape is a strongly rhizomatous shrub with ascending to erect, aerial stems, 10-60 cm long. The evergreen leaves are compound and alternate, but often appear clustered at the end of upright, bare stems. The pinnately compound leaflets number 9-21 and are 3-6 cm long.

- leaves dark green, leathery, somewhat glossy
- leaflets pointed, prickly at the tips of leaf lobes, with 3 central veins
- flowers yellow in spike-like racemes, to 20 cm long
- fruits edible, dark blue-purple berries, 1 cm thick, borne in clusters

Habitat: Shade-tolerant species that grows in shady, upland woods adjacent to wetland areas. Occurs in forests with salal *(Gaultheria shallon)*, sword fern *(Polystichum munitum)*, ocean-spray *(Holodiscus discolor)*, Douglas fir *(Pseudotsuga menziesii)*, and western hemlock *(Tsuga heterophylla)*.

Range: Common west of the Cascades from southern British Columbia to central California. Occurs in all counties in our area.

Similar Species: Tall Oregon grape *(Mahonia aquifolia)* commonly grows to 2 m tall, has fewer leaflets (5-7), each leaflet having only 1 central vein; it prefers sunnier conditions, and therefore is found in open spaces and on the edges of woods. Holly *(Ilex aquifolium)* is a tall, branched shrub to 6 m tall with darker, stouter green twigs, stiffer spines on the leaf tips, small, creamy white flowers, and bright red fruits. Salal *(Gaultheria shallon)* grows in similar conditions, but has finely toothed leaves on short stalks, and white to pink flowers loosely borne in hanging racemes.

Functional Value: Leaves and twigs are browsed by deer and the fruits are eaten by birds.

Ethnobotanical Uses: The berries are sour, but somewhat edible and contain vitamin C. The roots contain alkaloids and acids. Root bark has been used medicinally for centuries as a tonic, fever remedy, and cathartic. Teas from the roots were used by Native Americans for sore throats, stomach disorders, and as a cough medicine. Oregon grape was also used to treat gallstones and liver diseases. A yellow dye can be made from the roots. Foliage is used by florists as an ornamental.

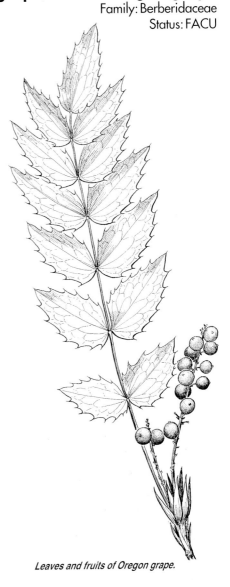

Leaves and fruits of Oregon grape.

Malus fusca
(Pyrus fusca)
western crabapple; Pacific crabapple

Family: Rosaceae
Status: FACW
Color photo page 77

Western crabapple in flower and with fruits; some leaves have a "mitten" shape.

Western crabapple is a several-stemmed deciduous shrub to small tree 3-12 m tall, often with a "messy" growth habit of many, intertwining branches in the crown. Twigs are less than 4 mm in diameter, short-hairy when new and smooth with age. Leaves are oval at the base with a pointed tip and finely toothed margins. Blooms late April to early July.

- bark black, crusty, crumbles to a black powder
- dark twigs and multiple branches with blunt spurs that resemble thorns
- some leaves lobed on either or both sides giving them a "mitten" profile, dark green above, paler underneath, 5 cm long
- flowers 2 cm wide, with white to pink petals, up to 20 stamens, borne in clusters
- fruits small, cherry-shaped, yellowish to dull red when ripe, 10-16 mm in diameter

Habitat: On the margins and within the saturated edges of forested and shrub swamps. One of the most common shrub/tree species on the outer margins of sphagnum bogs. Also common to the fringes of coastal estuaries.

Range: Southern Alaska south to Sonoma County, California; from the coast to the western foothills of the Cascades to 1,000 m elevation.

Similar Species: There are many species of escaped, naturalized domestic apples and pears that are very similar to this native species. However, most domesticated species, even when escaped, do not tend to colonize in the same saturated conditions of western crabapple. Black hawthorn *(Crataegus douglasii)* grows in similar habitats and has thorns that may be confused with spurs, but it is generally shorter and less densely twigged. No other native species has the same dark bark with spurs, a messy, freely branched crown, and leaves that are mitten-shaped.

Functional Value: Herbivores may browse on leaves, twigs, and buds. Fruits are consumed by birds, including upland game birds such as grouse. When crabapple forms a dense thicket, it provides excellent escape habitat and nesting locations for many songbirds.

Ethnobotanical Uses: The fruits are edible and have been used in preserves, jams, jellies, pies, and applesauce. Native Americans reduced the tartness of the fruits by storing them over winter and eating them in spring. The wood was used in building, and for ax and tool handles. Crabapple bark has been used as a tea to soothe sore throat, reduce fever, and for intestinal disorders. As in commercial apples, the seeds of crabapples contain cyanide-producing compounds that are toxic.

Menziesia ferruginea
rusty Menziesia; mock azalea; fool's huckleberry

Family: Ericaceae
Status: FACU+
Color photo page 78

Rusty Menziesia is a straggling or erect deciduous shrub 0.5-3 m tall. Leaves are thin, papery with indented veins, bright green, oval-elliptic, 4-6 cm long, with slightly toothed to wavy-fringed margins; they are often sparsely clustered at stem ends and appear to be horizontally arranged. Leaf surfaces are covered with glands and have a skunk-like smell. Blooms May to July.

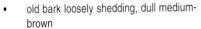

- old bark loosely shedding, dull medium-brown
- young branches covered with fine gland-tipped, rust-colored hairs
- leaves bright red-orange in fall
- flowers single or double, pinkish orange, urn-shaped, small (6-8 mm long), on smooth stalks, 1-2 cm long
- fruits woody capsules, 5 mm long, with pointed tip 4-8 mm long

Habitat: Shady, moist woods and along stream banks. Also found on hummocks in scrub-shrub wetlands.

Range: Alaska south along the coast and in the Cascades to northern California.

Similar Species: Twinberries *(Lonicera* species) are similar when plants are young, but the leaves of twinberry are net-veined, drooping, not as bright green, rounded or papery, and the bark is shiny silvery-tan. Blueberries and huckleberries *(Vaccinium* species) have bark that does not shed, leaves that are more highly veined and nonindented, white or pink flowers, and fruits that are berries.

Functional Value: Fruits and buds are consumed by upland game birds, such as grouse.

Branch of rusty Menziesia in leaf and flower.

Ethnobotanical Uses: Rusty Menziesia can not be used as an ornamental because it requires a special soil fungus to survive that does not thrive when transplanted.

Genus: *Myrica*
Family: Myricaceae

The gales or wax myrtles are aromatic shrubs to small trees that are commonly associated with bogs or scrub-shrub wetlands. They are often covered with glands and slightly to very aromatic. The leaves are alternate; leaves and fruits are waxy.

Functional Value: Fruits are eaten by some songbirds. Pacific wax-myrtle aids dune stabilization and has nitrogen-fixing bacteria that enriches the soil. The dense shrub cover provides habitat and cover for birds.

Ethnobotanical Uses: Sweetgale is used for scenting wax, as a tea for tuberculosis, as a steambath switch, and for flavoring homebrew beer and gale beer. Both species are valuable ornamentals, particularly Pacific wax-myrtle because it is tolerant of salt spray and is effective in highway plantings in sandy areas.

Myrica californica
Pacific wax-myrtle; California wax-myrtle; bayberry
Status: FACW

Leaves and fruits of Pacific wax-myrtle with detail of fruit cluster.

Pacific wax-myrtle is a densely bushy, dark green, evergreen shrub to small tree, 2-6 m tall. Bark is thin, smooth, and brown to light gray. Twigs are stout, dark green, slightly ridged, and short-hairy the first year. Older twigs are round and brown-green to steel gray. It is faintly aromatic. Unlike sweetgale, separate male and female flowers are borne on the same plant. Male catkins are approximately 5 mm long; female catkins 1-2 cm long. Blooms from April to May.

- leaves dark green, elliptic or elliptic-oblong with pointed tips, 5-8 cm long, smooth-margined to remotely toothed, short-hairy and finely black-dotted beneath
- young growth short-hairy and finely wax-dotted, but ultimately smooth; top of leaf lustrous, underneath pale
- flowers inconspicuous; females on top of plant, males below
- fruits small (4-8 mm), rounded, dark purplish, berry-like nuts, borne in clusters

Habitat: Pacific wax-myrtle occurs in shrub communites with moist but well-drained sandy or gravelly soils. It is typical of northwest Oregon coastal dune landscapes. It grows in the open or in shade. Associates include salal *(Gaultheria shallon),* evergreen huckleberry *(Vaccinium ovatum),* coast pine *(Pinus contorta),* bristly manza-nita *(Arctostaphylos columbiana),* and bigleaf rhododendron *(Rhododendron macrophyllum).* Also frequently found in shrub communities on flood-plains, inundated with surface water 3-4 months of the year. In these con-ditions, wax myrtle is as-sociated with Hooker wil-low *(Salix hookeriana),* coast pine *(Pinus contorta)* and sitka spruce *(Picea sitchensis).*

Range: Pacific wax-myrtle occurs in coastal counties from Washing-ton, to California.

Myrica gale var. *gale*
sweetgale; Pacific bayberry
Status: OBL
Color photo page 78

Sweetgale is a small deciduous shrub 0.5-2 m tall. The bark and twigs are dark gray- to red-brown and slender. A profusion of yellow wax glands on the leaves give this plant its characteristic sweet odor. Male and female flowers are borne on separate plants. Male catkins are 1-2 cm long. Blooms between April and June.

Leaves and female catkins of sweetgale.

- leaves oval with rounded tip, 3-6 cm long, mostly smooth-margined with coarse teeth on the outer half, may appear dusty gray; stalks short (0.3 cm)
- young leaves densely hairy
- flowers many, clustered in catkins that appear prior to leaves
- female catkins oval, cone-like, 8-10 mm long, covered with yellow, scented wax
- fruits beaked nutlets, 2-3 mm long, winged at the base

Habitat: Sweetgale occurs in lowland to montane bogs and coastal swamps, along lake margins and riverbanks; also grows well on the upper fringes of salt marshes. It prefers full sun and wet moderately nitrogen-rich soils. It is symbiotic with a nitrogen-fixing bacterium. Often associated with slough sedge *(Carex obnupta)*, water sedge *(Carex aquatilis)*, and Douglas spirea *(Spiraea douglasii)*.

Range: Sweetgale has circumpolar distribution. Alaska to Newfoundland, south to northwest Oregon, British Columbia, Michigan, Wisconsin, Virginia; and in the Appalachians to Tennessee and North Carolina.

Oemleria cerasiformis
(Osmaronia cerasiformis)
Indian plum; osoberry

Family: Rosaceae
Status: FACU
Color photos page 78

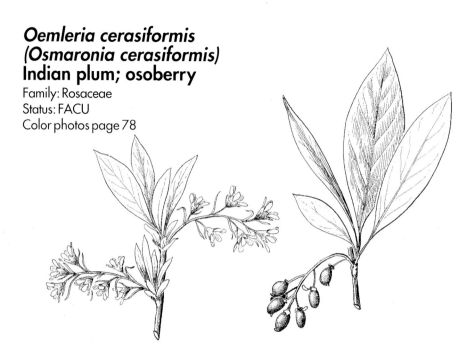

Leaves and flowers (left) and leaves and fruits (right) of Indian plum.

Indian plum is a deciduous shrub to small tree, to 5 m tall, with one or several, equal-sized stems. Buds are bright green in winter and turn red by early spring. Leaves have smooth margins, are 5-15 cm long, 2-4 cm wide, and oblong to lance-shaped. Male and female flowers occur on separate or on the same plant. Female flowers have a pleasant odor; however, the male flowers smell like cat urine. Blossoms precede, or coincide with, the emergence of the leaves in February through early March.

- one of the first shrubs to flower in spring
- bark on young twigs and older branches smooth, deep red-brown, with round, gray pores
- new leaves tend to stand upright or at 45-degree angle from twig
- leaves alternate, bright green above, paler and waxy underneath, 10 cm long
- flowers creamy white-green, 5-petaled, in hanging clusters
- fruits yellow-red turning deep purple

Habitat: Along stream banks, roadsides, and the edges of open woods. Tolerant of fluctuating water table, grows in moister sites than many upland shrubs. Prefers nutrient-rich soils. Slightly shade-tolerant; therefore, found in forest openings and edges. Commonly associated with red elderberry *(Sambucus racemosa)*.

Range: British Columbia to northern California and the west side of the Sierra Nevada; from the Pacific Coast to the west slope of the Cascades. Occurs in all counties in our area.

Similar Species: Black twinberry *(Lonicera involucrata)* has bright green and distinctly ridged young twigs, yellow-tan and shaggy mature bark, opposite leaves, and paired, yellow flowers subtended by a purple-red bract. Western serviceberry *(Amelanchier alnifolia)* also has oblong leaves with smooth margins, but the tips are toothed, and the buds are purple.

Functional Value: Fruits are eaten by birds. Indian plum is often used as a nesting habitat by small songbirds.

Ethnobotanical Uses: The fruits are edible fresh or dried. Native Americans made preserves from the fruits and used the leaves, in small amounts, in salads.

Oplopanax horridus
devil's club
Family: Araliaceae
Status: FAC+
Color photos page 78

SHRUBS

This is a fiercely spiny, deciduous shrub with stems 1-3 m tall. Stem color is usually a pale buff with yellow-tinged, long spines. The large, deeply palmate leaves have 7-9 lobes, are unevenly toothed, bright green, alternate, and 10-35 cm wide.

- entire shrub covered with stiff spines 5-10 mm long, including the leaf veins
- foliage and stems with musky aroma
- flowers pyramid-shaped, greenish white, 5-petaled, 5-6 mm long
- fruits bright red, 4 mm long, with 2-3 seeds, in terminal panicles

Habitat: Moist, forested conditions associated with hillside seeps and springs, stream corridors, or roadside ditches. Prefers shaded conditions in nitrogen-rich soils. Associates include understory plants such as lady fern *(Athyrium filix-femina)*, bedstraws *(Galium* species), skunk-cabbage *(Lysichiton americanum)*, and three-leaf foam-flower *(Tiarella trifoliata)*.

Range: Alaska south to Oregon, east and west sides of the Cascades, east as far as Michigan and Ontario.

Similar Species: Swamp gooseberry *(Ribes lacustre)* is much smaller with finer spines, and palmately lobed leaves that are deeply indented and much smaller than those of devil's club. The leaves, stems, and foliage of the gooseberry are not aromatic. Thimbleberry *(Rubus parviflorus)* has large palmate leaves, but no spines on either the leaves or stems.

Functional Value: Leaves are eaten by slugs; fruits eaten by bears. Devil's club makes a very effective

Flowers and painfully spiny leaves and stems of devil's club; detail of fruit above.

buffer to prevent human and/or livestock intrusion into wetland habitats. Often indicates the location of seeps.

Ethnobotanical Uses: Fruits are inedible. Native Americans used the inner bark and roots for many medicines. They rubbed the berries into the scalp to repel lice, treat dandruff, and make hair shiny. The stems were used to make fishhooks and lures. The outer bark can be used as a dye or deodorant.

Physocarpus capitatus
Pacific ninebark

Family: Rosaceae
Status: FACW-
Color photo page 79

Leaves and flowers of Pacific ninebark.

Pacific ninebark is a spreading to erect deciduous shrub, 2-4 m tall. Twigs are large, 5 mm in diameter, and heavily ridged on both sides. Leaves are broadly rounded at the base and have a toothed margin. Flowers have 5 short petals (3.5 mm) and up to 30 stamens. Blooms May to June.

- bark thin shedding to flaking, light tan to dark reddish brown, peeling in strips on older stems and twigs
- leaves alternate, palmately 3- to 5-lobed, 4-8 cm long, dark green above and lighter underneath, bright yellow in fall
- flowers creamy white, in terminal, dense, round-topped clusters, highly visible from a distance
- fruits woody follicles, reddish brown, 0.6-1 cm long

Habitat: Low elevation stream banks, swamps, lake margins, and the edges of woods and meadows in nitrogen-rich soils or on mineral, alluvial soils. Also grows in semi-open or open canopy forest. Tolerant of water table fluctuations. Often associated with redstem dogwood *(Cornus sericea)* and salmonberry *(Rubus spectabilis)*.

Range: Southern Alaska south to the central Sierras, and east to northern Idaho. Most common in the western Cascades at low elevations. Occurs in all counties in our area.

Similar Species: Another shrub with palmately lobed leaves is vine maple *(Acer circinatum)*, but it has green twigs and opposite leaves with red leaf stalks. Pacific ninebark may also be confused with salmonberry *(Rubus spectabilis)*, which is found in the same habitats, has similar shedding bark, and tri-lobed leaves. However, salmonberry has leaves that are pinnately lobed, single magenta flowers, and orange to red berries. The bark of thimbleberry *(Rubus parviflorus)* is also brown and shredding, but it has much larger leaves, crimson berries similar to blackberries, and prefers full sun along roadsides.

Functional Value: The twigs, buds, and foliage are browsed by herbivores.

Ethnobotanical Uses: Native Northwest peoples used the wood for toys and knitting needles. The bark is believed to be toxic and should not be eaten. Used to a limited extent as an ornamental.

Genus: *Rhododendron*
Family: Ericaceae

The rhododendrons are evergreen shrubs. Leaves are alternate, leathery, and glandular, with smooth margins that curl under. Flowers have 5 white petals and are borne in terminal racemes. There are 5-12 stamens.

Similar Species: Bog rosemary *(Andromeda polifolia)* and bog laurel *(Kalmia microphylla* ssp. *occidentalis)* are other members of the heath family found in bogs, but both have a white midstripe, on the upper leaf surface, which is lacking in the Labrador-tea species. Bog rosemary generally is a much more delicate plant with narrow leaves that are not hairy below. Bog laurel has smaller, upright leaves that are dark green above and waxy white, or with fine gray hairs, below. Labrador-tea is the only member of the heath family in bogs to have the dense rusty hairs on the underside of the older leaves, as well as the distinctive pungent odor.

Ethnobotanical Uses: Labrador-tea can be used as a tea to treat colds, sore throats, headache, heart troubles, and indigestion. May produce an allergic reaction causing dizziness and diarrhea.

Rhododendron groenlandicum (Ledum groenlandicum)
Labrador-tea
Status: OBL
Color photo page 79

- multibranched shrub to 2.5 m tall; twigs with dense rusty hairs
- leaves olive green, 6 cm long, covered with dense, rust-colored, cottony hairs on the undersides; hairs can be pure white on new leaves
- all parts of plant strongly glandular with very distinctive, pleasant, resinous odor from crushed leaves or stems
- flowers densely clustered, 1 cm wide
- fruits oval, hairy, woody capsules 7 mm wide
- blooms May to July

Habitat: Commonly found in sphagnum bogs and may also occur in forested or shrub swamps with little or no sphagnum present. Labrador-tea is intolerant of shade and prefers soils that are at least periodically saturated during the growing season.

Range: Alaska to Greenland, south along the coast to northwestern Oregon.

Stems, leaves, and flowers of Labrador-tea with detail of woody capsules.

Rhododendrons continued on next page...

SHRUBS

37

Rhododendron neoglandulosum
(Ledum glandulosum)
smooth Labrador-tea; trapper's tea

Status: FACW+
Color photo page 79

Leaves flowers, and fruits of smooth Labrador-tea.

- small shrub (less than 1 m)
- leaves elliptical to lance-shaped, usually rounded at the tip, 5 cm long, with white hairs (not densely hairy) below
- flowers few, large (to 3 cm long), creamy to pink
- fruits oval, glandular, woody capsules, 5 mm wide
- blooms June to August

Habitat: Same as Labrador-tea. In addition, smooth Labrador-tea grows in coastal areas.

Range: Same as Labrador-tea. Smooth Labrador-tea is more common in the south of our range than Labrador-tea.

Ribes bracteosum
stink currant; California black currant

Family: Grossulariaceae
Status: FAC
Color photo page 79

Stink currant is an erect, but straggly, deciduous shrub 1.5-3 m tall. Leaves are the largest of all currants in our area. Blooms May to June.

- no thorns or spines
- stems and leaves with small, yellow glands that have a sweetish skunk-like or cat-like odor (somewhat unpleasant) when crushed
- leaves 4-18 cm wide, palmately lobed, with 5-7 deep lobes
- flowers green-purple, disk- or saucer-shaped, borne in upright, erect spikes 15-30 cm long
- fruits large berries (1 cm long), purple, with white waxy blush, edible, arranged on an erect spike

Detail of individual flower and berries.

Leaves and flower spikes of stink currant.

Habitat: Stream banks and moist woods, often where there is at least periodic saturation or seepage. Common in the upland/wetland transition zone within forested wetlands.

Range: Alaska, south to northwestern California; most common on the west side of the Cascades in Washington, although occasionally found on the east side. Occurs in all counties in our area.

Similar Species: Other currant species have similar leaves, but this species is distinguished by the large leaf size, absence of spines, and most distinctly — the smell of the stems and leaves. Red currant *(Ribes sanguineum)* also lacks spines, but has much smaller leaves. Wax currant *(Ribes divaricatum)* has smaller leaves, thorns at the nodes, and drooping, white-petaled flowers. Thimbleberry *(Rubus parviflorus)* has single, large, 5-petaled white flowers, red multicelled berries, leaves that are not as deeply lobed as those of stink currant, and no glands. Rose species usually have spines or thorns, compound leaves, and woody hips.

Functional Value: Wildlife eat the fruits and foliage.

Ethnobotanical Uses: Native Americans ate the berries and used the twigs and leaves to line baskets.

Ribes divaricatum var. *divaricatum*
wax currant; coast black currant
Family: Grossulariaceae
Status: FAC

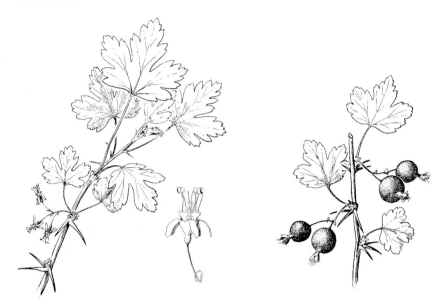

Leaves and flowers of wax currant with a detail of individual flower; and branch with berries.

Wax currant is a deciduous, multiple-branched, sometimes short-hairy, spreading shrub 1.5-3 m tall. It commonly has several robust limbs which bend over. Bark is gray to brownish and unarmed except where the leaves attach. Twigs are whitish or purplish gray and 2-3 mm in diameter. Stamens extend 1-2 mm past the petals. Blooms April to May.

- 1-3 robust, downward-curving spines (10-20 mm) where leaves attach
- leaves small, 2-6 cm wide, palmately 3- to 5-lobed
- flowers white-petaled with purplish backward-bent sepals, grouped in 2's or 3's, borne in lateral, drooping clusters from where the leaves attach to stem
- berries 1 cm long, purple-red, in 2s or 3s, rounded

Habitat: Open woods to moist hillsides, very common in forested transition zones and along streams.

Range: Western Cascades in British Columbia to mid-California coast to lower foothills; up the Columbia Gorge to Klickitat County. Occurs in all counties in our area.

Similar Species: Swamp gooseberry *(Ribes lacustre)* has stems that are covered with spines and much larger leaves. Stink currant *(Ribes bracteosum)* has larger leaves and an inflorescence that is a terminal, erect spike with red-petaled flowers. Red currant *(Ribes sanguineum)* is found in upland habitats, has no spines, and deep magenta flowers.

Ethnobotanical Uses: Fruit is edible.

Ribes lacustre
swamp gooseberry; prickly currant

Family: Grossulariaceae
status: FAC+
Color photos page 79

Swamp gooseberry is an erect to spreading decidu-ous shrub mostly 1-2 m tall. The young branches are densely soft-prickly. Leaves are often sparsely soft-prickly along the veins. Blooms April to July.

- stems copper-colored, thickly bristled with slender, sharp, golden prickles and larger spines (to 12 mm long) where the leaves attach
- leaves 2-5 cm long, palmately 3- to 5-lobed, toothed, indented, broad, mostly smooth-sur-faced
- flowers greenish pink, saucer-shaped (fused at base), 1 mm, borne in drooping clusters of 7-15; petal color usually deepens with age to dark pink, red, or maroon
- berries 6-8 mm long, dark purple, usually covered with glands

Leaves, flowers, and very prickly stems of swamp currant.

Individual flower and berries.

Habitat: Moist, open woods and stream banks to drier forest slopes or subalpine ridges. Very com-mon in the wetland/upland transition zone.

Range: Alaska to Newfoundland, south to Califor-nia. Occurs in all counties in our area.

Similar Species: Other currant species have similar, palmately lobed leaves, but swamp goose-berry is the only one that has spines along the stem. Wax currant *(Ribes divaricatum)* is closest in ap-pearance and also has spines only where leaves

are attached to stem, but has smaller leaves. Devil's club *(Oplopanax horridus)* is taller and with single stems, longer spines, and much larger leaves. The roses also have prickly stems, but the leaves are compound and flowers petals are separate.

Functional Value: Wildlife commonly eat the fruits.

Ethnobotanical Uses: Fruits are edible and the largest of the common currants. Leaves and ber-ries can be made into a tea. Spines can cause an allergic reaction on the skin.

SHRUBS

Ribes sanguineum
red currant; red-flowering currant

Family: Grossulariaceae
Status: NI (upl)
Color photo page 80

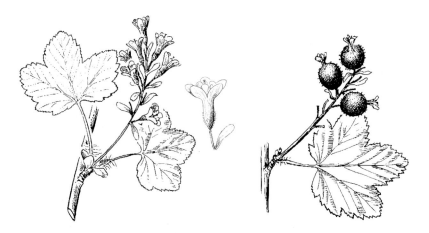

Leaves and flowers of red currant with a detail of individual flower; and branch with berries.

This is an erect, upland deciduous shrub 1-3 m tall. Flowers are present in early spring, prior to dense leaf emergence, making this species easy to spot throughout open woodlands. Fruits are black, round, 2-9 mm long, and rarely seen.

- no thorns or spines
- leaves 2.5-6 cm wide, palmately 3- to 5-lobed
- flowers pale magenta to deep red, tubular, 3-5 mm, borne in erect to drooping clusters of 10-20

Habitat: Common in dry, open woods adjacent to wetlands. Red currant is shade-intolerant.

Range: British Columbia to the Coast Range of California south of San Francisco; from the coast to the east slope of the Cascades in Washington and Oregon, but only found west of the Cascades in Washington. Occurs in all counties in our area.

Similar Species: Wax currant *(Ribes divaricatum)* and swamp gooseberry *(Ribes lacustre)* have prickly stems and spines where the leaves attach. Stink currant *(Ribes bracteosum)* is also lacking spines, but has a distinctive odor and leaves 4-18 cm wide.

Functional Value: Leaves are browsed by herbivores and the fruits are eaten by a wide variety of wildlife species.

Ethnobotanical Uses: Commonly used as an ornamental. Berries are edible but unpalatable.

Rosa eglanteria
sweetbrier rose; ornamental rose

Family: Rosaceae
Status: FACW
Color photo page 80

Sweetbrier rose is a deciduous escaped ornamental, 1-2 m tall, often found around wetlands. It is the only rose that is highly armed with stout and strongly curved spines. Flowers are usually multiple and borne in clusters. Blooms June to July.

- stems with many spines, 10-20 mm, along the entire length
- leaves compound, 5-7 leaflets per leaf, lower leaf surface with many fine spines, sweet smelling
- flowers dark pink, petals 2 cm long
- hips bright red, nearly round, 1-1.5 cm long

Flower with petals and after petals have dropped.

Leaves, hips, and flowers of sweetbrier rose with detail of hip.

Habitat: Along roadsides and drainage swales, and in pastures and abandoned fields. Grows well in moist soils in open habitats. Sweetbrier rose is shade-intolerant.

Range: Western Cascades, along coast to lower foothills; also occurs along East Coast of United States.

Similar Species: The native roses, baldhip rose *(Rosa gymnocarpa)*, Nootka rose *(Rosa nutkana)*, and peafruit rose *(Rosa pisocarpa)*, have more delicate spines.

Functional Value: This is a valuable hedge shrub that provides a protective screen and nesting habitat.

Ethnobotanical Uses: Hips are edible and can be used for tea. Used in hedgerows as an ornamental.

Genus: *Rosa*
Roses (native species)
Family: Rosaceae

These three native roses are quite similar. (A non-native, sweetbrier rose, *Rosa eglanteria*, is treated separately.) They are all deciduous shrubs that usually grow 1-2 m tall. They have alternate, pinnately compound leaves, and flowers that are pink to deep rose. There are, however, subtle differences in prickles, leaflet shape and number, flower size, and shape and size of fruits (hips).

Similar Species: Most similar to each other. Some of the currants *(Ribes* species) also have bristly stems, but do not have compound leaves.

Functional Value: Fruits are consumed by various herbivores and upland game birds. Leaves and twigs are eaten by browsers. Thickets provide excellent nesting and escape habitat for songbirds.

Ethnobotanical Uses: As a source of vitamin C, the hips may be prepared as a tea and the rinds of hips may be eaten raw (seeds are irritating). These species can be used for hedgerows or as ornamentals. Native Americans made a poultice by mashing the leaves of the Nootka rose and applied it on sore eyes, abscesses, and bee stings.

Rosa gymnocarpa var. *gymnocarpa*
baldhip rose; wild rose; wood rose
Status: FACU
Color photos page 80

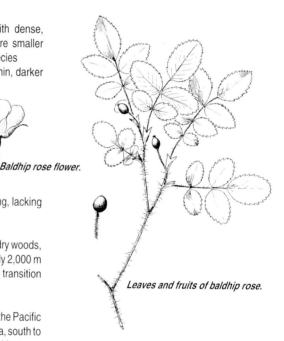

- stems nearly always covered with dense, straight, soft, fine prickles that are smaller than the other two native rose species
- leaflets 5-9, round at tip, elliptic, thin, darker green above, margins double-toothed with the teeth generally gland-tipped
- flowers small, 1-2 cm across, often solitary at branch ends
- hips smooth, tip rather pointed, red to orange, 6-8 mm long, lacking sepals and dried stamens at tip

Baldhip rose flower.

Leaves and fruits of baldhip rose.

Habitat: Baldhip rose grows in moist to dry woods, often in open sites from sea level to nearly 2,000 m and is restricted to upland areas and the transition zone between upland and wetland.

Range: Baldhip rose occurs throughout the Pacific Northwest from southern British Columbia, south to the Sierra Nevada and east to northeast Montana. Occurs in all counties in our area.

Rosa nutkana
Nootka rose

Status: FAC
Color photos page 80

- prickles, if present, curved backward, borne just below the stipules; mostly larger and stouter than those of the other two native rose species
- stems green, but sometimes with red hue, to 3 m tall, more robust than others, grow straight-erect, not intertwining
- leaflets 5-7, round at tip, dark green above, paler and slightly hairy underneath, margins double-toothed with glands, or single-toothed with no glands
- flowers large, 5-8 cm across, solitary or 2-3, at the ends of new, prickleless side branches
- hips spherical, orange-red, large, 1-2 cm broad, sepals and dried stamens remain attached to tip

Habitat: Nootka rose occurs in upland wooded regions or in open shrub wetlands in northern Washington.

Leaves, flower bud, flower, and hip of Nootka rose.

Range: Nootka rose is found throughout Oregon and Washington, north to British Columbia. Occurs in all counties in our area.

Rosa pisocarpa
peafruit rose; clustered wild rose; swamp rose

Status: FAC
Color photo page 80

- prickles, if present, stout, straight, borne below the stipules
- stems dark red, occasionally green and intertwining, to 2.5 m tall
- leaflets 5-9, sharp-toothed, sharply pointed at the tip
- flowers generally less than 4-5 cm across, seldom solitary
- hips egg-shaped, reddish purple, 1.2 cm long, sepals remain attached to tips, backs of the sepals are almost always coarsely glandular

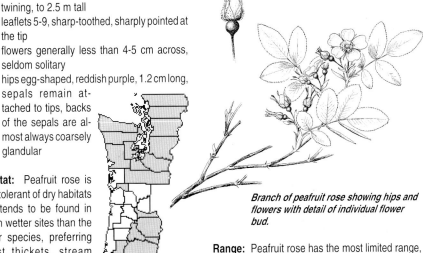

Habitat: Peafruit rose is less tolerant of dry habitats and tends to be found in much wetter sites than the other species, preferring moist thickets, stream banks, and swamps; it is shade-tolerant.

Branch of peafruit rose showing hips and flowers with detail of individual flower bud.

Range: Peafruit rose has the most limited range, from southern British Columbia to northern California and west of the Cascades.

Genus: *Rubus*
blackberries (non-native species)
Family: Rosaceae
Color photo page 81

The two, non-native blackberry species described here are invasive with sprawling, strongly armored stems that can be erect and form an impenetrable tangle. Both Himalayan *(Rubus procerus)* and evergreen *(Rubus laciniatus)* blackberries have prickles that are strong and sharp. The palmately compound leaves of each are essentially evergreen. Both species have white to pinkish flowers and fleshy, black-purple fruits, 1.5 cm thick. Bloom April to June.

Similar Species: Trailing blackberry *(Rubus ursinus)* has distinctly 3-lobed leaves, and stems are delicate and creeping. Blackcap *(Rubus leucodermis)* has pale, waxy, blue-green stems, smaller, hard fruits, and fine white hairs on the undersides of the leaves.

Functional Value: The fruits are used by numerous birds, and large and small mammals. Thickets provide excellent escape habitat and impenetrable buffers. Some songbirds, primarily sparrow species, use the tangle of branches as nest sites. Himalayan blackberry has been used in the past to stabilize road cuts; however, it can form complete monocultures eliminating all other species.

Ethnobotanical Uses: Himalayan blackberry was originally introduced as a horticultural species and was raised for its fruit. Gatherers still collect the succulent, though somewhat seedy, fruit for jams, pies, and eating in late summer. Commercial cultivation is now limited. The fruits of evergreen blackberry are also collected recreationally, although they contain more seeds.

Rubus laciniatus
evergreen blackberry; cut-leaf blackberry
Status: FACU+
Color photos page 81

The leaflets of evergreen blackberry are deeply divided and sharply toothed. Flower petals are 9-14 mm long. Stamens usually number more than 75.

- stems thinner (about 1.5 cm wide) than Himalayan, reddish green, to 12 m long with downward pointing prickles, more curving than Himalayan
- leaves dark green above, gray-green and partially hairy below
- leaflets 5 or 3, with many prickles, incised, deeply lobed, with coarsely toothed margins
- many hard seeds noticeable in fruits

Stems, leaves, and fruits of evergreen blackberry.

Habitat: A pioneering, invasive species of disturbed upland sites. Prefers bright sun and is intolerant of deep shade. Grows along roadsides, railroad grades, disturbed pastures, and fence rows. Evergreen blackberry, although not as common as Himalayan, is usually not found without the presence of Himalayan blackberry.

Range: An escaped and naturalized Eurasian species found from British Columbia south to California, mostly on the west side of the Cascades. Occurs in all counties in our area.

Rubus procerus
(Rubus discolor)
Himalayan blackberry

Status: FACU (fac)
Color photo page 81

The young stems of Himalayan blackberry are often green; older growth can be deep red to burgundy. Dead stems are pale tan and often persist within the thicket tangle. Petals are 10-15 mm long. Stamens often number more than 100.

- stems stout (about 2 cm wide), strongly 4-angled, to 10 m long, with thick back-pointing prickles
- leaves alternate, 12-25 cm wide, green above, with white hairs below
- leaflets 3-5, oval, with toothed margins

Habitat: Same as evergreen blackberry. Himalayan blackberry can dominate wetlands.

Range: Same as evergreen blackberry.

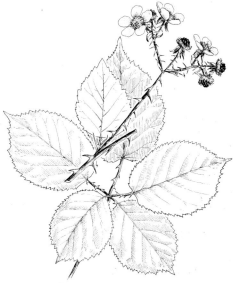

Stems, leaves, flowers, and immature fruits of Himalayan blackberry.

SHRUBS

Rubus parviflorus var. *parviflorus*
thimbleberry; western thimbleberry

Status: FAC-
Color photo page 81

*Twigs, leaves, and flowers of
thimbleberry with a detail of fruit.*

Habitat: Open moist to dry sites. In our range thimbleberry is most common in areas of bright sun, such as roadsides, edges of forests, and logged slopes. Often found in the transition zone associated with wetlands. Associates include red alder *(Alnus rubra)* and red elderberry *(Sambucus racemosa)*.

Range: Sea level to subalpine mountain slopes, from Alaska south to southern California, east to the Great Lakes region. Occurs in all counties in our area.

Similar Species: The large, bright green leaves with a fuzzy, felt-like texture and the crimson, cone-like berries of thimbleberry are quite unique. The bark of salmonberry *(Rubus spectabilis)* is similar although shiny, has stems with prickles, smaller and pinnately compound leaves, and orange-yellow or red fruits. The bark of western serviceberry *(Amelanchier alnifolia)* is also similar, but has simple leaves with round, toothed tips, and fruits that are a reddish brown, fleshy, dark purple, and blueberry-like. Pacific ninebark *(Physocarpus capitatus)* has brown shedding bark, but much smaller leaves, and fruits that are a woody capsule. Stink currant *(Ribes bracteosum)* has green-purple flowers and deeply lobed leaves with yellow glands that emit a skunk-like odor when crushed.

Thimbleberry is an erect deciduous shrub 0.5-2.5 m tall. Leaves are most often somewhat short-hairy, giving them a very soft, felt-like texture. Flowers are usually white, 2.5 cm across, in loose, 3- to 11-flowered clusters; petals are 30 mm long. Fruits are fleshy berries that separate from the inner pith in a thimble or hemispherical shape. Blooms June to July.

- stems with dull brown shedding bark, weak, no prickles
- leaves bright light green, palmately 5-lobed, doubly toothed, 6-15 cm long and somewhat broader, lobes triangular
- fruits edible, crimson, with many seeds

Functional Value: Fruits are eaten by many species of wildlife from songbirds and upland game birds to small and large mammals, such as black bears. Leaves and twigs are grazed by browsers. Thimbleberry often forms thickets that are excellent for cover and nesting.

Ethnobotanical Uses: The tart fruits are well liked by some, avoided by others. Those who appreciate them have described them as "red velvet raspberries." The leaves make an excellent source of woodland tissue paper.

Rubus spectabilis var. *spectabilis*
salmonberry
Status: FAC+
Color photos page 82

Salmonberry is a deciduous rhizomatous shrub, usually 1-4 m tall, with erect or arching stems. Stems are often densely prickly on the upper portions of new growth. The twigs in winter tend to have a distinctive golden-brown to rust-red color. Blooms April to July.

* old stems lack prickles; bark paper-thin, shedding
* leaves pinnately compound, dark green, with 3, or sometimes 5, toothed leaflets
* flowers bright magenta, relatively large, 2 cm across
* fruits fleshy berries commonly yellow to golden orange or deep scarlet

Habitat: Lowland moist woods, stream banks, and wetlands. Can form dense thickets or grow individually. Young stems in open settings are often unbranched and form a single, slender arching stem.

Range: Alaska south to northwestern California, from the coast to the Cascades, rarely east of the Cascades. Occurs in all counties in our area.

Twigs, leaves, and flowers of salmonberry.

Similar Species: The currants *(Ribes* species) and thimbleberry *(Rubus parviflorus)* have leaves that are palmately lobed, not pinnately compound. With their stout prickles, blackberries species of *Rubus* are much better armored than salmonberry. Pacific ninebark *(Physocarpus capitatus)* occurs in the same habitats and has similar reddish brown shedding bark, but has no prickles, palmately lobed leaves, creamy white flowers in dense flat-topped clusters, and reddish brown, woody fruits. In winter, stems of Douglas spirea *(Spiraea douglasii)* look similar to those of salmonberry, but spirea has smooth, deep red bark with short knobs along the stem.

Functional Value: Fruits are eaten by a variety of wildlife and bird species. The early blooming flowers are important for various insects including bees, as well as for hummingbirds. Leaves, twigs, and stems are grazed by browsers, such as deer. Thickets provide excellent escape habitats and nesting sites for songbirds.

Ethnobotanical Uses: Fruits were an important food source for Native Americans and are still collected today. Salmonberry is a useful shrub in created wetlands because it transplants easily.

Rubus ursinus ssp. *macropetalus*
trailing blackberry; dewberry

Status: FACU

Color photo page 82

*Stems, leaves, and flowers of trailing
blackberry.*

Under a forested canopy, trailing blackberry often grows as a slender, single, trailing or climbing stem to 6 m long. In open areas, multiple stems can form dense tangles over stumps and logs. It is semi-evergreen. Male and female flowers are borne on separate plants. Flowers are white and 5-petaled; the petals of the male flowers are larger, to 1.5 cm long. Usually only bears fruit in open, sunny sites. Blooms April to August.

- stems covered with fine, waxy powder, light green to green, with tiny, sharply recurved, hooked spines
- leaves alternate, composed of 3 leaflets, dark green above, pale white-green underneath, with prickles on the stalks and major veins
- fruits fleshy berries, deep red to shiny blue-black, 2.5 cm long, 1 cm wide

Habitat: Clearings and open to fairly dense woods. Grows in upland or transition zones. Thrives in clear-cuts, fire scars, and under transmission lines.

Range: British Columbia to northern California, from the coast to middle elevations in the mountains, east to central Idaho. Occurs in all counties in our area.

Similar Species: Himalayan blackberry *(Rubus procerus)* is similar in the leaf formation, but is erect and much more robust. Blackcap *(Rubus leucodermis)*, a less common native, has similar leaves and fruits, but the stems are pale green-blue and erect, leaves have fine white hairs underneath, and fruits are purple when ripe.

Functional Value: The fruit is a valuable food source for a variety of birds and mammals, especially small mammals because it is at ground level.

Ethnobotanical Uses: Important source for many commercial blackberry cultivars, such as loganberries and boysenberries. As one of the only native blackberries, it is prized by gatherers for its flavor and firm texture.

Sambucus racemosa ssp. *pubens*
red elderberry; European red elderberry

Family: Caprifoliaceae
Status: FACU
Color photo page 82

Red elderberry forms a deciduous shrub 3-6 m tall. Branches are opposite. Twigs are quite large in diameter, deeply furrowed and lined, and greenish brown. Inside the stems and branches is very dry-spongy, old pith which is dark red-beige. Blooms May to July.

- stems gray with pattern of whitish to orange raised spots on bark; new twigs purple
- leaves opposite, pinnately compound, 4.5-17 cm long
- leaflets number 5-7, oval, sharply toothed along margins
- flowers creamy white, concentrated in a dense, usually erect to drooping, pyramidal cluster
- fruits clustered in erect spike; fleshy and bright red when ripe

Range: Circumboreal; west of the Cascades in our area. Occurs in all counties in our range.

Leaves and flower cluster of red elderberry.

Habitat: Common in moist, disturbed habitats adjacent to wetlands and along stream banks.

Similar Species: Blue elderberry *(Sambucus cerulea)* is smaller (3-4 m tall), has flat-topped clusters of flowers or fruits, and the berries are blue-black with a "bloom" of wax and yeast on the surface that gives them a light blue appearance. Blue elderberry occurs more frequently in the Willamette Valley region in Oregon and from Olympia to the Washington coast range; common around Mount St. Helens, even at 300 m elevation.

Functional Value: Fruits are eaten by many mammals and birds. Foliage and twigs are consumed by browsers.

Ethnobotanical Uses: Raw fruits may cause nausea but when cooked they can be made into syrup and jam. Occasionally used as an ornamental.

Sorbus scopulina
Greene's mountain ash; western mountain ash
Family: Rosaceae
Status: FACU

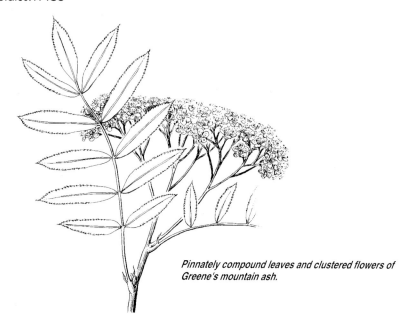

Pinnately compound leaves and clustered flowers of Greene's mountain ash.

Greene's mountain ash is an erect, several-stemmed, deciduous shrub to small tree, from 1-4 m tall. Twigs are round, 2-4 mm in diameter, brown, wrinkled, and slightly short hairy, with vertical, white to orange raised areas. Compound leaves have sharp-pointed and finely toothed leaflets. Blooms from May to early July.

*   winter buds dark brown, sticky, sparsely covered with white hairs
*   leaves alternate, pinnately compound, with 9-13 leaflets
*   flowers whitish, in a flat-topped cluster
*   fruits small (1 cm long), orange to scarlet, in clusters; from August through fall

Habitat: Upland woods, adjacent to woodlands.

Range: Alaska south to northern California, east to Alberta, the Dakotas and New Mexico. Most common east of the Cascades, but found from the foothills to the subalpine on the west side. Occurs in all counties in our area.

Similar Species: It is most likely that a mountain ash found within urban or rural (nonwilderness) areas of this region is one of the many escaped and naturalized non-native species such as Rowan tree *(Sorbus aucuparia)* and American mountain ash *(Sorbus americana)*. These species usually have more than 13 leaflets, with rounded tips and more coarsely toothed margins, and winter buds that are densely covered with long grayish hairs.

Functional Value: Fruits are a favorite food of songbirds and small mammals, and are an important source of winter food, even after they have rotted and fermented.

Ethnobotanical Uses: The native species are not as commonly used as ornamentals as the eastern species and cultivars, which are planted for their fall colors and distinctive fruits. The berries can be used to make a piquant jam.

Spiraea douglasii
Douglas spirea; hardhack

Family: Rosaceae
Status: FACW
Color photo page 82

Douglas spirea is a deciduous shrub 1-2.5 m tall. New growth in open settings can consist of vertical, thin, unbranched stems. Leaves are generally from 4-6 cm long but vary widely in shape and size. The undersides of the leaves can be very woolly to just slightly short-hairy and light in color. Blooms June to July.

- stems narrow (less than 1 cm wide), brittle, shiny medium-brown to purple-brown, with many old leaf nodes giving it a knobbly appearance; bark on older stems thin and shedding
- leaves alternate, oval to oblong, with toothed margins from the midpoint to the tip
- flowers pink in dense, terminal, upright, elongated spikes, several times longer than wide
- seed heads remain intact throughout the winter leaving a dark brown, distinctive elongated cluster at tops of stems

Habitat: Occurs in stream banks, swamps, bogs, along lake margins, and in damp meadows from sea level to subalpine; shade-intolerant. Very tolerant of fluctuating water table. Tolerates periodic to lengthy shallow inundation. Can often form dense monocultures on the disturbed edges of wetland communities, including bogs. Associates with salal *(Gaultheria shallon)*, soft rush *(Juncus effusus)*, salmonberry *(Rubus spectabilis)*, and cattails *(Typha* species).

Range: Southern Alaska south along the coast and inland to northern California, east to southeastern British Columbia, northern and central Idaho, and northeastern Oregon. Occurs in all counties in our area.

Similar Species: The distinctive pink inflorescences and long-lasting seed clusters make Douglas spirea easily distinguishable from other species. Salmonberry *(Rubus spectabilis)* appears similar in winter, but the branches have rust-red, peeling bark, prickles, and lack knobs. Common snowberry *(Symphoricarpos albus)* has narrower twigs and opposite leaves.

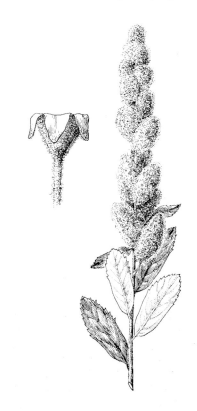

Erect stem of Douglas spirea showing flower cluster, and detail of individual flower.

Functional Value: Dense, nearly impenetrable thickets prevent human and/or livestock intrusion into wetlands. Douglas spirea also prevents other native species from surviving. Provides valuable escape habitat and nesting locations for many birds. Birds and small mammals feed on the seed heads, and large herbivores graze on the twigs and leaves.

Ethnobotanical Uses: May be used as an ornamental.

Symphoricarpos albus var. laevigatus
common snowberry

Family: Caprifoliaceae
Status: FACU
Color photo page 83

Branch of common snowberry showing leaves and small flowers.

Common snowberry is an erect deciduous shrub, generally 1-2 m tall. Twigs are very narrow, 1-5 mm, and brittle, and branch to form a "T". On the same plant, leaves can be simple and smooth-margined or coarsely toothed, or even lobed. Flowers are small, tiny, 5-7 mm long, pink to white, and borne in terminal or axillary racemes or spikes. Blooms May to August.

- branches many, fine, opposite; young branches light yellow-brown, older branches gray-brown; twigs upright
- leaves round to elliptic, opposite, with widely variable margins, 1.5-5 cm long, 1-3.5 cm wide
- fruits fleshy, white, round, 6-14 mm across, often borne in dense clusters, or sometimes singly

Habitat: Thickets, woodlands, and open slopes. Common snowberry is more common in deciduous than coniferous woods. Can tolerate fluctuating water tables, but prefers well-drained upland sites, except north of the Puget Basin, where it often tolerates saturated soils. A common component of the understory of woodlands, especially on edges and near openings where light is more available.

Range: From lowlands to moderate elevations. Alaska panhandle to Quebec, south to California, central Idaho, Colorado, Nebraska, and Virginia. Occurs in all counties in our area.

Similar Species: Douglas spirea *(Spiraea douglasii)* has larger twigs that are knobby and shiny reddish, and alternate leaves. Black twin-berry *(Lonicera involucrata)* also has yellow-silver-tan bark and opposite leaves, but twigs are bright green and ridged, bark sheds in strips, leaves are long and lance-shaped, and fruits are purple berries.

Functional Value: Fruits are valuable food for sharp-tailed and Franklin grouse, pine grosbeak, robins, and varied thrush. Snowberry is especially important because the fruit can hang on the shrub through the winter months. Twigs and foliage are also a valuable browse food for herbivores, such as deer.

Ethnobotanical Uses: May be used as an ornamental.

Vaccinium alaskaense
Alaska blueberry
Family: Ericaceae
Status: NI

Alaska blueberry is an erect, deciduous shrub 50-200 cm tall. Young twigs are yellow-green and somewhat angled; old bark is grayish. The underside of the leaf is lighter in color than the upper surface. Leaf veins, which are not prominent, have sparse glands. The single style extends just beyond the mouth of the corolla. Petals of the fused tube are round and shallowly lobed. Blooms May through June.

- leaves alternate, oval to elliptic, 2.5-6 cm long, with smooth margins or inconspicuously toothed on the bottom half, usually slightly hairy
- flowers bronzy pink, lantern-shaped, single, 7 mm long on stalks 5-15 mm long
- fruits blue-black to purplish black, 7-10 mm in diameter

Habitat: Grows in acidic, organic-rich soil in coniferous forests, in coastal to subalpine temperate and boreal climates. Often associated with Pacific rhododendron *(Rhododendron macrophyllum)* and bunchberry *(Cornus unalaschkensis)*.

Range: Along the coast and in the Cascades from Alaska to northwestern Oregon. Eastward in British Columbia to the Selkirk Mountains.

Similar Species: Other *Vaccinium* species, particularly the less common oval-leaved blueberry *(Vaccinium ovalifolium)*, are usually somewhat smaller (rarely greater than 60 cm), have prominent leaf veins that lack glands, shorter leaf stalks (less than 1 cm long), and a style that usually does not exceed the petals. Red huckleberry *(Vaccinium parvifolium)* is taller, has fewer leaves, bright green ridged stems, and red fruits.

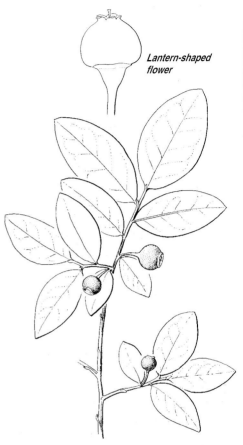

Lantern-shaped flower

Leaves and single flowers of Alaska blueberry.

Functional Value: Food for a variety of species; provides cover and perching sites.

Ethnobotanical Uses: *Vaccinium* species in general were used by Northwest native peoples as a source of food and dye. It is still popular fresh off the bush and for pies and jams.

Vaccinium oxycoccos var. *intermedius*
bog cranberry; small cranberry

Family: Ericaceae
Status: OBL
Color photo page 83

The vine-like stems of wild cranberry with detail of flower.

The evergreen leaves of wild cranberry are very small, with margins that are strongly turned under. Flowers are inconspicuous, usually solitary, and borne from midway to the tip of the branch. They are tiny (less than 1 cm long), deep pink, with 4 petals which are bent backwards. Leaves and berries often persist throughout the winter. Blooms June to July.

- tiny shrub, 10-40 cm, low-creeping, vine-like, with tangled, reddish brown stems 1 mm wide
- leaves alternate, thick, dark shiny green above and grayish white below, 2-6 mm long, 1.5-2 mm wide, oval-elliptic with pointed tip
- fruits 5-10 mm broad, ripening to deep red in the late fall

Habitat: Found in this region only within open sphagnum bogs from lowland to montane elevations. Creeps along the surface of the bog mat, often inconspicuous at first, however, fruits can be quite showy when they are present.

Range: Circumboreal; Alaska, Yukon, British Columbia and Alberta, south to Oregon and Idaho in the western United States.

Similar Species: None. Bog cranberry is the only bog shrub with slender, creeping stems.

Functional Value: Fruits are consumed by a variety of songbirds and upland game birds, as well as by various small mammals found within bog habitats.

Ethnobotanical Uses: Fruits are edible and were used by Native Americans across the continent. Wild cranberries are still collected by those who know where to find them and have the patience for picking them.

Vaccinium parvifolium
red huckleberry; red bilberry

Family: Ericaceae
Status: facu
Color photos page 83

Red huckleberry is an erect, deciduous shrub 1-4 m tall. Leaves are 1-3 cm long, usually smooth-margined, but can be slightly toothed on younger growth. Blooms May to June.

- stems bright green, slender (1-4 mm), distinctly angular-ridged, finely branched, often zigzag in shape
- bud scales often red in winter and early spring
- leaves alternate, thin, oval to oblong-elliptic, bright green, comparatively round-tipped
- Flowers are urn-shaped, whitish pink to green, 5 mm long.
- fruits bright red, fleshy, globose, translucent, 6-9 mm broad, contrasting sharply with the green twigs

Habitat: Most often grows on old decaying stumps or logs in moist coniferous woods, wetlands, or in the transition zone of wetlands. It is absent or scarce in dry woods. It is very shade-tolerant. Red huckleberry is one of the most frequent pioneering species on old stumps in association with western hemlock *(Tsuga heterophylla)* seedlings.

Range: Southeast Alaska to central California; west side of the Cascades. Occurs in all counties in our area.

Similar Species: Although similar to other *Vaccinium* species, red huckleberry is the most common in our area and is distinguished by its red fruits and bright green twigs. Other, lowland, tall shrub species of *Vaccinium* have blue-purple fruits. The winter twigs of vine maple *(Acer circinatum)* are also green, but are thicker and lack angular ridges. Rusty menziesia *(Menziesia ferruginea)* has net-veined leaves that are attached in a palmate pattern, orange flowers, and capsule fruits.

Fruiting branch of red huckleberry with detail of flower.

Functional Value: Fruits are an important food source for songbirds and upland game birds. Many mammals, from black bears to mice, feed on red huckleberries. Herbivores graze on the entire plant; it appears to be a favorite browse of deer.

Ethnobotanical Uses: Fruits are edible, though some people dislike the very tart flavor. Can be dried, mashed, or pressed for the juice. Frequently used as an ornamental.

Vaccinium uliginosum
bog blueberry

Family: Ericaceae
Status: FACW+
Color photo page 83

*Fruiting branch of bog blueberry
with detail of flower.*

Bog blueberry is a 20-50 cm tall, deciduous, mat-forming shrub of coastal bogs. It is freely branching and can be prostrate to erect. Younger branches are yellowish green and finely hairy; older branches have grayish red bark. Leaves are strongly net-veined on the lower surface. Flowers are pink, urn-shaped, with deeply triangular-lobed petals 5-6 mm long and usually 1-4 per cluster. Blooms May to July.

- leaves alternate, smooth-margined, oblong with widest point in the middle, 1-3 cm long, firm, leathery, with a rounded but slightly pointed tip, green above, pale green below
- buds with 4-7 conspicuous scales at base of stalk
- berries blue, 6-8 mm broad, covered with a thin waxy layer

Habitat: Very moist to wet, nitrogen-poor soils within tundra; boreal; cool temperate and cool moist climates; shade-intolerant. From lowlands to midmontane.

Range: Circumpolar and transcontinental in North America. Coastal from Alaska to northern California, eastwards in Canada to the Atlantic Coast; Eurasia.

Similar Species: Red huckleberry *(Vaccinium parvifolium)* is the most similar *Vaccinium* species, but it has narrower leaves that are not strongly net-veined, stems that are bright green with angular ridges and zigzag outline, and red berries. Many other *Vaccinium* species are found in Washington and Oregon but very few of these are found in the Puget lowlands, most others occur in higher elevations in the Olympic Mountains and/or are coastal-oriented.

Functional Value: Fruits are an important food for many songbirds and game birds. Mammals, especially deer, browse on the entire plant.

Ethnobotanical Uses: Very valuable to northern Native Americans as a source of food and dyes.

Introduction to the Willows (Genus: *Salix*)

Family: Salicaceae

Willows are common deciduous shrubs and trees associated with wet areas. They bear specialized floral structures, called ***catkins***, which are naked or petal-less flowers arranged in a compact cylindrical raceme or spike. Catkins are composed of either all male or female flowers. Plants are unisexual — either male or female. The furry "pussywillows" associated with willows in the spring are usually the male catkins; female catkins are more robust and may or may not be furry. Each flower on the catkin cylinder has a single, leaf-like ***floral bract***. A single, yellow ***gland*** may be present at the base of the pistil and occasionally at the base of the stamen(s). There are usually 2 ***stamens***, but sometimes 1,3,4,5,6,7 or 8, depending on the species. ***Stigmas*** are 2 in number and are whole or branched at the tip. The fruit is a dry ***capsule*** that is commonly attached to the central stem *(axil)* of the catkin by a small stem called a ***stipe***, however, in a few species, capsules are attached directly to the catkin axil. The capsule opens when mature to yield a cottony fluff that carries the seeds. Leaves are alternate, lance-shaped, and with a pointed tip, or oblong with a large, rounded tip. They are either smooth and slightly waxy coated; hairy with the hairs all trending in the same direction giving a velvet-like sheen (Sitka willow); or with hairs arranged in all directions. Leaves can emerge in the spring either before the catkins, with the catkins or after the catkins depending upon the particular species. As a result, the order in which leaves and catkins develop is a characteristic helpful to identifying a species. ***Stipules*** are wing-like leafy appendages at the base of new leaves on most willows. These are either deciduous or persistent during the growing season. ***Leaf buds*** are set in the fall for the next year and are covered by a single shell-like ***scale***, which falls off at the beginning of the season to yield a scar at the base of the new leaf or branch. Willows often have ***leaf galls*** which are swollen growths on the leaves or stems of particular species resulting from the presence of insect larvae within the gall.

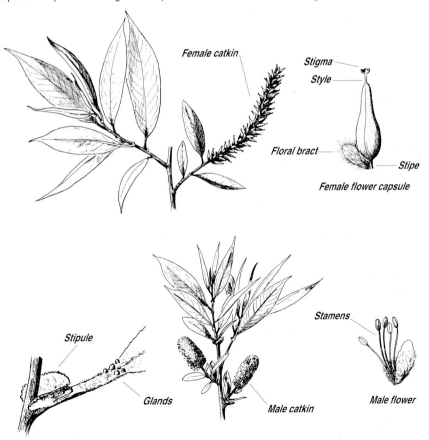

Female catkin

Stigma

Style

Floral bract

Stipe

Female flower capsule

Stipule

Glands

Male catkin

Stamens

Male flower

Eleven species of willow that are native to our region, or that have become widely naturalized are described. All of our lowland willows prefer a sunny, damp to wet habitat, and some require it; only Scouler willow thrives on well-drained slopes and tolerates shade. Many exotic species are used for horticultural purposes and are not naturalized. Many eastern Washington species, and species from other locations around the United States have been used in bioengineering projects along shorelines. These species are occasionally found but are not yet known to have become established; these often include the weeping or drooping willows.

The leaf shape of each species varies and is not the best feature for identification. Fruits should be examined whenever possible (spring). Characters to examine include glands, stamens, the capsule hairs, stigma, stipe, and floral bracts. Most of these features are easier to see using at least a 10x hand lens. Flower parts can be seen if the catkin is twisted to break it apart which exposes the capsules, floral bracts, glands or stamens, and filaments. It is common for willows to hybridize and so do not be surprised if the willow you are examining has intermediate characteristics of two different species.

Functional Value: Willows are highly favored by wildlife in our area. Willow buds are eaten by birds and small mammals. Deer and elk eat the twigs and leaves. Rabbits, mice, and beavers eat the bark. Beavers use willows to build their dams. Willows are often the dominant streambank plants where they prevent erosion by stabilizing the banks and providing nesting habitat for birds and mammals. Willows also shade stream banks enhancing fish habitat. Willow leaves provide a food source for aquatic bacteria during the fall and winter. The decaying leaves provides nutrients for the aquatic food chain.

Ethnobotanical Uses: Willows are used for ornamental plantings near water sources. They bloom early, can be used as shade trees, and the "pussy willows" (unopened male catkins) are used for decoration. Macerated willow wood contains a plant hormone that stimulates root growth. Native people of western Washington and Oregon used willow wood for construction and fibers were used for fishing and hunting. Most important was the use of bark of Hooker and Pacific willows to make string for fishing lines and nets, and even ropes strong enough for anchor lines and harpoon lines for sea lion hunting; also the wood was used for drills for starting fires by friction. Fibers were collected and prepared for use for baskets, mats and clothing. Bark was boiled to produce a tonic for sore throat, tuberculosis and shellfish poisoning. Leaves were cooked with food to flavor it. The bark, which contains salicin, the origin of common aspirin, has been used to alleviate pain and reduce fever.

Flowering Chart of the Willow Species

Species	Flowering time	Flowers with, before, or after leaf emergence
white & golden willows *(Salix alba* varieties)	early April to May	with
sandbar willow *(Salix exigua)*	May and June	with and after
Columbia River willow *(Salix fluviatilis)*	June to July	after & occasionally with
Geyer willow *(Salix geyeriana)*	May	with
Hooker willow *(Salix hookeriana)*	April to May	before and occasionally with
Pacific willow *(Salix lucida)*	mid-April to mid-May	with
Piper willow *(Salix piperi)*	March to April	before
heartleaf willow *(Salix rigida)*	March to May	before or with
Scouler willow *(Salix scouleriana)*	February to March	before and occasionally after
soft-leaved willow *(Salix sessilifolia)*	May to July	after
Sitka willow *(Salix sitchensis)*	March to April	before or with

Vegetative Key to the Willows

1a. Mature leaves typically with an evident, thin, whitish, waxy coating (easily rubbed off) beneath...2
1b. Mature leaves typically not waxy underneath..6

2a Leaves lance-shaped (at least coming to a long point)..3
2b. Leaves typically wider beyond the midpoint...4

3a. Hair lacking on underside of leaf, though a few hairs resident above; leaves typically 5-10 cm long/1-3 cm wide (3-5 length to width ratio); shrub 2-4 m in height; along shores, low terraces above streams, along roadsides..
....heartleaf willow *(Salix rigida var. macrogemma)*
3b. Leaves with hairs on underside; (4-15 leaf length to width ratio)......................................8

4a. Hairs beneath only on veins and reddish when mature, creamy white and all over when young, hairs straight and appressed pointing in all directions; wooly not velvety; leaves typically 3.5-8 cm long/1-3.5 cm wide {2-3 length to width ratio); shrub/tree 2-12 m in height; stream banks and along sloughs and ditches, lowlands to moderate elevations in mountains..Scouler willow *(Salix scouleriana)*
4b. No reddish pubescence, upper or lower portion of the leaf, mature leaves typically greater than 2 cm wide; leaf stalks 5-20 mm...5

5a. Stipules well developed and leafy, leaving a prominant scar; leaves 9-20 cm long/3-6 cm wide (3-4 length to width ratio); stream banks, shores of lakes and ponds, roadside ditches, and not confined to maritime areas; 2-6m in height....................
....Piper willow *(Salix piperi)*
5b. Stipules mostly small and falling off early with no scar; leaves 5-12 cm long/2-5 cm wide (1.5-3 length to width ratio); along seacoast and about Puget Sound within 5 miles of salt water; shrub 2-6 m in height.............Hooker willow *(Salix hookeriana)*

6a. Leaf stalk bearing two or more large yellowish glands and glands along the leaf margin at the teeth tips; leaf typically 5-15 cm long/1-3 cm wide (3-5 length to width ratio); stipules typically well developed and leafy in texture, broadly rounded, gland-toothed, 2-10 mm long, sooner or later deciduous; along streams; a tree up to 10m in height..
....Pacific willow *(Salix lucida var. lasiandra)*
6b. Leaf stalk and leaf without yellowish glands...7

7a. Leaf edge commonly inrolled, smooth to sparsely hairy above; dense short-velvety-hairy below, hairs reflect light like velvet; leaves 4-10 cm long/1.5-3.5 cm wide (2-4 length to width ratio); shrub height 2-6 m; stream banks and moist woods..
....Sitka willow *(Salix sitchensis)*
7b. Leaf edges not inrolled; blades greater than 3 times as long as wide; margin with few scattered small sharp teeth or entire; leaves 3-10 cm long/1-3.5 cm wide (3-7 length to width)...10

8a. Leaf margin entire or nearly so..9
8b. Leaf margin with scattered small teeth or almost entire; leaf with silvery appressed unidirectional hairs when young, later smooth to waxy; leaves typically 5-15 cm long/4-15 mm wide (7-15 length to width ratio); shrub 2-6 m in height; banks of the Columbia River, from the mouth of the Deschutes River to below the mouth of the Willamette River, and extending a few miles up the Willamette..............Columbia River willow *(Salix fluviatilis)*

Vegetative Key to the Willows continued on next page...

9a. Leaves with silky hairs at first, usually sooner or later smooth, or sometimes more or less persistently hairy, especially beneath; hairs commonly somewhat rusty in color; leaves typically 3.5-5.5 cm long/6-15 mm wide (4x length to width ratio); shrub 1.5-4.5m in height; wet meadows and stream banks...
....Geyer willow *(Salix geyeriana var. meleina)*

9b. Leaves densely short-hairy with bent scattered hairs; older leaves typically 1.5 cm long by 0.4-2 cm [7-35:1 ratio] shrub 1.5-3 m tall; floodplains with coarse gravel, low elevation...Sandbar willow *(Salix exigua ssp. melanopsis)*

10a. Young leaves with loose wooly or velvety hair, mature leaves smooth above, less hairy below; leaf margin with few, scattered, small, sharp, glandular teeth; shrub 2-8 m in height; stream banks..soft-leaved willow *(Salix sessilifolia)*

10b. New twigs/leaves are short moderately-hairy on both sides but soon become more or less smooth on both sides, strongly waxy below; leaf margin with 3-4 forward-pointing teeth per cm; leaves up to 17 cm long; tree up to 23 m high.....................................

    1)   branchlets greenish gray to dark brown and a single finger-like glandular process up to 6 mm long at the tip of the leaf stalk.................................
....white willow *(Salix alba var. calva)*

    2)   branchlets yellow with no glandular process on the leaf stalk..................
....golden willow *(Salix alba var. vitellina)*

Catkin Identification Chart for the Wetland Willows

Species	female catkin	floral bract description	capsule length	stipe length	stigma shape	male catkin	Number of stamens
white & golden willows (*Salix alba* varieties)	5-7 cm	greenish-yellow, 1 mm, deciduous, medium-long-hairy	4-5 mm smooth	<1 mm		3-5 cm	2
sandbar willow (*Salix exigua*)	3-5 cm 8 mm thick	green then yellow,1 mm, deciduous, lightly hairy	3-8 mm smooth to slightly hairy	no stipe	no style stigma forked	3.5-5 cm 4-6 mm thick	2
Columbia River willow (*Salix fluviatilis*)	4-10 cm 8 mm thick	yellow, 2 mm, deciduous, dense short-hairy	4-6 mm hairy, to smooth	<1mm	style/stigma long forked	3-5 cm 4-6 mm thick	2
Geyer willow (*Salix geyeriana*)	1.5-2.5 cm 1 cm thick	yellow-brown to blackish, 3 mm, persistent, densely long-hairy	3-6 mm few short hairs	1-2.5 mm	1 style stig stubby forked	7-15 mm 7-10 mm thick	2
Hooker willow (*Salix hookeriana*)	3-4 cm 4-12 mm thick	black to dark brown, 1-3 mm, persistent, long woolly-hairy	6-8 mm smooth,tip short-hairy	1 mm	1 style stigma stubby	3-4 cm 1.5-2.5 cm thick	2
Pacific willow (*Salix lucida*)	3-12 cm 1.5 cm thick	yellow, 7-8 mm, deciduous, medium-long-hairy	4-8 mm smooth	0.7-1.5 mm	1 style forked stigma	2-7 cm 1-1.5 cm thick	3-8
Piper willow (*Salix piperi*)	4-10 cm 2 cm thick	brown to black, 2-3 mm, persistent dense-long-silky-hairy	4-6 mm smooth	2 mm	1 style stigma stubby	5 cm 1.5 cm thick	2
heartleaf willow (*Salix rigida*)	3-6 cm 1.4 cm thick	light to dark brown, 1 mm persistent, smooth	3-7 mm smooth	7 mm	1 style stigma stubby	2-5 cm 8-15 mm thick	2
Scouler willow (*Salix scouleriana*)	2-6 cm 2 cm thick	brown to black, 4-5 mm, persistent, long-silky-hairy	5-8 mm dense short-hairy	2 mm	1 style stigma forked or not	2-4 cm 2 cm thick	2
soft-leaved willow (*Salix sessilifolia*)	3-8 cm 7-10 mm thick	yellow, 6-10 mm, deciduous, dense long-hairy	3-5 mm short-hairy	<1mm	1 style stigma forked	3-5 cm .8-10 mm thick	2
Sitka willow (*Salix sitchensis*)	3-8 cm 2 cm thick	black to brown, 2 mm, persistent dense-long & long hairy	3.5-5 mm dense short-hairy	<1 mm	forked style stigma stubby	2.5-5 cm 1-1.5 cm thick	1

SHRUBS

Salix alba vars. *calva* and *vitellina*
white willow (var. *calva*), golden willow (var. *vitellina*)
Status: FACW
Color photo page 84

Two varieties of *Salix alba* were introduced from Europe. Both grow to 20 m tall and form either a shrub or a tree. The mature bark is dark and furrowed or ridged. White willow has greenish gray twigs and golden willow has yellowish twigs on young branches. Leaf buds of both are about 6-9 mm and usually lance-shaped. There are often a few hairs near the base of the leaf buds and on the twigs around the nodes; new twigs and leaves are hairy on both sides but become more or less smooth by the end of the growing season. Leaves can be up to 15 cm long, 4-5 times longer than they are wide, and are glossy green above and whiter and strongly waxy below. Leaf galls are common. Blooms early April to May.

- leaves usually lance-shaped with very slender or pointed tips; margins with 3-4 forward-pointing teeth per cm; borne on short stalk 1-2 cm long
- stipules early deciduous, scars absent
- catkins emerge with leaves
- male catkins to 5 cm long; 2 stamens hairy near base
- female catkins to 7 cm in fruit; capsule 4-5 mm long, oval, smooth, 1.4 mm long; style 0.2-0.4 mm long; gland present; stipe short (5-7 cm long)
- floral bracts deciduous, greenish or yellowish, commonly hairy on both sides with a marginal fringe of hairs

Illustration not available for this species.

Habitat: White willow colonizes wet, silty mud of somewhat swampy river floodplains. In cultivation it will tolerate moderately well-drained conditions. Golden willow inhabits similar habitats to Scouler willow *(Salix scouleriana)*.

Range: These varieties are not a natural component of any native communities in Washington or Oregon; however, both have been planted and have become naturalized. White willow can be expected throughout our area wherever there is suitable habitat but is more common in Thurston County and south. Golden willow is common in King, Snohomish, Pierce, and Skagit counties.

Similar Species: Pacific willow (*Salix lucida*) has callous, gland-tipped teeth on the leaves; smaller and more numerous teeth; more rounded leaf bases and longer and more slender leaf tips; large and leafy stipules with stipule scars present; 5 stamens per male flower; and female catkins and capsules that are commonly somewhat longer than those of the white or golden willow.

Functional Value: White willow is used to shade out reed canarygrass *(Phalaris arundinacea)*. Golden willow was one of the first willows to be introduced to our area from Europe. It was especially popular as a shade tree at the turn of the century because of the beautiful yellow twigs which are evident in winter. Old specimens can get quite large. They are occasionally seen at abandoned homesites. Weeping willow *(Salix alba var. tristis)*, which almost never escapes cultivation, is now the horticultural willow of choice.

Salix exigua ssp. *melanopsis*
sandbar willow; dusky willow

Status: OBL

Color photo page 84

Sandbar willow is the smallest of our lowland native willows generally growing 1.5-3 m tall; however, it will occasionally form a slender tree to 8 m. Plants grow in spreading colonies commonly becoming thickets. Twigs are slender and the new leaves are densely short-hairy with soft, bent, and spreading hairs that are not directionally oriented. Older leaves are less hairy with predominantly bent, loosely appressed, forward-pointing hairs, eventually becoming smooth or nearly so. The young leaves are less than 6 cm long, and mature leaves grow to 15 cm long, and 4-20 mm wide. Male plants are much more common than female plants. Catkins are very hairy. The first catkins are borne on leafy twigs about 2 cm from axillary buds of the previous season. Catkins that appear later are found on the longer, leafy branches of the current season. Insect galls are rare or absent in our area. Blooms in May and June.

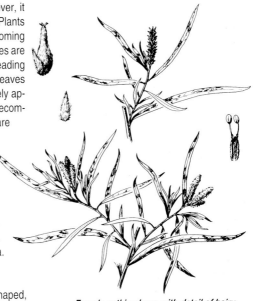

Female catkin above with detail of hairy capsule and floral bract; male catkins below with detail of 2 stamens with hairy base.

- leaves linear-elliptic to slightly lance-shaped, toothed, especially near the tip, or smooth-margined; callous glands more or less forward-pointing; leaves attached directly to twig with a 2 mm leaf stalk
- stipules tiny and early deciduous
- catkins appear with and after leaves
- male catkins slender, 3.5-5 cm long, 4-6 mm wide, very hairy near base; 2 stamens; 2 cylindrical glands
- female catkins 3-5 cm long, 5-8 mm wide; capsules 3-8 mm long, conic, smooth or slightly hairy; 2 stigmas whole to slightly forked, 0.1mm long; 1 flattened gland
- floral bracts green, then yellow, and deciduous in late season, hairy towards the base, round to lance-shaped with rounded tip

Habitat: Sandbar willow colonizes floodplains with coarse gravel and bar islands in wide sunny valleys.

Usually grows partly submerged, or at water elevation. Often found with Sitka willow *(Salix sitchensis)* and Pacific willow *(Salix lucida)*.

Range: Common in the Willamette Valley in Oregon, occurs along the Skagit and Cowlitz rivers in Washington. Occasionally found scattered in Washington and Oregon.

Similar Species: Sandbar willow, Columbia River willow *(Salix fluviatilis)*, and soft-leaved willow *(Salix sessilifolia)* often hybridize, making identification difficult. The other two species have hairy capsules, forked stigmas with long, slender lobes, and wider male catkins (8 mm or more). The very new leaves of Columbia River willow have hairs that are appressed and forward-pointing; the mature leaves of both willows become less hairy with predominately bent, appressed, forward-pointing hairs remaining; however, the hairs of the Columbia River willow are not deciduous.

Salix fluviatilis
Columbia River willow; river willow
Status: OBL
Color photo page 84

A branch of Columbia River willow from a female plant showing hairy capsule with forked stigma on left and stamens of the male flower on right.

Columbia River willow is a multistemmed, compact shrub 2-6 m tall. The main trunk can be up to 100 cm thick; however, it is more commonly a spreading shrub with many sucker stems. New twigs and leaves are brown or green and copiously covered by loosely appressed, forward-pointing hairs. When mature, twigs and leaves are smooth and/or occasionally waxy. Older bark is gray-brown and scaly. Leaves taper to a short stalk (1-5 mm long), are less than 1 cm wide when young, but widen with maturity, eventually becoming 5 times longer than they are wide (5-15 cm long by 4-15 mm wide). Most plants are male. Twig seldom have galls. Blooms June through July.

- leaves variable but usually elliptic to lance-shaped; margins with small, forward-pointing gland-tipped teeth, or occasionally smooth-margined

- stipules oval, 5 mm long, early deciduous
- catkins appear mostly after but sometimes with leaves
- male catkins 3-5 cm long, 4-6 mm wide; 2 stamens, filaments densely hairy toward the base; 2 glands of unequal size
- female catkins 4-10 cm long, 5-8 mm wide; capsules 4-6 mm long, oval, with dense, usually persistent, forward-pointing, slightly bent hairs; 1 style 0.5 mm long; stigma forked; 1 gland, tapering from the base; stipe short
- floral bracts yellow, very hairy, eventually deciduous, generally oblong-lance-shaped and often widest near the rounded, or slender pointed tip

Habitat: Columbia River willow is often found in sandy habitats above the water level. Colonizes by rooting shoots; established plants often survive being deeply buried. It is often found with Sitka willow *(Salix sitchensis)* and soft-leaved willow *(Salix sessilifolia)*. It grows in gravelly substrates in the Willamette Valley.

Range: Common along sandy banks of the Columbia River west of Portland. Columbia River willow is found as far south as Lynn and Lane counties in Oregon, but not farther north than southern Washington.

Similar Species: Columbia River willow commonly hybridizes with sandbar willow and soft-leaved willow. Neither sandbar nor soft-leaved willow have leaves with forward-pointing hairs. Soft-leaved willow also has hairy capsules and forked stigmas, but the leaves are only 3 times as long as wide. The female catkins of sandbar willow are smooth or only slightly hairy.

Salix geyeriana var. meleina
Geyer willow
Status: FACW+

Geyer willow is a shrub that grows 4-6 m tall. Leaves and twigs are smooth and covered with a waxy coating. When young, twigs are slender, 1-2 mm thick, and covered with silky hairs. Leaf buds are flattened, oval, and with a forward-pointing and appressed tip. Mature leaves are smooth above with a fringe of short hairs on the margin, and often with a few short, appressed, rusty colored hairs below, or if smooth then also waxy. Leaves are 4-6 times as long as wide (3-8 cm long by 6-15 mm wide). Twig galls are uncommon. Blooms in May.

- leaves oblong and lance-shaped to elliptic with sharp tip; margins smooth
- stipules tiny and early deciduous
- catkins appear with the leaves, on short leafy stalks 2-10 mm long
- male catkins very small, 7-15 mm long, 7-10 mm wide; 2 stamens; filaments hairy near the base
- female catkins 1.5-2.5 cm long, 7-10 mm wide; capsules 3-6 mm, conic, thinly short-hairy; 1 style with a forked tip; stigma and style = 0.4 mm; 1 gland; stipe 1-2.5 mm long
- floral bracts about 3 mm long, light yellow-brown to blackish, linear-lance-shaped, densely long-hairy, occasionally with a reddish tip, persistent

Mature leaves of Geyer willow, upper left; upper right, capsule and long, hairy-tipped floral bract; lower left, branch with female catkins; lower right, male catkins.

Habitat: Preferred habitat is on the inundated banks of very slow-moving streams. Also occurs in muddy substrates along the shores of small ponds and in wet meadows. Geyer willow is shade-intolerant. It is occasionally found in roadside ditches.

Similar Species: Sandbar willow *(Salix exigua ssp. melanopsis)* has similar leaves and twigs but the leaf margins are usually gland-tipped and not waxy below. Scouler willow *(Salix scouleriana)* has longer leaf buds and catkins, and the leaves are not pointed.

SHRUBS

Salix hookeriana
Hooker willow

Status: FACW-
Color photo page 84

Above left, female catkins; above right male catkins; lower left, rounded leaves; lower capsule with long-hairy floral bract.

Hooker willow is a stout shrub or small tree that grows to 6 m tall. The trunk can be to 40 cm thick. Twigs average 4 mm thick. Young twigs and leaves densely long-silky. Leaf buds are long-oval 5-6 mm long with a flattened tip. Mature leaves are dark green and shiny above, and persistently hairy or eventually smooth and lightly coated with wax below, and 1.5-3 times longer than they are wide (4-13 cm long by 2.5-5 cm wide). Leaf stalks are 0.5-2 cm long. Galls are rare. Blooms from April though May.

- leaves wide, oval, to rounded and broadest at tip; margins smooth or scalloped
- stipules inconspicuous or absent, less than 5 mm long; early deciduous
- catkins on short 1 cm long, leafy stalks, ap-

pear before (and occasionally with) the leaves
- male catkins 3-4 cm long, 1.5-2.5 cm wide; 2 stamens, filaments smooth
- female catkins 4-12 cm long, 2 cm wide; capsules 6-8 mm long, conic or oval, smooth or with a hairy tip; 1 style 1.5 mm long; stigmas shorter, stubby; stipe shorter than the style
- floral bracts small (1-3 cm long) persistent, black or dark brown, long-silky-woolly-hairy

Habitat: Common in sunny exposures in wet alluvial soil behind longshore bars, along the shores of streams, and small lakes and ponds within 5 miles of the coast. Occasionally along roadsides in ditches and on shoulders, and on moist coastal bluffs.

Range: Common on the Pacific Coast and Puget Sound usually within 5 miles of salt water.

Similar Species: Piper willow *(Salix piperi)* is a variety of Hooker willow that grows along acid bog margins. Both species have large leafy stipules and stipule scars, dark shiny leaves above, dull green leaves below. Piper willow is not restricted to within 5 miles of salt water. Scouler willow's *(Salix scouleriana)* leaves are more lance-shaped with a narrower tip. The stipules are small. The capsules are densely hairy.

Functional Value: Provides shelter and food for wildlife. Hooker willow is often used for riparian restoration for fish habitat because it grows in dense patches and provides excellent shading for fish.

Ethnobotanical Uses:
Indigenous peoples have used the bark of Hooker willow to make a strong cord for nets and slings; the wood for lures; the leaves in a tonic to treat shellfish poisoning; and the roots in shampoo.

Salix lucida var. lasiandra
(Salix lasiandra)
Pacific willow
Status: FACW+
Color photo page 84

SHRUBS

Pacific willow is a common native, usually multistemmed tree that grows to 20 m tall. The trunk can be up to 60 cm thick. The bark is dark gray to dark brown and ridged vertically when mature. Twigs are brittle. Young twigs and leaves are covered with fine spreading hairs; older stems and leaves are smooth. Leaf buds are duckbill-shaped and both buds and twigs are orange or yellow and smooth during the winter. Leaf buds are about 10 cm long with a narrow heel and lateral veins on each side. Leaves are 5-15 cm long (may be to 19 cm), 3-5 times longer than they are wide, and have a rounded base. Leaf stalks are 1-2 cm long and have a gland near the base. Older leaves are glossy above and smooth and/or waxy below, with a few hairs persisting near the junction of the blade and leaf stalk. Fibrous, 4 cm diameter galls occur near the tops of twigs and are locally common. Blooms from mid-April to mid-May.

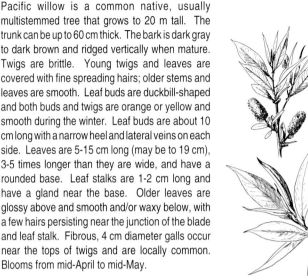

- leaves narrow, lance-shaped, tapering to long slender tip; margins with fine, forward-pointing, yellow, gland-tipped teeth, 6-8 per cm
- stipules large, leafy, kidney-shaped, persistent but eventually deciduous, scars are obvious
- catkins appear with the leaves, the central stalk of the catkins is hairy
- male catkins 2-7 cm long, 1-1.5 cm thick; 3-8 (commonly 5) stamens; filaments hairy at base; 2 glands per flower
- female catkins 3-12 cm long, 1.5 cm thick; capsules 4-8 mm long, smooth; 1 style, 0.5 mm long; stigma 0.5 mm; stipe long 0.7-1.5 mm, glands 1.4 mm long with 2 per flower
- floral bracts deciduous, yellow, hairy

Above, from left to right, male catkins, male flower with 5 stamens and floral bract, and capsule and floral bract; center, branch showing stipules and glands near leaf base; below, female catkin.

Similar Species: Soft-leaved willow *(Salix sessilifolia)* has shorter leaves (to 8 cm long) that are soft and succulent with the midvein raised on both surfaces. Geyer willow *(Salix geyeriana)* has smaller leaves (to 8 cm long), very small stipules and black floral bracts. White and golden willows *(Salix alba)* have leaves with smooth margins (no teeth) that emerge with the catkins, and obvious stipules. Heartleaf willow *(Salix rigida)* only grows as a shrub 2-4 m tall and has no glands on the leaves.

Habitat: Pacific willow is common to river habitats, especially floodplains. Most common on the stream banks but also common in freshwater wetland depressions, and alluvial bottomlands. Usually found associated with deep, sandy or sandy loam alluvial soils, It often becomes a tall tree. It is often associated with Sitka willow *(Salix sitchensis)*, and white and golden willows *(Salix alba)*, near the coast it may occur with Hooker willow *(Salix hookeriana)*.

Range: Widespread and common throughout our area; var. *caudata* is the eastern variety.

Functional Value: Nehalem Pacific willow, a cultivated variety has been planted for erosion control along shorelines and dikes. It has also been used to hold both natural shorelines and dikes in place. It is often also used to improve fish habitat by shading streams and thereby reducing water temperatures in summer.

Ethnobotanical Uses: The inner bark has been used to make two-ply cord and the wood for the drill of a fire drill.

Salix piperi
Piper willow; dune willow
Status: FACW

Above left, female catkins; above right, male catkins; below left, leaves and stipules; capsule with persistent, long-hairy floral bract.

Piper willow grows as a shrub to 5 m tall. Young twigs and leaves are long-silky-hairy but soon become smooth. Mature leaves are dark green and shiny above and mostly smooth and waxy below. Leaves 4 times as long as wide (20 cm long). Leaf stalks 5-20 mm long. Blooms from March to April.

- leaves lance-shaped to oval-elliptic, broadest near the middle; margins bluntly toothed to shallowly scalloped
- stipules large and leafy, narrowly elliptic to linear, positioned at an angle to the leaf scars; scars conspicuous
- catkins appearing before the leaves
- male catkins commonly 5 cm long, 1.5 cm thick; 2 stamens
- female catkins 4-10 cm long, 2 cm thick; capsule smooth, 4-6 mm long; 1 style with a stubby stigma; stipe longer than style
- floral bract brown to black, very long-hairy, persistent

Habitat: Most common on the margins of acid bogs. Grows in standing water on stream banks and along the shores of lakes and ponds.

Range: Occasional to common throughout most of our area west of the Cascades in Washington and Oregon, south to California and up the Columbia to Bingen, Washington.

Similar Species: Piper willow is a variety of Hooker willow *(Salix hookeriana)*; however, Hooker willow has stipules that are inconspicuous, more hairy and hairs are persistent, and the stipe is shorter than the style. It is limited to within 5 miles of salt water and not found at the margins of acid bogs.

Ethnobotanical Uses: Indigenous peoples harvested young trees to make weirs for fish pools; used the bark for basketry; and added the leaves to cooking as a flavoring.

Salix rigida var. *macrogemma*
heartleaf willow

Status: OBL
Color photo page 84

Heartleaf willow grows as a multistemmed shrub 2-4 m (occasionally up to 9 m) tall. It will form a small tree with a single, 10 cm thick trunk, and smooth gray bark. Young twigs are abundant, spreading, and can be hairy. Winter twigs and buds are densely short-hairy and slender. Leaf buds are lance-shaped, about 9 mm long, often with a slender upturned tip. Young leaves are dark green above and light green below 3-5 times as long as wide, 5-10 cm long and 1-3 cm wide. Mature leaves are smooth above, except on the leaf stalks and midribs, and smooth and waxy below. Leaf stalks are short (1-2 cm in length). Twig galls are seldom seen. Blooms from March to May.

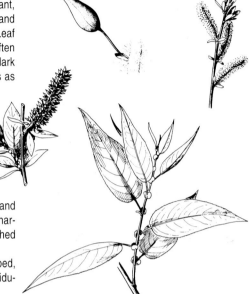

- leaves are oblong-lance-shaped, widest and rounded at the base, usually abruptly narrowed to a slender tip; margin finely toothed to smooth
- stipules usually small, leafy, kidney-shaped, with gland-tipped teeth, eventually deciduous
- catkins with a short woolly-hairy central stalk, borne on short twigs with a few leafy bracts either before or with the leaves
- male catkins 2-5 cm long, 0.8-1.5 cm thick; 2 stamens; filaments smooth, joined at base
- female catkins 3-6 cm long, 1.4 cm thick; capsules 3-7 mm, conic and smooth; styles longer than stigma (0.2- 0.7 mm); 1 gland; stipe very long (2-4 mm)
- floral bracts smooth, small, light to dark brown, persistent

Far left, female catkins; above left, smooth capsule and inconspicuous floral bract; above right, male catkin; and lower center, leaves and stipules.

Habitat: Wet sites along shores, or low terraces above streams, and along roadsides.

Range: Occasional throughout the western Cascades from northern Washington to the upper Willamette Valley. The

species has 6 varieties which are transcontinental from Newfoundland to Virginia and the Yukon to Arizona.

Similar Species: Heartleaf willow has floral bracts and filaments that are different from any other willow. Geyer willow *(Salix geyeriana)* also has long linear leaves, but the leaf margin is smooth, and capsules are hairy. Pacific willow *(Salix lucida)* has very linear leaves, but the base is more narrow, the twigs and leaves are smooth, not hairy, and glands usually occur above at the tip of the leaf stalk and along the leaf margin at each tooth.

Ethnobotanical Uses: Heartleaf willow has been used for basketry.

Salix scouleriana
Scouler willow
Status: FAC
Color photos page 85

Left, male catkins; right, short, hairy capsule with long-hairy floral bract.

- catkins covered with long, silky hairs may appear as early as January before the leaves; others appear later in spring on stalks with bracts at the base
- male catkins 2-4 cm long, 2 cm thick, sparsely hairy near base; 2 stamens; 1 gland per flower
- female catkins 2-6 cm long, 2 cm thick; capsule densely short-hairy, conic; style short (0.5 mm long); stigma forked or not (0.5 mm long); stigma and style are 1 mm
- floral bracts brown to black, 4-5 mm long, long-hairy, persistent

Above, female catkins; below, leaves with triangular stipules.

Scouler willow is a tall spindly tree to 12 m tall with a trunk to 40 cm thick. The bark is smooth, greenish gray, yellow-brown to reddish brown when mature. Young twigs and leaves are velvety-hairy, but become smooth above, and smooth-waxy below. Leaves are commonly 3-8 cm (sometimes 12 cm) long; 2-3 times as long as wide. Older leaves are leathery, dark green above, yellow green below. Leaf stalks are 5-10 mm long. Galls form mostly on the stem, not the leaves, and they are persistent in the branch junctions.

- leaves oval-lance-shaped with the widest part 1/3 down from the tip, pointed to round at the tip, with rusty hairs on the main veins below when mature; smooth-margined
- stipules triangular, early deciduous

Habitat: Scouler willow grows in uplands as well as wetlands. It is the most shade-tolerant of our willows. It does not grow in standing water.

Range: Alaska and Yukon to California; Arizona to New Mexico; black hills of North Dakota to Manitoba. Occurs in all counties in our area.

Similar Species: Hooker willow *(Salix hookeriana)* has broader and more elliptic leaves and is found within five miles of salt water. Piper willow *(Salix piperi)* has similar leaves, but they are shiny above and have large leafy stipules. Piper willow is usually found in or near bogs. Sitka willow *(Salix sitchensis)* also has similar leaves, but these are very hairy below and have a distinctive, contrasting light reflectivity on either side of the midrib.

Ethnobotanical Uses: The roots have been used for a fire drill and fire hearth. The catkins are often collected and used for decoration.

Salix sessilifolia
soft-leaved willow; Northwest willow
Status: FACW

Soft-leaved willow is a small shrub to tree that grows to 8 m tall with a trunk to 10 cm thick. Young twigs and leaves are densely and loosely hairy. Mature leaves lose most of the hairs, especially on top. Branches without catkins are the most hairy. Mature leaves are typically 3-10 cm long, 1-3.5 cm wide, and 3 (occasionally up to 7) times longer than they are wide. Leaves narrow to a short leaf stalk, 1-5 mm long. Leaf and stem galls are uncommon, 0.5-1.5 cm long, and borne on lateral twigs. Blooms from May to July.

- leaves oval-elliptic, lance-shaped; short gland-tipped, 7-15 per side
- stipules oval, 5 mm long, and early deciduous
- catkins appear after the leaves
- male catkins 3-5 cm long, 8-10 mm wide; 2 stamens; filaments hairy near the base; 2 subequal glands
- female catkins 3-8 cm long, 7-10 mm wide; capsules 3-5 mm long, oval, hairy; style 0.3 mm long; stigma forked; style + stigma to 1.5 mm long; 1 gland broader at base; stipe short
- floral bracts deciduous, yellow to green, densely long-hairy, widest near the tip

Above left, male catkins; above right, leaves that are densely hairy when young; below left, female catkin; and below right, long and hairy capsule.

Habitat: Similar to Columbia River willow *(Salix fluviatilis)*, but soft-leaved willow cannot survive burial in sediment.

Range: Same range as Columbia River willow, but is less common. One population has been found on the Skagit River. Otherwise, this species is found along the Columbia River in Wahkiakum and Clatsop Counties, and along the Willamette River and tributaries in Lane County, Oregon.

Similar Species: Columbia River willow is very similar except twigs and leaves have no hair above and less hair below, and the hairs do not point forward. The leaves of Columbia River willow and sandbar willow *(Salix exigua)* are linear and lance-shaped. The capsules of Columbia River willow and sandbar willows are less hairy than soft-leaved willow and the hairs are short.

73

Salix sitchensis
Sitka willow
Status: FACW
Color photo page 85

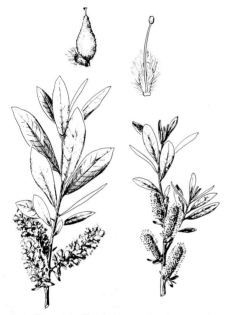

Above left, short-hairy capsule with long-hairy floral bract; above right, single stamen with long-hairy floral bract; below left, female catkins, and; below right, male catkins.

Sitka willow is a multistemmed shrub that grows to 8 m tall. It is one of the most common willows in our region. The bark is gray to dark brown and smooth. Young twigs are usually densely velvety-short-hairy. Leaf buds are erect, cylindrical with a rounded tip, have a longitudinal groove facing the twig, and are densely covered by forward-pointing, appressed, short hairs. The undersides of the leaves are densely covered in unidirectional hairs which give the the leaf a nap that reflects light when rotated. Leaves are 3.5-10 cm long and 1.8-3.5 cm wide; 2-4 times as long as wide. Leaf stalks are 5-15 mm long. Round galls that are red above and green below are common. Blooms March to April.

- leaves oblong-lance-shaped; margins smooth, rarely with a few scattered callous glands, widest at the tip
- stipules large and leafy in young shoots, persistent
- catkins with stems 1 cm long; appear before or with the leaves
- male catkins 2.5-5 mm long, 1-1.5 cm wide, brown or the base light colored, 1 stamen, no hairs
- female catkins 3-8 cm long, 2 cm thick; capsules 3-5.5 mm long, densely short-hairy, hairs more or less forward-pointing; style 0.3-0.8 mm; stigma stubby; stipe short (less than 1 mm)
- floral bracts black, occasionally brown or the base light-colored, long-hairy, 2 mm long, persistent

Habitat: Sitka willow is common in many habitat types: sandy floodplains, gravel shores, and muddy stream banks. It is a weedy species and will invade wet areas such as ditches, stream banks, and cleared wetlands. It is occasionally found on drier sites.

Range: Coast of south Alaska to San Louis Obispo California; west Cascades, eastern Oregon north to British Columbia.

Similar Species: Sitka willow is readily recognized by how light reflects differently underneath the leaf; no other species has hairs that do this. Scouler willow *(Salix scouleriana)* has similar leaves, but catkins appear before the leaves, stigmas are long, capsules are large, and the hairs fall off on the undersides of the older leaves except along the veins where they are rusty-red. In addition, it blooms in February.

Acer circinatum (vine maple)
Photo by Clayton Antieau

Acer circinatum (vine maple)
Photo by Fred Weinmann

Amelanchier alnifolia (western serviceberry)
Photo by Al Hanners

Acer circinatum (vine maple)
Photo by Fred Weinmann

Betula glandulosa (bog birch)
Photo by Fred Weinmann

Cornus sericea ssp. sericea (redstem dogwood)
Photo by Sarah Spear Cooke

Cornus sericea ssp. sericea (redstem dogwood)
Photo by Sarah Spear Cooke

Corylus cornuta (beaked hazelnut)
Photo by Marty Chaney

Crataegus douglasii (black hawthorn)
Photo by Mike Zierke

Gaultheria shallon (salal)
Photo by Fred Weinmann

Ilex aquifolium (holly)
Photo by Sarah Spear Cooke

Kalmia microphylla (bog laurel)
Photo by Dyanne Sheldon

Kalmia microphylla (bog laurel)
Photo by Fred Weinmann

Lonicera involucrata (black twinberry)
Photo by Fred Weinmann

Lonicera involucrata (black twinberry)
Photo by Clayton Antieau

Malus fusca (western crabapple)
Photo by Fred Weinmann

Malus fusca (western crabapple)
Photo by Al Hanners

Menziesia ferruginea (rusty menziesia)
Photo by Al Hanners

Myrica gale (sweetgale)
Photo by Binda Colebrook

Oemleria cerasiformis (Indian plum)
Photo by Sarah Spear Cooke

Oemleria cerasiformis (Indian plum)
Photo by Binda Colebrook

Oplopanax horridus (devil's-club)
Photo by Sarah Spear Cooke

Oplopanax horridus (devil's-club)
Photo by Sarah Spear Cooke

Rhododendron groenlandicum (Labrador-tea)
Photo by Sarah Spear Cooke

Physocarpus capitatus (Pacific ninebark)
Photo by Clayton Antieau

Rhododendron neoglandulosum (smooth Labrador-tea)
Photo by Clayton Antieau

Ribes bracteosum (stink currant)
Photo by Al Hanners

Ribes lacustre (swamp gooseberry)
Photo by Fred Weinmann

Ribes lacustre (swamp gooseberry)
Photo by Sarah Spear Cooke

Ribes sanguineum (red currant)
Photo by Sarah Spear Cooke

Rosa eglanteria (sweetbrier rose)
Photo by Sarah Spear Cooke

Rosa gymnocarpa (baldhip rose)
Photo by Al Hanners

Rosa gymnocarpa (baldhip rose)
Photo by Lois Kemp

Rosa nutkana (Nootka rose)
Photo by Fred Weinmann

Rosa nutkana (Nootka rose)
Photo by Clayton Antieau

Rosa pisocarpa (peafruit rose)
Photo by Al Hanners

*Rubus laciniatus & Rubus procerus
(evergreen & Himalayan blackberry)*
Photo by Sarah Spear Cooke

Rubus parviflorus (thimbleberry)
Photo by Sarah Spear Cooke

Rubus parviflorus (thimbleberry)
Photo by Fred Weinmann

Rubus procerus (Himalaya blackberry)
Photo by Sarah Spear Cooke

Rubus procerus (Himalaya blackberry)
Photo by Tom Dubendorfer

Rubus spectabilis (salmonberry)
Photo by Fred Weinmann

Rubus spectabilis (salmonberry)
Photo by Sarah Spear Cooke

Rubus ursinus (trailing blackberry)
Photo by Fred Weinmann

Sambucus racemosa (red elderberry)
Photo by Sarah Spear Cooke

Sambucus racemosa (red elderberry)
Photo by Sarah Spear Cooke

Spiraea douglasii (Douglas spirea)
Photo by Sarah Spear Cooke

Symphoricarpos albus (common snowberry)
Photo by Clayton Antieau

Vaccinium oxycoccos (wild cranberry)
Photo by Lois Kemp

Vaccinium parvifolium (red huckleberry)
Photo by Fred Weinmann

Vaccinium parvifolium (red huckleberry)
Photo by Sarah Spear Cooke

Vaccinium uliginosum (bog blueberry)
Photo by Clayton Antieau

Salix alba var. calva (white willow)
Photo by Sarah Spear Cooke

Salix exigua (sandbar willow)
Photo by Mike Zierke

Salix fluviatilis (Columbia River willow)
Photo by Al Hanners

Salix hookeriana (Hooker willow)
Photo by Rick Pratt

Salix lucida var. lasiandra (Pacific willow)
Photo by Clayton Antieau

Salix rigida var. macrogemma (heartleaf willow)
Photo by Al Hanners

Salix scouleriana (Scouler willow)
Photo by Clayton Antieau

Salix scouleriana (Scouler willow)
Photo by Sarah Spear Cooke

Salix sitchensis (Sitka willow)
Photo by Al Hanners

Salix sitchensis (Sitka willow)
Photo by Binda Colebrook

Angelica genuflexa
kneeling angelica

Family: Apiaceae (Umbelliferae)
Status: FACW
Color photo page 224

Kneeling angelica is a 1.5 m tall herbaceous plant that arises from a large perennial taproot. The species name is derived from its most obvious identifying feature: the leaf stalk is bent at the point of attachment of the leaflets, particularly at the first pair. This feature is especially apparent when viewing the plant in its entirety. Blooms July to August.

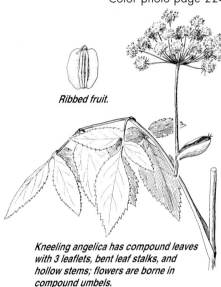

Ribbed fruit.

- stem purple, covered with a white powder, hollow; arise from a chambered base
- leaves twice compound with 3 leaflets; leaflets sharply to coarsely toothed, 4-10 cm long, 1.5-5 cm wide; veins end at the leaf tips
- leaf stalk broadened at the base and sheathing the main stem
- flowers white or pinkish, tiny, in numerous compact, compound umbels with more than 20 flower clusters per umbel
- fruits round to egg-shaped, 3-4 mm long, hairless, with broad, lateral ribbing

Kneeling angelica has compound leaves with 3 leaflets, bent leaf stalks, and hollow stems; flowers are borne in compound umbels.

Habitat: Often occurs in nutrient-rich freshwater marshes that are flooded or ponded at least until summer. Not generally found in highly disturbed sites. Infrequently encountered, perhaps because little suitable habitat now remains. Associates often include red alder *(Alnus rubra)*, Sitka spruce *(Picea sitchensis)*, lady fern *(Athyrium filix-femina)*, and skunk-cabbage *(Lysichiton americanum)*, sedges, mannagrass, willows, etc.

Range: West of the Cascades from Alaska to Northern California. Occurs in all counties in our area.

Similar Species: With the exception of its unique genuflexed leaves, this large, robust plant resembles other members of the parsley family. It has toothed compound leaves, orbs of small white flowers borne in umbels, and tuberous or thick chambered stem bases. Seawatch angelica *(Angelica lucida)* is similar but occurs only in maritime

habitats. Sharptooth angelica *(Angelica arguta)* has a similar leaf shape but leaf stalks that do not bend; this species is common in Oregon, but uncommon in Washington. Western water-hemlock *(Cicuta douglasii)* has a chambered stem base. Poison-hemlock *(Conium maculatum)* has a musky odor, purple splotches on the stems, and leaves with many small, finely divided leaflets. Water-parsley *(Oenanthe sarmentosa)* has finely divided, compound leaves.

Ethnobotanical Uses: Many species of angelica have been used in medicines for thousands of years. The stem and roots contain volatile oils and coumarins that stimulate gastric secretion. It has been used for intestinal cramps. Because the constituents in angelica are complex, different preparations yield different effects. In China, angelica is the source of "Dong-qwai" or the "women's ginseng," and is used as a general female tonic. However, angelica is a member of a family that is known to contain plants with lethal toxins, such as poison-hemlock, and should be used only with the guidance of a medical or naturopathic physician.

HERBS

Angelica lucida
seawatch angelica

Family: Apiaceae (Umbelliferae)
Status: FAC+

Fruits with thin-edged ribs.

Seawatch angelica is a robust, perennial herb with a single stem that often exceeds 1 m in height. Stems arise from a stout taproot. Flower umbels are borne on long stalks that are sheathed at the base. Blooms July to August.

- leaves twice palmately compound; leaflets hairless, oval, with terminal leaflets being 3-lobed or maple-shaped, 3-7 cm long, 2-6 cm wide with irregular teeth
- leaf sheath broad, sheathing the stem
- flowers white, borne in 1- to several compound umbels, to 10 cm long
- fruits oblong to elliptic, 4-9 mm long, 2-5 mm wide, with thin-edged ribs

Habitat: Grows in upper reaches of emergent salt marshes, often at the transition between herbaceous species such as tufted hairgrass *(Deschampsia caespitosa)* and woody species such as twinberry *(Lonicera* species). Frequently associated with cow-parsnip *(Heracleum lanatum)*.

Range: Coastal Northwest, Siberia, and Kuril Islands; also Labrador to New York. All counties in our area bordering salt water.

Similar Species: Resembles other angelica species, but its maritime habitat is unusual. Henderson's angelica *(Angelica hendersonii)* is similar overall and also maritime, but has woolly-hairy leaves and is rare. All species described as similar to kneeling angelica *(Angelica genuflexa)* are also similar to seawatch angelica.

Ethnobotanical Uses:
Stems and leaf stalks, known as wild celery, were eaten by West Coast native peoples. Fumes from the roasted roots were used as a sea-sickness remedy by the Siberian Inuit. See also note under kneeling angelica *(Angelica genuflexa)*.

This tall, saltmarsh species has twice compound leaves with a 3-lobed, terminal leaflet; small flowers are borne in compound umbels.

Asarum caudatum
wild ginger

Family: Aristolochiaceae
Status: FACU
Color photo page 224

This low-growing, evergreen, aromatic perennial grows from rhizomes. Leaves emerge in pairs along the rhizome and are held on leaf stalks 5-30 cm long. The flowers grow just above the forest floor, and are borne on stalks 1-3 cm long. Fruits are fleshy, 6-chambered capsules. Blooms from April through July.

- strong smell of ginger, especially rhizomes
- leaves dark green, heart-shaped with net-like venation, 5-10 cm long and to 15 cm wide, with scattered hairs on the underside of veins
- leaf stalks long, usually copiously hairy, although can be waxy and lacking hairs
- flowers brownish red, formed by 3 petal-like sepals fused at the base, with tail-like tips to 7.5 cm long, true petals inconspicuous

Habitat: Wild ginger grows in moist, deeply shaded forests. It can form scattered mats, isolated clumps or dense ground cover. Because of its low-growing habit, it can be lost in heavy litter where it occurs among mosses and other shade-tolerant herbs. It often grows under western red-cedar *(Thuja plicata).*

Range: Native to North America and the north temperate latitudes; wild ginger is common in the Pacific Northwest north to Canada, and east to Montana.

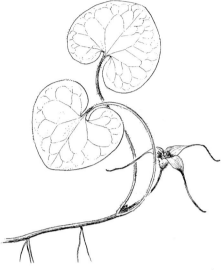

Wild ginger has aromatic, ginger-fragrant rhizomes. Leaves are net-veined and flower sepals have long, tail-like tips.

Similar Species: False lily-of-the-valley *(Maianthemum dilatatum)* has similarly shaped leaves, but they are lighter green with parallel (not net-like) veins, and clustered white flowers that are 2-3 mm long.

Ethnobotanical Uses: The rhizome of wild ginger has been dried, candied, and used as a substitute for the tropical ginger.

HERBS

Aster subspicatus
Douglas aster

Family: Asteraceae (Compositae)
Status: FACW
Color photo page 224

Douglas aster has long, lance-shaped leaves and lavender to violet flower heads.

- stems 1 m tall, usually unbranched, sparsely to densely hairy, especially on the upper plant
- leaves alternate, lance-shaped, 1-2 cm wide, with margins usually toothed above the middle
- involucre 5-6 mm high
- involucral bracts linear, outer involucral bracts sometimes leaf-like only at the tip, loosely overlapping, with pressed down or spreading green tips; basal portion yellowish or brownish with dry, often hairy margins
- ray flowers number 20-30, lavender to violet; disc flowers yellow to reddish purple
- achenes hairy and ribbed; pappus hairs often reddish at maturity

Habitat: Occurs mostly in coastal areas, along seashores, streamsides, and in uplands and emergent wetlands. Common associates include beaked sedge *(Carex utriculata)*, Canada goldenrod *(Solidago canadensis)*, bulrushes *(Scirpus* species), and rushes *(Juncus* species).

Range: Coastal Alaska south to northeastern Oregon and east to Montana.

Similar Species: Douglas aster is similar to several other species of *Aster*, although most of these do not occur in western Washington or Oregon. Where it grows with closely related species of *Aster*, it may form hybrids and can not always be identified with certainty. Leafy aster *(Aster foliaceus)* has clasping, smooth-margined leaves, outer involucral bracts that are all green and leaf-like, and occurs at higher elevations in the Cascades. California aster *(Aster chilensis)* has outer involucral bracts that are obtuse and not leaf-like. Species of fleabane *(Erigeron)* tend to have numerous narrow ray flowers, achenes with two nerves, and involucral bracts in one series.

Douglas aster is a perennial and rhizomatous herb with leaves, involucral bracts, and radiate flower heads that vary widely in size and shape. It is the most common purple aster at lower elevations in our area. It begins to flower in early summer and continues late into the fall. Some plants can be found blooming in winter.

Atriplex patula
fat-hen saltbush; halberd-leaf saltbush; spearscale

Family: Chenopodiaceae
FACW
Color photo page 224

Fat-hen saltbush is a succulent, annual, salt marsh herb that is 20-100 cm tall. Leaves are opposite at the base and alternate above. Flowers are either male or female and are borne in the same inflorescence, with male flowers often above the female flowers. Fruits are bladder-like and enclosed in two triangular bracts. Blooms June to September.

• leaves fleshy, covered by a whitish powder, distinctly arrowhead-shaped
• leaves turning from green to reddish purple in late summer
• flowers greenish, inconspicuous, in terminal spikes

Habitat: Widespread in tidal salt marshes, usually at upper edges, but rarely a dominant species. Tolerates inundation and highly saline conditions, such as in salt pans. Also occurs in dredge disposal areas where diking prevents runoff of rainwater and salt is concentrated at the surface. In highly saline situations fat-hen saltbush is found in monotypic stands, although Puget-Sound gumweed *(Grindelia integrifolia)*, seashore saltgrass *(Distichlis spicata)*, and pickleweed *(Salicornia virginica)* may be present. Fat-hen saltbush is also found commonly in alkaline soils east of the Cascades.

Range: Along Pacific and Atlantic coasts, as well as inland where saline or alkaline conditions exist; also in Eurasia.

Similar Species: Red goosefoot *(Chenopodium rubrum)* and lamb's quarters *(Chenopodium album)* have similar leaves, but have flowers with both male and female parts which are lo-

Fruits are enclosed in triangular bracts.

This saltmarsh species has fleshy, arrow-shaped leaves that become reddish by late summer.

cated in the leaf axils and lack bracts enclosing the flower. In addition, these species are uncommonly found in saline situations in the north of our region.

Functional Value: Succulent leaves grazed by waterfowl. Adds to diversity and community structure in salt marshes.

Ethnobotanical Uses: Fat-hen saltbush has been cultivated in Asia and Africa since ancient times. Seeds are reported to be nutritious and palatable when ground, mixed with water, and drunk. Leaves and young shoots make edible, albeit salty, greens. They are particularly tasty when boiled with meat.

Bidens cernua
nodding beggarticks; nodding beggar-ticks

Family: Asteraceae (Compositae)
Status: FACW+
Color photo page 224

Bristled achene.

Involu-cral bracts.

Nodding beggarticks has opposite leaves and yellow flowers.

- leaves opposite, attached directly to stem, lance-shaped, 4-20 cm long, 5-45 mm wide, with coarsely toothed to nearly smooth margins
- involucral bracts in 2 series, outer series number 5-8, narrow, spreading or bent backwards; inner series broad and striped
- ray flowers yellow, usually number 6-8 (although occasionally lacking), 1.5 cm long, 1.2-2.5 cm wide; disc flowers numerous, yellow to brown, with yellow stamens
- achenes 5-8 mm long, tan, long wedge-shaped with hard convex tip and 4 backwards-barbed bristles, 2-3 mm long; pappus with 3-4 barbed bristles

Habitat: Emergent wetlands in low elevation sites, wet ditches, shallow ponds, and lake shores. Common associates are smartweeds *(Polygonum* species), common cattail *(Typha latifolia)*, and yellow pond-lily *(Nuphar luteum)*.

Range: Widespread in temperate Northern Hemisphere. Introduced from the East Coast into our area.

Similar Species: Other genera of composites that superficially resemble nodding beggarticks lack the 2-4 firm, backwards-barbed bristles found on the achenes of the genus *Bidens*, and typically also lack the two distinct series of involucral bracts. Other common species of beggarticks in our area, such as common beggarticks *(Bidens frondosa)*, have compound leaves borne on stalks with 3-5 leaflets, orange disc flowers, and achenes that are 2-bristled.

Nodding beggarticks, a weedy annual herb, is the most common daisy in habitats with standing water. Plants are 10-100 cm tall, smooth- or slightly rough-surfaced, often branched, and always leafy. The roots are fibrous. Cernua means "drooping" or "nodding", and refers to how the flower heads bend over at maturity. Bidens means "two teeth" and refers to the two pappus bristles found in most (but not this) species. Blooms July though September.

Genus: *Boykinia*

Family: Saxifragaceae

These two boykinias are rhizomatous, perennial herbs with alternate, heart- to kidney-shaped leaves that have angular lobes and toothed margins. Stipules are present on the leaf bases. Leaves are borne on long stalks at the base of plants, and on very short stems above. Petals are opposite sepals, white, strongly short-clawed, and tapering where they attach.

Similar Species: Boykinias are most likely confused with other members of the Saxifrage family, especially fringecup *(Tellima grandiflora)*, piggy-back plant *(Tolmiea menziesii)*, and three-leaf foamflower *(Tiarella trifoliata)*. Fringecups have leaves with toothed margins but the clefts are not deep, and flowers are yellow-green with turned backwards, branched, and bristle-like petals. Piggy-back plant has similar leaves, but they often develop small buds where the leaf stalk joins the leaf blade, and the flowers are red-brown. Three-leaf foamflower has a compound leaf with three leaflets, and the leaves are mostly basal.

Boykinia major var. *intermedia*
greater mountain boykinia; mountain brookfoam

status: FACW

HERBS

Greater mountain boykinia is 30-100 cm tall with stout stems that lack glandular hairs. Blooms June through September.

- leaves unequally 3- to 7-lobed, but mostly 3-lobed leaves, to 20 cm wide
- stipules brown, membranous, leaf-like, toothed, often clasping the stem, greater than or equal to 1 cm long
- inflorescence 30-100 cm long, flat-topped panicle; petals larger than 5 mm, round to elliptic

Habitat: Occurs in meadows, along stream banks, and in moist coniferous and deciduous forests at mid- to low elevations. Prefers flooded stream terraces and stream edge sites that are shady.

Range: Greater mountain boykinia is restricted to the coastal mountains and lowlands of the Olympic Peninsula south to Tillamook County, Oregon.

Greater mountain boykinia has 3-lobed leaves, stems lacking hairs, and flower petals that are greater than 5 mm long.

Boykinia species continued on next page...

93

Boykinia occidentalis
(Boykinia elata)
slender boykinia; Santa Lucia brookfoam; coast boykinia
Status: FAC

Slender boykinia is small (15-60 cm) and delicate. Stems are brown-glandular hairy. Blooms June through August.

- leaves 2-8 cm wide, 5- to 9-lobed
- stipules slender, inconspicuous, bristle-like, 2-4 mm long
- infloresence 30-60 cm long, open, cyme-like panicle, arranged on one side of stem; petals less than 5 mm long, oblong to oval

Habitat: Occurs in meadows, along streambanks, and in moist coniferous and deciduous forests at mid- to low elevations. Prefers flooded stream terraces and stream edge sites that are shady.

Range: Slender boykinia is found in British Columbia south in the western Cascades to the California Sierras and on the coast in Washington and Oregon.

Slender boykinia has 5- to 9-lobed leaves, very hairy stems stems, and flower petals that are less than 5 mm long.

Brasenia schreberi
watershield

Family: Cabombaceae (Nymphaeaceae)
Status: OBL
Color photo page 225

The floating leaves of this aquatic water lily are 4-15 cm wide and 3-12 cm long. Branching stems can be 30-200 cm long. The flowers, which sometimes open under water, have 3 petals, 3 sepals, and 12-18 stamens. Blooms June to August.

- leaves eye-shaped to oval, with stalk attached to center of each leaf, not notched at the base
- leaf undersides reddish and, along with leaf stalks, have a jelly-like coating
- petals and sepals small (10-15 mm long), purple-red
- seed pods leathery, containing 1-2 seeds each

Habitat: Watershield roots in the silty bottoms of shallow freshwater ponds and slow-moving streams. Often found with pondweeds *(Potamogeton* species) and cattails *(Typha* species).

Range: Introduced to the United States as a cultivated species, watershield is a widely distributed escapee.

Similar Species: The only other water lily with leaf stalks attached at the center of the leaf is *Nelumbo lutea*, which has much larger leaves and is not found in western Washington and Oregon except under cultivation. White water lily *(Nymphaea odorata)* has circular leaves and yellow pond-lily *(Nuphar luteum)* has heart-shaped leaves. The leaf stalks of both species attach at the base of a notched leaf and lack the jelly-like coating. White wa-ter lily has large (15 cm), showy, fragrant white flowers and yellow pond-lily has yellow flowers with red markings.

The leaf stalks of watershield are attached to the center of each leaf; stems and leaf undersides are covered with a jelly-like coating.

Functional Value: Ducks eat the leaves and seeds. The floating leaves provide roosts for aquatic organisms.

HERBS

Cakile edentula var. edentula
American searocket

Family: Brassicaceae (Cruciferae)
Status: FACU
Color photo page 225

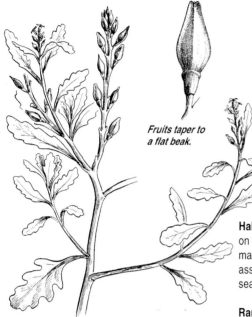

Fruits taper to a flat beak.

American searocket is a maritime species with succulent stems and leaves.

The thick fruits of American searocket, which taper to a flat beak, are unmistakable. Leaves are to 7 cm long and spreading. The small flowers are white to purple-tinged, 4-parted, rather short-lived, and inconspicuous. Blooms in July and August.

- plants to 50 cm tall, with a taproot
- leaves alternate, succulent, 5-7 cm long, with toothed, somewhat indented, wavy margins
- petals 6-8 mm long
- fruits double-jointed, 1.5-2.5 cm long, stems with mature fruits appearing like string of beads

Habitat: Found in sandy areas along sea coasts, on sand dunes, and at the highest reaches of salt marshes where sandy substrate occurs. Often associated with sandworts *(Arenaria* species) and seashore saltgrass *(Distichlis spicata).*

Range: Common on sandy coastal and estuarine beaches of Washington and Oregon. Native to the shores of the Great Lakes and Atlantic Coast.

Similar Species: A related species, European searocket *(Cakile maritima)*, occurs in coastal Oregon and California. It has finely divided leaves 4-8 cm long, petals 8-10 mm long, and fruits in which the lowest joint is flared into 2-4 lobes.

Ethnobotanical Uses: Young leaves and shoots have a strong peppery flavor, but are quite edible raw in salads. Cooking is necessary for older plants and improves palatability of young plants. No use by Native Americans has been reported.

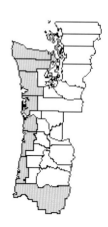

Callitriche heterophylla
different leaved water-starwort;
different leaved water-chickweed; different-leaved wort;
larger water-starwort

Family: Callitrichaceae
Status: OBL
Color photo page 225

This water-starwort typically forms continuous mats in shallow, stagnant water. Although mats appear to be free-floating, they are rooted in the mud. Stems are 5-40 cm long with opposite leaves. Minute, petal-less flowers are borne in the leaf axils and are attached to 2 small bracts. Blooms April through July; sometimes as late as September.

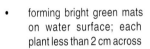

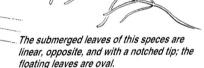

Fruit with notched tip.

Flowers.

- forming bright green mats on water surface; each plant less than 2 cm across
- floating leaves oval-oblong, 1 cm wide
- submersed leaves often linear with notched tips, 5-25 mm long
- fruits squarish-oval to oblong, 1 mm long, notched at the tip

The submerged leaves of this speces are linear, opposite, and with a notched tip; the floating leaves are oval.

Habitat: Found floating in drainage swales and on small shallow ponds. After the water has drained, water-starwort can cover the mud like a carpet and will continue to grow provided the soil stays moist. Often associated with duckweed *(Lemna minor)*, white water buttercup *(Ranunculus aquatilis)*, and yellow pond-lily *(Nuphar luteum)*.

Range: Throughout North America and in South America and Greenland. Occurs in all counties in our area.

Similar Species: Two similar aquatic species, duckweed *(Lemna minor)* and great duckweed *(Spirodela polyrhiza)*, have single pairs of flat, green, floating leaves. Another species of water starwort that is less common but does occur in our region is spring water-starwort *(Callitriche verna)*. The leaves and stems of this species are very similar to different-leaved water starwort, but the fruits are not prominently notched at the tip and the margins of the fruits are winged.

Functional Value: Provides forage for aquatic insects. Water-starwort filters and absorbs toxicants in bioswales and ditches.

HERBS

Caltha palustris var. *asarifolia*
yellow marshmarigold

Family: Ranunculaceae
Status: OBL

Yellow marshmarigold has fleshy to succulent leaves and yellow, petal-like sepals.

Yellow marshmarigold is a stout, somewhat fleshy, perennial herb. Basal leaves are borne singly at the ends of long stalks. Leaves borne on the flower stem are smaller than the basal leaves and are held on short stalks. Flowers lack true petals, but have brightly colored, modified sepals. Mature fruit is a crown-like aggregate of seed-filled capsules.

- flower stems weak, arched and prostrate, sometimes rooting at nodes, with several leaves
- leaves round to heart-shaped, 5-12 cm wide, with notched base forming 2 overlapping lobes; veins prominent, palmate; margins round- to sharp-toothed
- flowers 1-3, yellow, with 5-7 petal-like sepals, many stamens, and several to many ovaries attached on a common base

Habitat: Mostly in coastal bogs and marshes.

Range: Aleutian Islands and coastal Alaska, south to Oregon.

Similar Species: Yellow marshmarigold may be confused with other marshmarigold species (none of which are common in our area, but occur more frequently at higher elevations); however, the yellow flowers, several-leaved flower stem, and creeping manner of yellow marshmarigold make it unique. Deer-cabbage *(Fauria crista-galli)* has similarly shaped leaves with notched bases that form 2 lobes, but the lobes do not overlap, all leaves are basal with blunt-toothed, wavy margins, and flowers are white and foul smelling.

Genus: *Camassia*
camas
Family: Liliaceae

Camases are onion-like, perennial herbs that grow from an edible bulb. The two sub-species found in our region have fewer than 10 leaves per plant. Leaves are long and narrow, grass-like, and emerge from the base. Flowers are showy with 6 tepals, 6 stamens, and 3 stigmas. Inflorescence is a spike-like cluster borne on a leafless stem that is held above the leaves.

Similar Species: The bulbs of common camas when not in flower, and the plants themselves, look very similar to death camas *(Zigadenus venenosus)*. Be certain of your identification before eating common camas bulbs! Death camas, which has white flowers, can grow in a similar habitat, and cause abdominal pain, vomiting, diarrhea, and even death.

Ethnobotanical Uses: Camas bulbs were a staple food for many Native American groups living in the Pacific Northwest, and except for choice varieties of dried salmon, no other food item was more widely traded. Bulbs were gathered during or after flowering and steamed in pits lined with seaweed, blackberry, fern fronds, salal, or grand fir boughs. The bulbs were sometimes stored in bags woven from common cattail *(Typha latifolia)*, but they did not keep well. Another source states that the bulbs were stored fresh, dried, or cooked, and does not comment on their shelf life. Among some Northwest native peoples, camas beds were divided into family-owned plots that passed from generation to generation. See above note on death camas.

HERBS

Camassia quamash ssp. *breviflora*
common camas
Status: FACW
Color photo page 225

Common camas is a stout, robust plant with a dense inflorescence. It has slightly irregular flowers with the lowest tepal curving outward away from the stem. Blooms April through June.

- flowers light to deep blue; more than 3 flowers can be open at one time
- leaves narrow and not covered with fine, waxy powder
- tepals withering and falling off the fruit, not twisting together over the ovary
- anthers bright yellow

Habitat: Seasonally wet meadows, prairies, and hillsides where moist, and streamside areas, often where dry by late spring.

The leaves of common camas lack a powdery cover; many flowers open at once and have bright, yellow anthers.

Range: Throughout our area and east to southwest Alberta, Montana, Wyoming, and Utah. Hitchcock (1973) describes several varieties: var. *intermedia* has pale blue flowers and occurs from Lane County to southeast Oregon; var. *maxima* has deep blue to violet flowers and occurs from southwestern British Columbia through western Washington to the southeast end of the Willamette Valley, Oregon; var. *azurea* has pale bluish violet flowers and occurs in the Puget Basin from Pierce to Grays Harbor counties, and on both sides of the Olympic Peninsula.

Camas species continued on next page...

Camassia quamash ssp. quamash (Camassia leichtlinii)
great camas; Leichtlin's camas

Status: FACW-
Color photo page 225

The flowers of great camas resemble those of common camas, but the inflorescence is more open and more regularly and equally shaped and sized. Blooms June and July.

- flowers white (south of Pierce County) to deep blue-violet; no more than 3 flowers are open at one time
- leaves wide and covered with fine, waxy powder
- tepals 20-40 cm long, twisting together over the ovary after flowering
- anthers dull yellow to violet

Habitiat: Same as common camas.

The leaves of great camas are covered with a fine powder; flowers open three at a time and have dull yellow to violet anthers.

Ceratophyllum demersum
coontail; hornwort; common hornwort

Family: Ceratophyllaceae

Status: OBL

Coontail is an aquatic herb that is entirely submerged and without roots. The leaves are very finely dissected and attached in whorls around the stem, forming long cylinders that can grow to 4 m in length. Flowers are not obvious. Nut-like fruits are borne without stalks in the leaf axils.

- leaves forked, 5-12 per whorl, 5-25 mm long, stiff (will retain shape out of water), with fork-like teeth along one side

Habitat: Widely distributed in the Pacific Northwest, coontail is typically found in alkaline conditions, in standing to slow-moving fresh water.

Range: Considered cosmopolitan and commonly found in both Washington and Oregon.

Similar Species: Milfoil (*Myriophyllum* species) have feather-like leaves that lose their shape when removed from the water.

Functional Value: Although the seeds are eaten by various duck species, coontail is not considered an important food source. It provides shelter for small aquatic animals. Coontail can sometimes crowd out other, more desirable, aquatic plant species. It is used in fish bowls and aquaria.

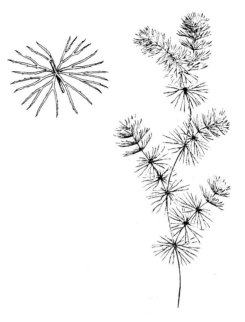

Coontail is an aquatic species with very fine, narrow leaves that are forked.

HERBS

Cicuta douglasii
western water-hemlock; Douglas' water hemlock

Family: Apiaceae (Umbelliferae)
Status: OBL
Color photo page 226

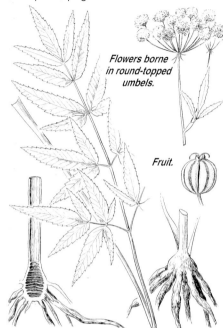

Flowers borne in round-topped umbels.

Fruit.

The base of western water-hemlock, when cut lengthwise, has horizontal partitions; leaves are compound with long, linear leaflets.

Western water-hemlock is a stout perennial that grows 0.5-2 m tall. It has a single taproot or a cluster of tuberous roots from which one to a few hairless stems arise. The stems will root at the nodes. Leaves are attached to the base of the plant and along the stem.

- tuberous-thickened stem base containing prominent horizontal partitions
- twice to thrice compound leaves; leaflets 1-3, linear, narrow, toothed, with lateral veins that end at the base of the indentation between the teeth, not at the tip of teeth
- flowers small, white or greenish, borne in several round-topped umbels
- fruits oval to egg-shaped, 2-4 mm long, unequal, with ribbing

Habitat: Grows in marshes, ditches, wet low places, along streams, and in disturbed areas. Can be found from the plains and lowlands to midmontane elevations.

Range: Western water-hemlock is widespread in western North America.

Similar Species: Many genera of the Apiaceae, including *Cicuta, Angelica, Sium, Conium,* and *Oenanthe,* have white-flowered umbel inflorescences, swollen tuberous underground structures, and compound leaves. *Cicuta* is the only species that has underground stems divided into distinct chambers. All can have purple-tinted stems but *Conium* is the only species that has purple spots on the stems, leaves that are more divided than the others, and a musty mouse-like odor. *Oenanthe* has flower lobes that are persistent on the fruits, and highly dissected leaflets on the compound leaves. *Angelica* has irregularly shaped and sized, mostly triangular, leaflets with sharply toothed margins. *Sium* has very narrow lance-shaped leaves with 7-15 leaflets that are only once-divided.

Functional Value: All parts of the plant are very poisonous to humans and cattle, especially the roots and stems; even a small quantity can cause illness and death. It is particularly hazardous to cattle because it grows in pastures along streams.

Cirsium arvense var. *horridum*
Canada thistle; creeping Canadian thistle; creeping thistle

Family: Asteraceae (Compositae)
Status: FACU+
Color photo page 226

Canada thistle is a perennial herb with extensive rhizomes that extend deep into the soil. Stems are usually 30-150 cm tall, thin, and branched. Leaves are smooth-surfaced above and soft white-hairy below, with leaf bases running down the stem in some forms. Flower heads are open and composed of either all male or all female flowers. Female flowers produce long, flattened, ribbed achenes. Blooms July to August.

- stems without spines
- leaves alternate, long, lance-shaped, spiny, wavy to deeply lobed, delicate
- involucre about 1-2 cm high; involucral bracts numerous in several series, not spiny, or the outer with a weak spine tip about 1 mm long
- flower heads 1-2 cm tall, pale lavender to purple, or white, numerous, composed of disc flowers only
- pappus hairs of female heads are longer than the petals, those of the male heads are shorter than the petals

Habitat: Common in pastures, meadows, and other open areas, mostly in upland habitats, but also found in emergent wetlands. Canada thistle is a noxious weed that, once established, is difficult to eradicate.

Range: Native of Europe; it is now widespread in temperate areas of the world. Occurs in all counties in our area.

Similar Species: Other thistle species confused with Canada thistle have larger flower heads, stems with spines, leaves that are stout, and occur in drier sites. Bull thistle *(Cirsium vulgare)* is often found near, and sometimes in, wetlands, but it is twice the size of Canada thistle, has involucres that are 2.5-4 cm long, flower heads with both male

Involucre.

Canada thistle has spiny leaves that are long and lance-shaped; flowers can be pale lavender to purple, or white.

and female flowers, grows in a huge tuft, and has conspicuous, stiff, prickly hairs on the upper leaf surfaces.

Ethnobotanical Uses: The stems and roots may be eaten when peeled.

HERBS

Claytonia lanceolata
western springbeauty; lance-leaf springbeauty
Family: Portulacaceae
Status: FAC-

The stems of western springbeauty are attached underground to a round corm; leaves are succulent; flowers are white with pink veins.

Western springbeauty is a small, slender, delicate, perennial herb that emerges in early spring. Leaves are sometimes lacking on flowering plants. The inflorescence is a loose raceme with 3-20 flowers borne on stout to slender stalks, 1-5 cm long. Flowers have 5 petals that are 7-12 mm long and fused into a tube at the base, with 5 stamens and 3 styles. The fruit is an oval, firm-walled capsule about 4 mm long. Seeds number 3-6, are black, shiny, and 2-2.5 mm long. Plants blooms late March to late July.

- stems 1- to several, 6-20 cm long, attached underground to a 5-20 mm diameter round corm
- leaves waxy and smooth-surfaced, 2 per flowering stem, opposite, oval to narrowly lance-shaped, 5-20 mm broad and 1.5-6 cm long, attached directly to stem or nearly so
- flowers pure white to occasionally deep pink with deep pink veins, rarely light to deep yellow or orange

Habitat: Found in subalpine meadows on both sides of the Cascades; often abundant near snowbanks in open grassy meadows. Usually it occurs in places moist at least in the early spring. Often found in the lower subalpine silver fir *(Abies amabilis)* zone in the thimbleberry *(Rubus parviflorus)* — fireweed *(Epilobium angustifolium)* community with yellow fawnlily *(Erythronium grandiflorum)*.

Range: Southern British Columbia southward, on both sides of the Cascades, to southern California, east to Alberta and New Mexico. Several regional varieties, including *Claytonia lanceolata* var. *pacifica*, found only in the Olympic Mountains, are on the Washington State list of sensitive plants.

Similar Species: Miner's lettuce *(Montia* species) have the same general growth form, but lack corms.

Ethnobotanical Uses: The starchy corms are edible prior to flowering and taste like potatoes. They were steamed or dried by the native peoples of the Pacific Northwest, particularly those of British Columbia and the Okanogan.

Conium maculatum
poison-hemlock

Family: Apiaceae (Umbelliferae)
Status: FAC+
Color photos page 226

Poison-hemlock is a hairless biennial that forms a rosette of leaves and grows to 1 m tall. The plant arises from a robust, white, carrot-like taproot. Entire plant emits a musty, mouse-like odor when crushed. Flowering stems, to 3 m tall, are produced only in the second year. Blooms from May to August.

- stems hollow, multiple-branched, purple-spotted
- leaves twice to thrice pinnately compound, carrot-like, finely dissected, 15-30 cm long
- leaf stalks sheathing at the base
- flowers small, white, numerous, in many compound umbels, with involucral bracts
- fruits oval-flattened, 2-3 mm long, with raised, prominent, wavy ribs

Habitat: Usually found along roadsides, in abandoned fields, ditches, and other moist, disturbed areas.

Range: Introduced from Europe many years ago and now grows throughout most of North America. Common in all counties in our area.

Similar Species: Several genera of the Apiaceae, including *Cicuta, Angelica, Sium, Conium,* and *Oenanthe,* have white-flowered umbel inflorescences, swollen tuberous underground structures, and compound leaves. *Conium* is the only species that has purple spots on the stems, leaves that are more divided than the others, and has a musty mouse-like odor. *Cicuta* have a chambered base, and broader and less dissected leaves. *Oenanthe* typically grows in shallow standing water and has fibrous roots, and no purple spotting on the stem. *Angelica* has irregularly shaped and sized, mostly triangular and once-divided leaflets with sharp-toothed edges. *Sium* has very narrow lance-shaped leaves with 7-15 leaflets that are only once-divided. Queen Anne's lace *(Daucus carota)* has a single unbranched stem, a small white tap root, no purple spotting on the stem, and grows in drier sites in meadows, pastures, and waste places.

Fruit.

Poison-hemlock has finely dissected, compound leaves, and purple-spotted stems.

Ethnobotanical Uses: Poison hemlock is *extremely poisonous* and is purported to be the same hemlock taken by Socrates. All parts of the plant may cause dermatitis and are poisonous if ingested. Unfortunately, since poison hemlock resembles parsley, carrots, and other edible members of the parsley family, every few years children or adults experimenting with wild foods die after eating raw or cooked leaves, roots, or even just the seeds. After the plant was introduced, Native Americans used poison-hemlock roots in various ways to bring good luck. The Snohomish rubbed it on their fish hooks to mask the fisherman's odor; S'klallam women wanting to attract a mate rubbed the root on their bodies after bathing.

HERBS

Cornus unalaschkensis
(Cornus canadensis)
bunchberry, dwarf dogwood
Family: Cornaceae
Status: FAC

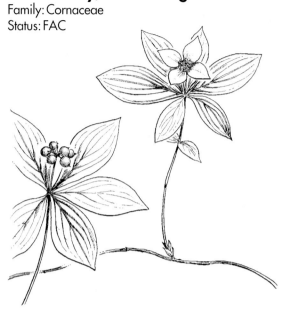

Bunchberry is an evergreen groundcover; leaves have parallel veins and fruits are red berries.

Bunchberry is a small, low-trailing, perennial herb that grows in forested wetland and upland communities. Stems are short, only 5-20 cm tall, erect, slightly hairy, and semi-woody. Leaves are borne at the top of the stem, and are whorled, with 4-7 leaves per whorl. Stems have 1-2 pairs of leafy bracts below the leaves. Blooms from June through August.

- leaves evergreen, green to occasionally reddish-green, whitish waxy below, 2-8 cm long, oval-elliptic, with parallel veins; borne directly on stem
- inflorescence consisting of 4 white to purplish-white, petal-like bracts surrounding a cluster of inconspicuous flowers
- fruits berries, 5-9 mm wide, red, pithy; edible

Habitat: Coniferous and mixed deciduous forests, and small forest openings where conditions are moist. Common on logs and stumps. Bunchberry is found from 1,500 m in elevation to sea level.

Range: Alaska to Greenland, south to Pennsylvania, New Mexico and California. Occurs in all counties in our area.

Similar Species: None.

Ethnobotanical Uses: Often used as an ornamental because of its attractive foliage and fruits. Bunchberry rhizomes transplant easily but should not be removed from the wild.

Corydalis scouleri
Scouler corydalis

Family: Fumariaceae
Status: FAC+

Scouler corydalis is a tall (to 1 m), erect, perennial herb that is often covered with a fine waxy powder. It is easily identified by its lacy leaves and erect spikes of 15-35 flowers. It spreads by thick rhizomes. Blooms April to July.

- leaves borne above the middle of flowering stem
- leaves usually 3 per stem, lacy, round-lobed, compound, with narrow leaflets
- flowers spurred, purplish pink fading to white-pink, 2-3 cm long
- seeds shiny, black, 4 mm long, ejected from egg-shaped capsules

Habitat: Nearly always occurs in shady forested areas, frequently where soils are very moist and a seep is present. Usually seen as clusters of a few plants or small colonies rather than dominating large areas of land.

Range: Occurs from British Columbia to northern Oregon, both along the coast and inland to the Cascade slopes.

Similar Species: Bleeding heart *(Dicentra formosa)* has symmetrically pouched outer petals, more finely divided, pointed-tipped leaves, heart-shaped and dropping flowers, and grows in upland communities.

Ethnobotanical Uses: This plant is related to bleeding heart and contains at least ten alkaloids. Ingestion of just a small amount may affect the nervous system.

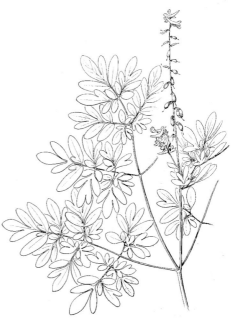

Scouler corydalis has compound leaves with finely dissected, round-tipped leaflets; flowers are purplish pink and have spurs.

HERBS

Cotula coronopifolia
brassbuttons

Family: Asteraceae (Compositae)
Status: FACW+
Color photo page 226

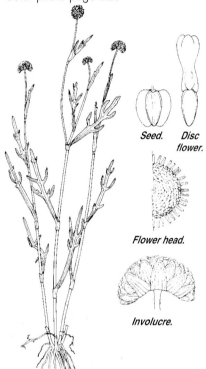

*Seed.   Disc
flower.*

Flower head.

Involucre.

*This small estuarine species has succulent
stems and flower heads composed of yellow
disc flowers.*

This member of the daisy family is an estuarine,
perennial herb with stems 5-30 cm long. Flower
heads are solitary, 5-11 mm wide, and flattened.
The outermost disc flowers consist of a single row
of female flowers that lack corollas. The inner rows
of flowers have both male and female parts.

- stems trailing, succulent, rooting at the nodes
- leaves alternate, attached directly to stem, lance-shaped to linear, sheathing, 1-6 cm long, 1-10 mm wide, with smooth, few-toothed or deeply lobed margins
- involucral bracts separate, slightly unequal, in 2 series, 3-5 mm long
- flower heads yellow, button-shaped, to 1 cm wide, composed of disc flowers only
- achenes of the outer flowers winged, others not winged; pappus lacking

Habitat: Occurs in estuarine salt marshes and on tidal mudflats; rarely inland in emergent wetlands.

Range: Native of South Africa; now widespread around the world. In the Pacific Northwest from the coast of British Columbia to California and inland along the Columbia River to the Cascade Mountains.

Similar Species: Brassbuttons is not easily confused with other yellow-flowered composites lacking rays because those species have pappus hairs on their achenes or the outer flowers have corollas. Australian cotula *(Cotula australis)*, a species that is occasionally found in the Willamette Valley, is an annual, is not succulent, and has leaves that are not sheathing. Smooth lasthenia *(Lasthenia glaberrima)* has a similar appearance, but the involucral bracts are united in a cup.

Cuscuta salina var. *major*
salt-marsh dodder

Family: Convolvulaceae (Cuscutaceae)
Status: Not listed (facw)
Color photo page 226

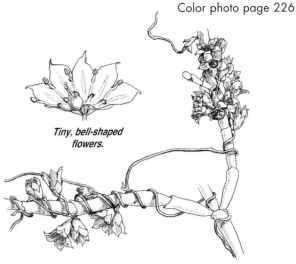

Tiny, bell-shaped flowers.

Salt-marsh dodder is a symbiotic species with twining orange stems.

This herbaceous plant is an entwining symbiont that lacks chlorophyll. Blooms June to August.

- stems bright orange, thread-like, lavishly twinning
- leaves reduced to microscopic scales, hardly noticeable
- flowers tiny, bell-shaped, white or cream, 2-5 mm, in loose clusters

Habitiat: Symbiotic on pickleweed *(Salicornia virginica)* and less commonly on jaumea *(Jaumea carnosa)* or other plants of emergent salt marshes.

Range: Pacific Coast from British Columbia to Mexico. Inland to Utah and Arizona.

Similar Species: Not easily distinguishable from other dodder species; however, salt-marsh dodder is the only species reported from Pacific Northwest salt marshes or inhabiting areas with saline soils, whereas other species are frequently associated with agricultural crops.

Functional Value: No apparent damage is caused to host plants.

Ethnobotanical Uses: Salt-marsh dodder has been used as a laxative-cathartic and to reduce spleen inflammations and lymph node swellings. The Chinese use it to treat impotence.

Drosera rotundifolia var. *rotundifolia*
roundleaf sundew; sundew

Family: Droseraceae
Status: OBL
Color photo page 227

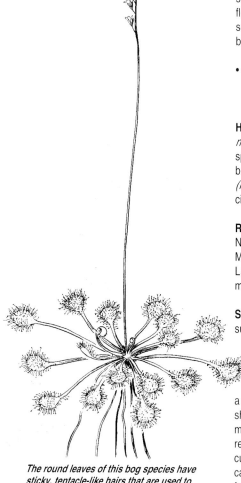

The round leaves of this bog species have sticky, tentacle-like hairs that are used to snare insects.

Roundleaf sundew is a small, perennial, bog plant with a flattened, basal rosette of rounded leaves covered with sticky hairs which are used to snare and digest insects. Sundew plants produce a one-sided raceme of white flowers in which the terminal flower blooms first, followed by the others in descending order. Flowers are 6-10 mm long and bloom May to July.

• leaves basal, round, reddish, covered with tentacle-like hairs each holding a drop of sticky sap at the tip

Habitat: Restricted to drier hummocks of *Sphagnum* moss-dominated bogs and fens. Associated species include *Aulacomnium* mosses, wild cranberry *(Vaccinium oxycoccus)*, bog Labrador-tea *(Rhododendron groenlandicum)*, and other species restricted to acidic, nutrient-poor habitats.

Range: Roundleaf sundew ranges from Alaska to Nevada and California, east to Idaho, Montana, Minnesota, Florida, Virginia, New England, and Labrador; also grows in Eurasia at low to midelevations. Occurs in all counties in our area.

Similar Species: A very similar species, great sundew *(Drosera anglica)*, occurs much less frequently than roundleaf sundew. Great sundew's leaves are oblong and held more erect.

Ethnobotanical Uses: Occasionally sold as a novelty item in grocery stores and souvenir shops. Otherwise, this fascinating little plant is much less known to the general public than its relative, Venus flytrap. The leaf sap is reported to curdle milk and has been used by Native Americans to remove corns, warts, and bunions on the feet. The sap contains an antibiotic that has been used to treat a variety of coughs and bacterial infections.

Elodea canadensis
Canada waterweed; broad waterweed

Family: Hydrocharitaceae
Status: OBL

Canada waterweed is a submerged, flexible, aquatic plant common in fresh water. It forms extensive beds or occurs as isolated stems. Plants are usually attached to the bottom during the early growing season and become detached later on. The foliage becomes widely spaced, and occasionally branched, towards the roots. Blooms midsummer.

- leaves simple, transparent with one vein, thin and straight to oblong, 1-2 mm wide and 6-15 mm long, minutely toothed near the tip, and in whorls of 3 near base
- male flowers persistent, white, lacking petals on a stalks to 15 cm long; female flowers solitary and 3-petaled

Habitat: Canada waterweed prefers calm or slow-moving water in streams, rivers, ponds, and lakes up to 3 m deep. It tolerates moderate over-fertilization and mild pollution. Found from the coast to midelevations in the mountains. Often associated with other aquatics such as pond-weeds *(Potamogeton* species), milfoils *(Myriophyllum* species), and bladderworts *(Utricularia* species).

Range: Native to North America, this species ranges from the Pacific to the Atlantic coasts, across southern Canada and the northern half of the United States, and now through Europe. Occurs in all counties in our area.

Similar Species: Nuttall's waterweed *(Elodea nuttallii)*, with leaves in whorls of three, is very similar and can be confidently distinguished only by its male flowers, which are not stalked and are shed after blooming (then float to the surface). No other flowering aquatic genus has only whorled simple leaves. Some nodes of the rare howellia *(Howellia aquatilis)* are whorled, but many leaves are alternate. The algae with whorled leaves are much more slender and branch repeatedly, unlike the little-branched waterweed. The rapidly spreading South American waterweed *(Elodea densa)* is

The leaves of this aquatic plant are tiny, linear, and transparent.

distinguished by its lance-shaped, 1-3 cm long by 1 mm wide, toothed leaves in whorls of 4-8. It has very dense foliage and showy flowers.

Functional Value: Dense beds of waterweed provide shelter to many invertebrates, turtles, frogs, and small fish.

Ethnobotanical Uses: Occasionally used as a decorative species in aquaria.

HERBS

Epilobium ciliatum
(Epilobium watsonii)
Watson willowherb; hairy willow-herb

Family: Onagraceae
Status: FACW -
Color photo page 227

Watson willowherb has reddish stems, opposite leaves, and flowers with deeply notched flower petals that are red to purple.

Watson willowherb is an erect herbaceous perennial that forms a basal rosette of leaves that are initially covered with a fine waxy powder and, with age, become hairy. It has fibrous roots, and occasionally, short rhizomes. Small flowers, on slender stems, are borne on leafy stalks. Sepals and petals of each flower number 4; sepals are 4-5 mm long and reddish, and petals are to 8-14 mm long, reddish to purplish, and deeply notched. Stamens number 8 and are of two lengths.

- stems erect, to 1 m tall, round to slightly square, coarse, often reddish when young, sometimes branched; ridges occur vertically down stem from under leaves

- leaves many, opposite, elliptic to lance-shaped, reddish to greenish, 3-6 mm long, toothed along margins, with short, broad leaf stalks

- fruits capsules, elongate, to 8 cm long splitting open lengthwise when mature, producing numerous seeds

- seeds tiny, 1 mm each, with a tuft of whitish hairs

Habitat: Common in moist open areas, from wet meadows to scrub-shrub wetlands, and often found near the edge of shrub or forested areas which contain small streams.

Range: A native to North America, it is common in the Pacific Northwest north to British Columbia.

Similar Species: Fireweed *(Epilobium angustifolium)* is usually, but not always found in dry, recently disturbed sites, such as logged areas and roadsides, grows much taller (to 2.5 m), bears longer and wider leaves, much larger and more open flowers, and longer fruits. When young, Watson willowherb is often mistaken for veronica *(Veronica* species) as all have reddish, round to slightly square stems and lance-shaped to linear leaves; however, the stems and leaves of the veronicas are creeping, plants root freely at the nodes, and stems lack vertical ridges and are less red. The stems of water purslane *(Ludwigia palustris)* and purple loosestrife *(Lythrum salicaria)* are also erect and similar in color and shape from a distance. On close examination, the stems of both these species tend to be square; in addition, the stems of purple loosestrife are almost woody, the leaves of water purslane are not lance-shaped and are more olive-red in color, the flower petals are lacking, and the sepals are fused.

Fauria crista-galli
(Nephrophyllidium crista-galli)
deer-cabbage

Family: Menyanthaceae
Status: OBL

Deer-cabbage is a rhizomatous, perennial herb that is smooth, shiny, and slightly fleshy. Stems are 5-30 cm long. Leaves are borne singly at the ends of long, 20-30 cm stalks that all attach at the base and have sheathing stipules. The three petals have fringed nerves, one along each midnerve and one along each margin ("crista-galli" means "crest of a fowl" or "cockscomb"). Blooms July through August.

- rhizomes thick and scaly
- leaves simple, heart- to kidney-shaped, 3-14 cm long, with notched base forming 2 nonoverlapping lobes; margins blunt-toothed
- inflorescence 5- to 10-flowered, loose cyme terminating stem
- flowers white, 6-8 mm long, with 5 petals fused at the base; emit foul, mildew-like scent

Habitat: Grows in bogs, swamps, and wet prairies. Occurs in depressions with saturation to the surface, wet to very wet nitrogen-poor soils, and nutrient-poor wetlands. Deer-cabbage is shade-intolerant. Commonly associated with *Sphagnum*.

Range: Olympic Peninsula north to Alaska; Japan.

Similar Species: The leaves of yellow marshmarigold *(Caltha palustris)* are similarly shaped with notched bases that form 2 lobes; however, leaves may be present along the flower stem, and flowers are yellow and not foul smelling.

Functional Value: A succulent browse for deer, this species also provides habitat for a number of beetles and flies. Deer-cabbage is pollinated by flies attracted to the foul smell.

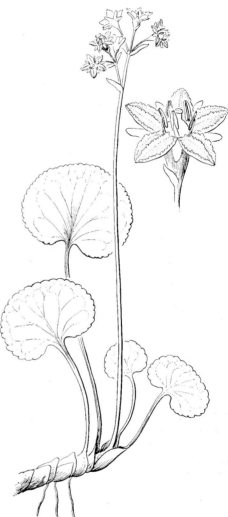

Deer cabbage has thick, scaly rhizomes and kidney-shaped, blunt-toothed leaves.

Genus: *Galium*
bedstraws

Family: Rubiaceae

Bedstraws are common herbs with weak, slender, 4-angled stems that have backward-facing bristles along the margin, and form dense tangles. They are easily uprooted. Leaves are smooth-margined and attach directly to the stem in whorls of 4-8. Flowers are minute with 3 or 4 greenish white petals that are fused to form a short tube that spreads into a saucer shape. Fruits are 2-parted, fused, and globular-shaped.

Similar Species: The bedstraws most closely resemble each other. Sweet woodruff *(Asperula odorata)* is similar to cleavers bedstaw because it also typically has leaves in whorls of 8, but has funnel-shaped flowers with a tube that is more or less equal in length to the lobes.

Ethnobotanical Uses: Bedstraws have long been used as matting and bedding materials. The roasted fruits are used as a coffee substitute. The entire dried herb may be brewed as a tea and has been used in medicines for treatment of urinary tract infections. The roots can be used as a red dye. Fresh plants are used as a filter for milk in Scandanavia.

Galium aparine
cleavers bedstraw; catchweed bedstraw

Status: FACU
Color photo page 227

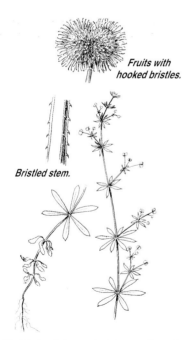

Fruits with hooked bristles.

Bristled stem.

The leaves of cleavers bedstraw are borne in whorls of 6-8 and have short-pointed tips.

This taprooted, annual bedstraw is the largest of the three bedstraws in our area. Leaves have stiff, barbed hairs on the margins and midrib underneath that cause stems to attach to clothes. Blooms April through June.

- stems 10-100 cm long, generally unbranched
- leaves in whorls of 6-8 (usually 8), 1-6 cm long, straight and narrow to oblong, with short-pointed tips
- inflorescence cluster of 3-5 flowers on erect stalks that originate in leaf axils
- flowers 1-2 mm wide, borne in small cluster of 3-5 flowers from leaf axils
- fruits with hooked bristles

Habitat: Cleavers bedstraw *(Galium aparine)* has been found in a variety of habitats, including thickets, coastal dunes, dry meadows, recent clearcuts, moist woodlands, gravel outwash, and open woods. It tends to grow in shady places but is not confined to them. Common associates include salal *(Gaultheria shallon)* and trailing blackberry *(Rubus ursinus)*.

Range: Circumboreal; cleavers bedstraw is probably native to both hemispheres and is now found over most of temperate North America.

Galium trifidum
small bedstraw

Status: FACW+
Color photo page 227

This widespread perennial has tiny flowers and relatively short, narrow leaves. It grows from very slender creeping rhizomes. Blooms June through September.

- stems 5-60 cm long
- leaves in whorls of 4 (sometimes 5 or 6), 0.5-2 cm long, narrow-linear to narrowly elliptic, with blunt or rounded tips
- inflorescence cluster of 1-3 flowers on nodding stalks that orginate in leaf axils and occur on branch tips
- flowers 1-2 mm wide, borne on long, narrow stalks from branch tips and leaf axils
- fruits smooth and waxy, lacking hooked bristles

Habitat: Small bedstraw *(Galium trifidum)* is found in moist areas in bogs, swamps, margins of ponds, along streams, saline and freshwater marshes, and lake shores.

Range: Circumboreal; small bedstraw occurs from Alaska and the Yukon eastward to the Atlantic Coast, and south through our area to California, Texas, Alabama, and Georgia; from sea level to high elevations in the mountains.

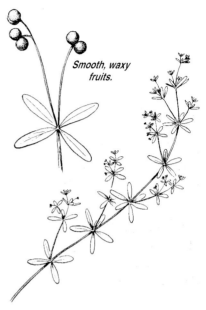

Smooth, waxy fruits.

The leaves of small bedstraw are borne in whorls of 4 and have blunt or rounded tips.

HERBS

Bedstraws continued on next page...

Galium trifidum var. pacificum
(Galium cymosum)
Pacific bedstraw

Status: FACW

This perennial bedstraw grows from creeping rhizomes and occurs mostly in our coastal areas. It is very similar to small bedstraw, but Pacific bedstraw has longer stems, and larger leaves and flowers. Blooms June through August.

- stems weak, freely branching to 80 cm
- leaves in whorls of 4-6, to 3 cm long, linear to narrowly elliptic, with blunt or rounded tips
- inflorescence an irregularly branched cluster of 1-3 flowers on trailing stalks that originate in leaf axils
- flowers 2-3 mm wide, borne in clusters of more than 5 flowers from leaf axils
- fruits smooth, in pairs or threes, lacking hooked bristles

Habitat: Pacific bedstraw *(Galium trifidum* var. *pacificum)* is found in moist places in thickets and wet meadows. It is the most common wetland-associated bedstraw.

Range: Pacific bedstraw occurs chiefly along the Pacific Coast and Puget Sound area from southern British Columbia to Oregon. Occasionally it is found inland to the west slope of the Cascades and to Missoula, Montana.

Pacific bedstraw is very similar to small bedstraw, but has longer stems and larger leaves and flowers.

Gentiana sceptrum
king gentian, staff gentian

Family: Gentianaceae
Status: OBL

This robust gentian is a tufted, waxy-surfaced, perennial herb that grows from fleshy roots. Stems are leafy with the lowest leaves reduced to short bracts. Flowers mostly clustered at the top but may appear in the leaf axils. Blooms July to September.

- stems 20-120 cm tall, scepter-shaped, crowned with several flowers
- leaves opposite, 10-15 pairs, lance-shaped to oblong-linear, upper leaves 3-8 cm long
- flowers 3-4 cm long, with infolded, tubular corolla terminating in 5 oval lobes, bluish purple often with greenish streaks or dots; sepals fused at the bottom with unequal lobes
- seeds spindle-shaped

Habitat: Grows on open lake and stream banks, bogs, wet meadows, and moist sandy flats behind coastal dunes. Most commonly occurs near the coast.

Range: British Columbia to northwest California, west of the Cascades.

Similar Species: Other members of the gentian family are similar, but king gentian is the only lowland, perennial, blue-purple-flowered species.

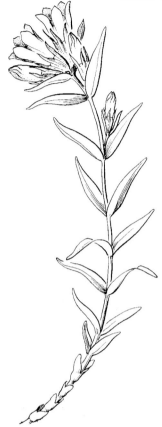

King gentian has succulent leaves and stems and flowers that are bluish purple with greenish dots.

HERBS

Geum macrophyllum
largeleaf avens

Family: Rosaceae
Status: FACW-
Color photo page 227

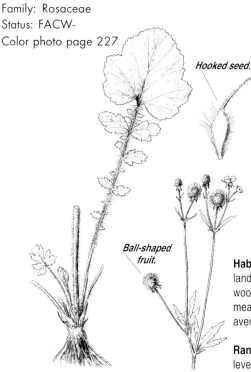

Hooked seed.

Ball-shaped fruit.

Largeleaf avens has bristly-hairy leaf stalks with many irregularly shaped leaflets.

Largeleaf avens is a leafy perennial herb with one to several angular flowering stems. It grows 30 cm to 1 m tall. Leaves are light green and borne both at the base and along the flowering stem. Stem leaves are 3-lobed, alternate near the base but opposite near the top. Flowers appear singly to several on branches at the tops of stems.

- stems bristly-hairy, with several simple, 3-lobed leaves on the flowering stem above the base
- basal leaves pinnately compound, roundish leaflets to 30 cm long, with heart-shaped, terminal leaflets and many small irregular leaflets towards the base
- flowers 5-parted, yellow, with broad, dull petals 6 mm long; sepals pointed; pistils and stamens many
- fruits ball-shaped, with many S-hook-tipped seeds

Habitat: Grows in emergent and forested wetlands, often in open disturbed sites of deciduous woods and clearings on mineral soils. Occurs in meadows and along stream banks. Largeleaf avens is tolerant of fluctuating water levels.

Range: Occurs throughout our range from sea level to subalpine areas, and from Alaska south to Baja, California. There are two varieties of largeleaf avens; one found west, and the other east, of the Cascades.

Similar Species: Buttercups *(Ranunculus* species) and Pacific silverweed *(Potentilla anserina)* also have 5-parted yellow flowers and similarly shaped leaves; however, buttercups have shiny petals and darker green leaves, and seeds lacking hooks. Creeping buttercup *(Ranunculus repens)* has silver markings and nonleafy flowering stems. Pacific silverweed is strictly coastal and has leaves with yellow-green tops and silver undersides.

Ethnobotanical Uses: Native people of the Pacific Northwest used the roots for flavoring stews and fish. In addition, the roots were brewed as tea for stomach pains, or boiled to make aromatic steam to treat rheumatism. The leaves were pounded into a poultice for relieving boils. Largeleaf avens reportly had many female-related uses from pregnancy and birth control to prevention of birthing complications.

Glaux maritima var. *obtusifolia*
sea-milkwort; saltwort

Family: Primulaceae
Status: FACW+
Color photo page 227

Sea-milkwort is a succulent, rhizomatous herb with small, smooth-margined leaves that are somewhat crowded at the tips of the stems. The solitary flowers have no petals, only sepals. Blooms between May and July.

- stems erect, 5-40 cm tall
- leaves opposite, attached directly to stem, oval to oblong, 5-25 mm long
- sepals white or light pink, small, cup-shaped, with 5 lobes, attached directly to stem at leaf axils

Habitat: Common in emergent tidal salt marshes. Associated in the high marsh with fat-hen saltbush *(Atriplex patula)*, Puget-Sound gumweed *(Grindelia integrifolia)*, fleshy jaumea *(Jaumea carnosa)*, and Pacific silverweed *(Potentilla anserina)*.

Range: Occurs in saline tidal marshes or on inland saline soils throughout Arctic and temperate North America and Eurasia. Common in coastal estuaries and salt marshes of Puget Sound.

Similar Species: Saltmarsh chickweed *(Stellaria humifusa)* has leaves that are less crowded on the stems and flowers borne on short stalks. Fleshy jaumea *(Jaumea carnosa)* has long (1.5-5 cm), narrow leaves and one terminal, daisy-like, yellow flower.

Functional Value: Contributes to habitat complexity and biodiversity.

Ethnobotanical Uses: Dried leaves were used by Native Americans as a tea for nursing mothers to increase their milk supply. Young stems and leaves may be pickled.

Sea-milkwort is a salt marsh species with linear, opposite leaves and small flowers that are nestled in leaf axils.

HERBS

Gnaphalium uliginosum
marsh cudweed; low cudweed

Family: Asteraceae (Compositae)
Status: FAC+
Color photo page228

Involucre.

The leaves of marsh cudweed are light blue-green and woolly.

- stems white or grayish woolly, branching from base, 3-25 cm tall
- leaves alternate, linear to lance-shaped, light blue-green, woolly or nearly hairless, 0.8-5 cm long, 1-4 mm wide
- involucral bracts papery, with pale green bases and dark brown tips
- disc flowers white, about 2.5 mm long, in small clusters at tips of stems and branches
- pappus hairs are distinct and detach from the achenes

Habitat: Occurs in low, moist places along roadsides, in drainage ditches, and on poorly drained fill or other highly disturbed habitats. Common associates include various species of willows *(Salix* species), rushes *(Juncus* species), and bedstraws *(Galium* species).

Range: Native to Europe; in our area mostly in the Puget Basin and along the Columbia River, but is found in all counties in our area.

Similar Species: Other species of cudweed are either taller, have unbranched stems, broader leaves, larger (4 mm) flower heads, or reduced, nonleafy involucral bracts. Lowland cudweed *(Gnaphalium palustre)*, which is otherwise very similar, has broad, oblong-lance-shaped to spatulate leaves that are loosely woolly.

Ethnobotanical Uses: Marsh cudweed is aromatic. It is sometimes used in dried flower arrangements.

Marsh cudweed is a highly adaptive annual or perennial weed that pioneers puddles, muddy surfaces, and seasonal ponds. Foliage has a silvery cast, and at first glance appears to be dried up and dead, even when blooming. The bases of the involucres are imbedded in brownish wool. Flower heads are 3-4 mm long and composed of disc flowers only; the numerous (94-108) outer flowers are female, the few (5-7) inner flowers have both male and female organs but are functionally male. Flower heads keep their papery texture after fruiting. Blooms June through October.

Grindelia integrifolia var. *macrophylla*
Puget-Sound gumweed

Family: Asteraceae (Compositae)
Status: FACW
Color photo page 228

Puget-Sound gumweed is a sticky, succulent, taprooted, perennial herb that emits a strong, musky-sweet odor. Stems are often stout, soft-hairy or nearly hairless, 15-80 cm tall, and branching from the base. Basal leaves are oblong to lance-shaped, to 40 cm long and 4 cm wide; stem leaves are alternate, lance-shaped, and attached directly to the stem or clasping. Its yellow flowers persist into late fall, making it a most conspicuous coastal plant. Blooms from June through November.

Involucre

- leaves with sticky resin glands and toothed or smooth margins
- involucre sticky with white gummy sap; bract tips slender and spreading
- flower heads sunflower-like, several to many
- ray flowers yellow, number 10-35, 8-20 mm long; disc flowers yellow, disc head 1-3 cm wide
- achene flattened; pappus of 2 to many deciduous bristles

Habitat: Occurs in coastal habitats, mostly on beaches, rocky outcrops, and emergent saline wetlands; occasionally found on freshwater coastal headlands. Associates include Pacific silverweed *(Potentilla anserina)*, seashore saltgrass *(Distichlis spicata)*, and tufted hairgrass *(Deschampsia caespitosa)*.

Range: British Columbia and Alaska to northern California; in Washington and Oregon along west side of Cascades.

Puget-Sound gumweed has a gummy, sticky-white involucre and yellow flower heads.

Similar Species: Puget-Sound gumweed is distinct from other wetland plants in our area because of its sticky foliage and involucral bracts, large flower heads, and pappus of deciduous bristles.

Ethnobotanical Uses: Grindelia, made from gum extracted from dried parts of some *Grindelia* species, has been used for treating asthma, bronchitis, whooping cough, and contact dermatitis from poison ivy. The medicinal properties of Puget-Sound gumweed are unknown.

HERBS

Hippuris vulgaris
common marestail

Family: Hippuridaceae
Status: OBL
Color photo page 228

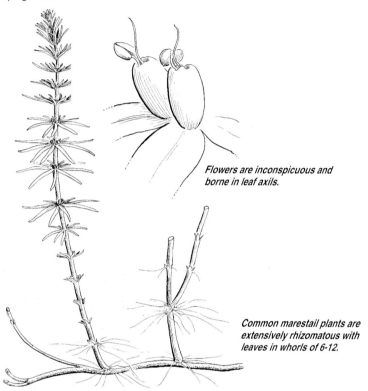

Flowers are inconspicuous and borne in leaf axils.

Common marestail plants are extensively rhizomatous with leaves in whorls of 6-12.

Common marestail is an aquatic or emergent perennial herb. It has extensive creeping rhizomes from which arise erect and spongy stems. It typically forms dense stands of small to moderately large colonies. Plants may be completely submerged, or only partially submerged with the upper portion of the stem held out of the water. Flowers are inconspicuous, borne one above the other in leaf axils; both male and female parts are present. Blooms May to June.

- stems erect, 5-40 cm tall, not hollow, appearing above the surface of a lake or pond
- leaves short (10-35 mm long), narrow (1-2 mm wide), in whorls of 6-12 per node
- leaves on the submerged portion of stem thin and lax; those on the aerial portion relatively stiff and held at right angles to stem

Habitat: Occurs at low elevations in pond and lake shallows, occasionally where water recedes during the growing season but soils remain saturated.

Range: Worldwide in the temperate zone; throughout our area and south in North America to California, New Mexico, and the central and eastern United States.

Similar Species: Mountain marestail *(Hippuris montana)* has leaves that are 5-10 mm long and 0.5-1 mm wide, generally with 5-8 leaves in each whorl, and grows in subalpine marshes, ponds, and lakes in the Olympic and Cascade mountains. Horsetails *(Equisetum* species) loosely resemble common maretail, but lack flowers and have hollow jointed stems.

Honkenya peploides
seabeach sandwort; sandwort; sea purslane

Family: Caryophyllaceae
Status: FACU
Color photo page 228

Seabeach sandwort's erect stems arise from slender rhizomes, although the "mother plant" is taprooted. Plants form mats along sandy beaches and typically these colonies can get quite large with age. Stems can have 3-10 pairs of auxilary stems. Inconspicuous, white-petaled flowers are borne singly in leaf axils of the upturned ends of stems. Blooms May to September.

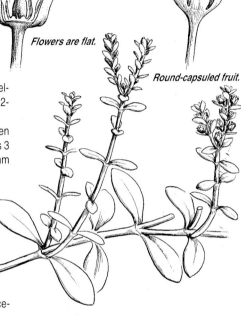

Flowers are flat.

Round-capsuled fruit.

- rooting stems partially buried
- leaves waxy and succulent, opposite, yellow-green, oval to broadly lance-shaped, 2-5 cm long
- flowers almost flat in profile; sepals green and longer than petals; stamens 10; styles 3
- fruits round capsules, smooth, brown, 3 mm long, with 5-10 seeds

Habitat: Forms mats on sandy and gravelly beaches near or just above high tide level along Oregon and Washington coasts. Often found among driftwood. Common associates include American searocket *(Cakile edentula)* and dune grasses.

Range: Coastal beaches of North America, Iceland, Greenland, and Eurasia.

This species, found on sandy beaches, has waxy and succulent stems and leaves.

Similar Species: None.

Functional Value: Seabeach sandwort is a beach stabilizer and provides excellent waterfowl forage.

HERBS

Hydrocotyle ranunculoides
marsh-pennywort; floating marsh-wort; floating penny-wort

Family: Apiaceae (Umbelliferae)
Status: OBL

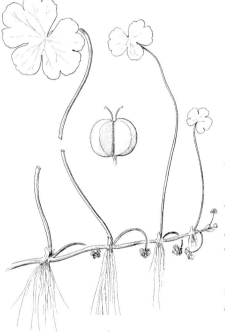

Marsh-pennywort has succulent, clover-shaped leaves that are floating; stems root freely at the nodes.

Marsh-pennywort is a low-growing, aquatic perennial herb with creeping stems and small leaves that are generally held parallel to the surface of the ground. The small flowers and fruits of marsh-pennywort are not useful for identification because they do not resemble those of other species in the parsley family. Blooms at any time during the summer months.

- stems root at nodes to form dense colonies or floating mats; anchored to the ground only at the water's edge
- leaves kidney- to clover-shaped, shallowly lobed, thick, succulent
- flowers 5-10, borne on small curved stalks
- fruits rounded to pumpkin-shaped, 1-3 mm long, 2-3 mm wide, ridges barely present

Habitat: Occurs along muddy shores of creeks and ponds.

Range: Tropical America north to Delaware, Arkansas, California, and west of the Cascade Mountains to the Puget Basin.

Similar Species: None.

Ethnobotanical Uses: A related species, *Hydrocotyle asiatica*, was important in Ayurvedic medicine and has been used on the Indian and African continents as a treatment for leprosy. The plant is considered poisonous.

Hydrophyllum tenuipes
Pacific waterleaf

Family: Hydrophyllaceae
Status: Not listed (fac)

Pacific waterleaf is a rhizomatous perennial herb with fleshy robust roots, and tender, highly dissected leaves. Plants produce one very long-bristly and hairy flowering stem that grows to 80 cm tall. Leaves are few, large, and borne on long stalks. The inflorescence is a terminal compact cluster. Sepals are prickly-bristly. Blooms from May through July.

- leaves alternate, 15 cm long, 10-15 cm wide, divided into 5-9, pointed, broad-toothed, with irregular lobes
- flowers greenish white, occasionally purple, bell-shaped, 5-7 mm long; stamens very long and very obvious
- fruits 1- to 3-seeded capsules

Habitat: Moist forests at low elevations.

Range: Western Washington to northern California. Occurs in all counties in our area.

Similar Species: None

Ethnobotanical Uses: The roots were reportedly eaten by the Cowlitz peoples at the turn of the century.

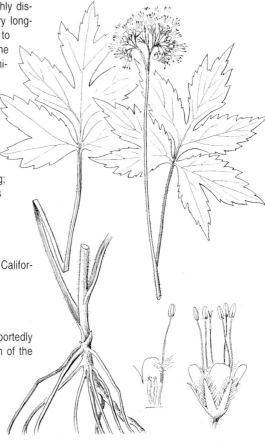

The leaves of Pacific waterleaf are few and borne on long stalks; flowers are greenish white with prickly-bristly sepals.

HERBS

Genus: *Hypericum*
St. John's wort
Family: Hypericaceae

The St. John's wort species in our area are slightly succulent to tender perennial herbs. Foliage is commonly bright blue-green with opposite and purplish, gland-dotted leaves that are attached directly to the stem. The inflorescence is compound with one to many flowers, the terminal flower blooming first. Flowers have five sepals, five yellow petals, and numerous stamens.

Similar Species: Klamath weed *(Hypericum perforatum)* looks very similar to western St. John's wort *(Hypericum formosum)* but it is tap-rooted, with large many-flowered heads. The leaves are lance-shaped, the petals are 10-17 mm long, the sepals 5-7 mm long and narrow with a pointed tip, and the seeds are brownish, more than 1mm long and have a longitudinal row of pits. It is an upland species found in dry disturbed sites – along roadsides, and in cultivated and abandoned fields.

Ethnobotanical Uses: Most species, especially common St. John's wort, contain a volatile oil, a glycoside, a flavonoid, tannins, carotene, and vitamin C. It has been used to treat superficial bruises and, when take internally, stimulates gastric and bile secretions. Also used to improve blood circulation and regulate menstruation, as a treatment for eye diseases, and as an anti-depressant, anti-spasmodic, and anti-viral medication. **CAUTION:** also has been known to cause photosensitization in light-skinned humans if eaten, leading to swelling and serious skin irritation. It is toxic to livestock.

Hypericum anagalloides
bog St. John's wort

Status: OBL

Color photo page 228

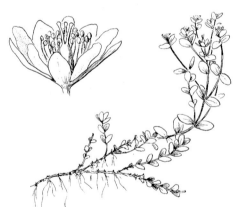

Plants are tiny and creep along in sphagnum moss bogs.

Bog St. John's wort is a tiny, 5-10 cm tall, almost succulent plant that is mat-forming. Stems root at the nodes. Flowers are borne singly or in few-flowered clumps. Blooms June through July.

- stems smooth, creeping, to 20 cm long
- leaves small, rounded to elliptic-oval, 5-15 mm long
- flowers golden to salmon-colored, 5-8 mm across, petals 3-3.5 mm long, sepals 2-3 mm long, stamens 15-25
- fruits capsules, narrow to oblong, to 3 mm long; seeds numerous, 0.5 mm long black, shiny

Habitat: Bog St. John's wort *(Hypericum anagalloides)* is commonly found in low, wet areas, ditches with slow-moving water, and at the edges of ponds, and in more pH-neutral converted bogs, from montane to coastal wetlands.

Range: Western North American native. Found scattered from British Columbia to California, and east to Montana and Wyoming. Bog St. John's wort may be found from British Columbia and Montana south to California.

Hypericum formosum
western St. John's wort

Status: FAC

Western St. John's wort is a fibrous rooted herb. The flowers of western St. John's wort are arranged in few-flowered clumps. Blooms July to September.

- stems smooth, unbranched to branched, erect, 10-80 cm tall
- leaves oval to oblong, 1-3 cm long, with dark purple-black dots on the margins
- flowers 2 cm in diameter; petals 7-10 mm long, dark dotted; sepals 4-5 mm long, rounded-triangular, dark dotted; stamens 50-80
- fruits 3-chambered capsules, narrow to cup-shaped; seeds less than 1mm long, veined, yellow to brownish, no pits

Habitat: Western St. John's wort *(Hypericum formosum)* is commonly found in moist open sites, and along stream banks. It competes well with other non-native weedy species.

Range: Same as bog St. John's wort. In addition, Western St. John's wort is extremely common in California and north through Oregon into Washington.

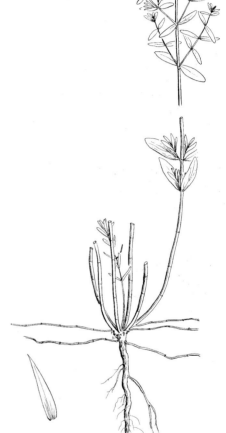

HERBS

Western St. John's wort has leaves with dark dots along the margins; flower heads are few-flowered.

127

Hypochaeris radicata
spotted cat's-ear

Family: Asteraceae (Compositae)
Status: FACU

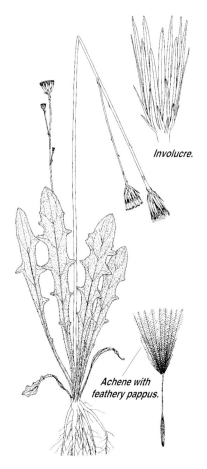

Involucre.

Achene with
feathery pappus.

The stems and leaves of spotted cat's-ear
produce a milky sap; flower heads are yellow.

Spotted cat's-ear is a perennial herb with an enlarged fleshy taproot. Flowering stems are 15-60 cm tall, lack leaves, but have minute bracts. Receptacles have delicate, thin, dry involucral bracts. Blooms from May to October.

- stems numerous, dark green, branched above; stems and leaves produce milky sap
- leaves basal, oblong-lance-shaped, toothed or lobed, 3-35 cm long, with scattered hairs on both leaf surfaces; margins with coarse, stiff, prickly hairs
- flower heads 2-3 cm wide, several per stem, composed of yellow ray flowers only
- involucre 10-15 mm long when flowering, enlarge in fruit (20 mm)
- achenes 4-5 mm long, red-brown, cylindrical with a slender beak about 2.5-13 mm long; pappus feathery, with branched hairs

Habitat: Spotted cat's-ear is a widespread weed in lawns, roadsides, pastures, and other disturbed habitats. Commonly found in, or adjacent to, emergent wetlands, especially wet pastures, in our area. Occurs in shade or full sun.

Range: Native to Europe; spotted cat's-ear is now widespread in the Pacific Northwest and the northeastern United States. Occurs in all counties in our area.

Similar Species: Spotted cat's-ear may easily be confused with other yellow ray-flowered composite species. Smooth cat's-ear *(Hypochaeris glabra)* is an annual herb that favors disturbed sandy soils, lacks hairs on leaves, and blooms only in full sunlight. Dandelion *(Taraxacum officinale)* has unbranched, lighter green or pinkish, translucent stems; lacks hairs on leaves; and has pappus hairs that are not branched. Smooth hawksbeard *(Crepis capillaris)* also has branched flowering stems but they bear leaves, and pappus hairs are not branched. Hawkbits *(Leontodon* species) have smaller flower heads that do not enlarge in fruit, receptacles that lack dry scales, and beakless achenes.

Impatiens noli-tangere
yellow touch-me-not; western touch-me-not; touch-me-not

Family: Balsaminaceae
Status: FACW
Color photo page 229

Yellow touch-me-not is found in our region as a tall annual herb 20-80 cm tall. Foliage deteriorates rapidly after the first frost, leaving virtually no trace of plants in the winter months. Leaves grow along the stem and are alternate and large, with wavy margins. Flowers are composed of 3 sepals, one of which extends as a downward curving spur, 6-10 mm long; and 5 petals, two of which are fused. Fruits are 5-chambered, succulent capsules, 2.5 cm long. Blooms from July to September.

- stems freely branching, juicy-succulent, erect, easily broken
- leaves elliptic to egg-shaped, 3-12 cm long, 2.5-5 cm wide, coarsely toothed, with widely pointed tips
- flowers yellow, 2.5-3.5 cm long, irregular, spurred, sac-like, sparsely spotted with purple-brown on the tube only (not extending to the upper lip)
- fruits waxy, "explode" to eject seeds when ripe

Habitat: Occurs along stream and lake boundaries and in moist woods.

Range: Yellow touch-me-not grows throughout the Pacific Northwest from Alaska south to Oregon, and east to Idaho. Occurs in all counties in our area.

Similar Species: Spotted touch-me-not *(Impatiens capensis*, color photo page 228), although very similar, has orange flowers with brown spots on both the tube and upper lip, and is found mostly south of the Columbia River. Policeman's helmet *(Impatiens glandulifera)*, an escaped Asian ornamental touch-me-not, has established itself in wetlands in the more urban centers in our region. It is much more robust with stems to 2 m tall and 4 cm wide, has opposite or whorled leaves that are finely toothed, and long (2-3 cm) reddish purple flowers with a short (4-5 mm) spur.

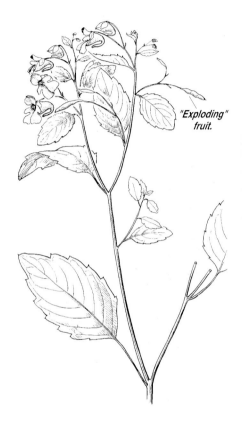

"Exploding" fruit.

HERBS

Yellow touch-me-not has juicy-succulent stems and yellow, spurred flowers.

Iris pseudacorus
yellow iris; yellow flag
Family: Iridaceae
Status: OBL
Color photo page 229

*This non-native species has edgewise
flattened leaves and showy yellow flowers.*

Yellow iris is a non-native perennial that is common in dense, robust stands along freshwater shorelines. Leaves are pointed at the tip, often blue-green, with the central leaves being the longest. This is the only yellow iris in our region. The blooms can appear over an extended period, often from April to August.

- 1 m tall with thick rhizomes
- leaves 20-35 mm broad, stiff, flattened edgewise, enfolding each other at the base; leaf sheaths flattened
- flowers yellow, showy, three-parted, sometimes with fine purple markings

Habitat: Limited to areas with permanent shallow water, generally at depths of less than 0.5 m. It is often found along the shores of streams and ponds, and in roadside ditches and swales. Often found growing with common cattail *(Typha latifolia)*, rushes *(Juncus* species), and sedges *(Carex* species).

Range: Yellow iris was introduced from Europe and has become a well-established and invasive species in the Pacific Northwest. It is found from Vancouver Island south into Washington, on both sides of the Cascades.

Similar Species: When not in flower, the emergent vegetation of yellow iris can be confused with that of common cattail *(Typha latifolia)*. However, cattail leaves have a rounded sheath, are longer (to 3 m long) and narrower (10-20 mm wide), and have leaf tips that are more pointed than those of iris.

Functional Value: As a result of its strong, thick rhizomes, yellow iris is a valuable species for sediment retention, shoreline stabilization, water quality enhancement, and wildlife refuge. Its flowers attract insects and birds. It is sometimes invasive.

Ethnobotanical Uses:
This is an obligate wetland species not often found as an ornamental; its showy flowers are an attractive addition to the shoreline habitat.

Jaumea carnosa
fleshy jaumea

Family: Asteraceae (Compositae)
Status: OBL
Color photo page 229

Fleshy jaumea is a succulent, rhizomatous perennial with lax stems giving it a matted appearance.
Flower heads are composed mostly of ray flowers,
but occasionally of disc flowers, and rarely appear
to be all the way open. Receptacle is 7-12 mm
wide surrounded by 6-10 narrow, inconspicuous
ray flowers, 3-5 mm long. Blooms July through
September.

- stems smooth-surfaced, weak, trailing, to 30
  cm long
- leaves opposite, united at the base, linear-
  lance-shaped, 1.5-5 cm long, and smooth-
  margined
- involucral bracts few, 8-12 mm long, overlapping in several rows, the outer row fleshy,
  striped, obtuse, often purplish or pink at ends
- flower heads usually solitary
- achenes long, linear, 10-nerved; pappus is a
  crown of short hairs or lacking

Habitat: Fleshy jaumea is an estuarine species
occurring in salt marshes and on tide flats. It can
form extensive colonies as a co-dominant with
pickleweed *(Salicornia virginica)* and seashore
saltgrass *(Distichlis spicata)*, or grow in single
species stands at, or just above, the mean high
water level.

Range: Occurs along the coast from Vancouver
Island, British Columbia, to California.

Similar Species: Smooth lasthenia *(Lasthenia
glaberrima)* is not succulent, has involucral bracts
that are fused in one row, flattened achenes, and

*Fleshy jaumea is an estaurine species with
succulent leaves and stems, and extensive
rhizomes.*

occurs in freshwater wetlands. Sea-milkwort
(Glaux maritima) also has succulent leaves, but
they are shorter (5-25 mm) and oval to oblong.

HERBS

Lemna minor
small duckweed; lesser duckweed; water lentil

Family: Lemnaceae

Status: OBL

Color photo page 229

Small duckweed plants are composed of a single, floating leaf with a single root.

Small duckweed is a free-floating aquatic plant. Each plant consists of a minute leaf, from which hangs one root and two reproductive pouches which house the three minute, inconspicuous flowers. Plants reproduce vegetatively from leaf tissue. Blooms June through October.

- commonly forming bright green mats on the surface of ponds
- root single, 1-12 cm long
- leaves often paired, disc-like, green and smooth above, sometimes purple below, 3-nerved, 2-5 mm in diameter

Habitat: Grows in quiet, shallow fresh water.

Range: Found around the world in temperate and subtropical areas. Occurs in all counties in our area.

Similar Species: Large duckweed *(Spirodela polyrhiza)* has larger (4-8 mm) leaves with minute purplish, warty projections beneath, 5-11 nerves, and 5-15 rootlets. Water-ferns *(Azolla* species) are more moss-like, khaki green to red in color, branched, and have leaflets about 1 mm long. Different leaved water-starwort *(Callitriche heterophylla)* can appear to have floating leaves in shallow standing water.

Lilaeopsis occidentalis
western lilaeopsis; lilaeopsis

Family: Apiaceae (Umbelliferae)
Status: OBL
Color photo page 229

Western lilaeopsis is a small, rhizomatous, creeping perennial herb with narrow (1-4 mm wide) leaves (actually the expanded leaf-stem, as lilaeopsis leaves have no blade.) These stem-like leaves grow in small bundles at each node along a creeping underground stem. Inconspicuous umbels of 3-12, small (.5-4 cm long), greenish-white flowers on slender stalks are produced at each rhizome node, and are shorter than the leaves. Blooms June through July.

- stems creeping, not erect
- leaves stem-like, hollow, succulent, segmented, light green, 4-15 cm long
- fruits egg-shaped, 2 mm long, brown with pale, lengthwise ridges

Habitat: Western lilaeopsis often grows in natural drainage channels of sandy mudflats in salt and brackish marshes.

Range: Coastal throughout our range, including Puget Sound, and from southern Vancouver Island to central California.

Similar Species: Although some rushes *(Juncus* species) have segmented leaves, none have the

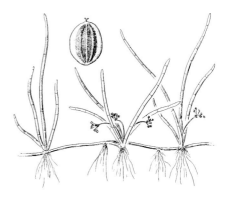

Western liaeopsis is a salt marsh species with stem-like leaves that are hollow and segmented; fruits are egg-shaped with ridges.

combined characteristics of brackish or salt marsh habitat, small stature, and hollow, light green leaves. Pickleweed *(Salicornia virginica)* also lacks obvious leaves and has segmented stems similar to the stem-like leaves of western liaeopsis; however, only the new growth of pickleweed is succulent and the green stems have a reddish or purplish cast.

HERBS

Lotus corniculatus
birdsfoot trefoil

Family: Fabaceae (Leguminosae)
Status: FAC
Color photo page 229

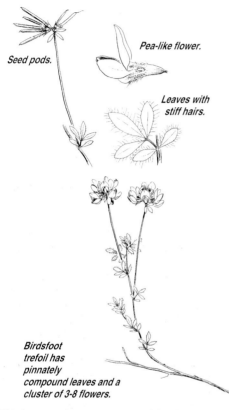

Seed pods.

Pea-like flower.

Leaves with stiff hairs.

Birdsfoot trefoil has pinnately compound leaves and a cluster of 3-8 flowers.

Habitat: Mostly in moist open, disturbed areas such as wet meadows or lawns. It occasionally grows near the edge of shrub or forested wetlands.

Range: Native to Europe, birdsfoot trefoil is becoming increasingly common in the Pacific Northwest, where it may invade and aggressively outcompete native wetland species. Occurs in all counties in our area.

Similar Species: Other species of lotus may have reduced (not leaf-like) stipules, more leaflets, or smaller and fewer flowers (usually purple) per umbel. Leaves of vetches *(Vicia* species), and sweet peas *(Lathyrus* species) typically have numerous leaflets, the terminal one of which is usually reduced to a tendril. Clovers *(Trifolium* species) have three leaflets and stipules that are often smaller and coarsely-toothed.

This is a creeping to erect perennial with bright green, leafy stems to 50 cm tall. It often grows in dense patches or mats. The inflorescence is a cluster of 3-8 flowers on short-stalked, axillary umbels. The fruits are narrow, elongated pods, 1.5-3.5 cm long, with many tiny, dark brown seeds.

- stems and leaves with stiff, straight hairs
- leaves alternate, pinnately compound, with 5 leaflets attached directly to stem
- stipules gland-like, at base of leaf stalk
- flowers pea-like, with yellow wings and keel, and yellow to reddish banner, entire flower 8-15 mm long
- dry fruits split into segments and twist into the shape of a bird's foot

Functional Value: Seeds and foliage are eaten by quail and small rodents. As a member of the pea family, birdsfoot trefoil hosts symbiotic bacteria and is capable of fixing atmospheric nitrogen, thus aiding in the nutrient cycling of exposed or poor soils. It is used in seed mixes for wetlands and erosion control, but often becomes an invasive weed in wetland restoration/mitigation projects if allowed to grow unchecked and therefore should not be used.

Ludwigia palustris
water-purslane; false loosestrife; marsh seedbox

Family: Onagraceae
Status: OBL
Color photo page 230

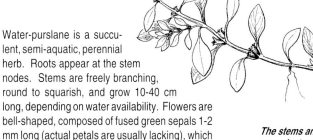

Water-purslane is a succulent, semi-aquatic, perennial herb. Roots appear at the stem nodes. Stems are freely branching, round to squarish, and grow 10-40 cm long, depending on water availability. Flowers are bell-shaped, composed of fused green sepals 1-2 mm long (actual petals are usually lacking), which attach directly to the stem in the leaf axils. Blooms July to September.

Bell-shaped flowers.

The stems and leaves of water-purslane are succulent and reddish olive green.

- mat-forming, either floating on the surface of the water or creeping in the mud
- leaves 1-3.5 cm long, varying in shape from oval to triangular to irregularly lance-shaped, opposite, often reddish olive green, borne on long stalks
- fruits 2-3 cm long, dry, with 4 green stripes

Habitat: Grows in drainage swales, shallow streams with muddy bottoms, intermittent natural swales, and margins of lakes and ponds. It is associated with veronica *(Veronica* species), Watson willowherb *(Epilobium ciliatum)*, and skunk-cabbage *(Lysichiton americanum)*.

Range: Greenland, North and South America, and Africa. Occurs in all counties in our area.

Similar Species: Water purslane is often confused with veronicas *(Veronica* species) and Watson willowherb*(Epilobium ciliatum)*; however, these species have separate petals and long, lance-like, regularly shaped, bright green leaves.

Functional Value: Useful for filtering and uptake of toxicants in bioswales and ditches. When sufficiently dense, water-purslane can provide some erosion control on mud banks. Used as forage by aquatic insects.

HERBS

Genus: *Lycopus*
bugleweeds

Family: Lamiaceae (Labiatae)

These rhizomatous perennials are non- to scarcely aromatic members of the mint family. Leaves are opposite, decrease in size up the stem, with coarsely and irregularly incised margins that vary from shallowly to deeply round-toothed. Minute flowers, borne in whorls in the leaf axils, are divided into two lips, the upper undivided, the lower divided into 3 lobes. The sepals are fused into a tube that is either the same length as the flowers or shorter than the flowers.

Similar Species: Mint *(Mentha* species) are aromatic, lack underground tubers, and have pointed leaf tips. The flowers of field mint *(Mentha arvensis)* are much larger (4-7 mm long), usually purple or pink (occasionally white), fused into a saucer with 4 equal lobes, and have stamens that extend well beyond the flower.

Functional Value: Tubers are eaten by small mammals, especially muskrats.

Ethnobotanical Uses: Bugleweeds of North America are known as a treatment for nervous indigestion, both as a tonic and a sedative. Because of their astringent constituents, bugleweeds have been used as a hemostat or coagulant for nosebleeds, hemorrhage, etc. Native Americans used bugleweeds in conjunction with other plants for treating childrens' colds. However, the two species in Washington have not been used for any of the above purposes, and their value is unknown.

Lycopus americanus
American bugleweed; cutleaved water horehound

Status: OBL
Color photo
page 230

- rhizomes elongate, not bearing tubers
- stems 20-80 cm tall, smooth-surfaced, but hairy at nodes
- leaves 3-8 cm long, 1-3.5 cm wide, deeply incised with irregular teeth; tips blunt
- flowers white, 2-3 mm long, barely longer than sepal tube
- blooms June to August

Habitat: American bugleweed occurs in marshes and moist low ground along streams in foothills and lowlands with nonalkaline soils.

Range: Northern temperate regions, British Columbia to Newfoundland, south to California and Florida.

The leaves of American bugleweed are deeply incised with irregular teeth.

- rhizomes elongate, bearing tubers
- stems 10-40 cm tall, slightly hairy
- leaves 2-8 cm long, 0.6-3 cm wide, slightly hairy, with slightly toothed but not deeply cut or lobbed margins; tips blunt
- flowers white to pinkish, 2.5-4 mm long, longer than calyx
- blooms July to September

Habitat: Northern bugleweed can be found in the same habitats and in peat bogs.

Range: Northern bugleweed occurs within the same range as American bugleweed.

HERBS

The leaves of northern bugleweed are slightly toothed and, unlike American bugleweed, the rhizomes bear tubers.

Lysichiton americanum
skunk-cabbage; swamp lantern

Family: Araceae
Status: OBL
Color photo page 230

Skunk-cabbage leaves emit a skunk-like odor. The tiny flowers (center) are borne on a cylindrical spike that is loosely covered by a yellow spathe (right).

Habitat: Prefers forested wetlands and shady open forests, but will grow in open areas along streams and at the shores of lakes, and persist in meadows and shrub wetlands after logging; also can be found in some bogs. If exposed to great amounts of sunlight, skunk-cabbage will remain small. Often associated with western red-cedar *(Thuja plicata)*, red alder *(Alnus rubra)*, vine maple *(Acer circinatum)*, lady fern *(Athyrium filix-femina)*, and water-parsley *(Oenanthe sarmentosa)*.

Range: Alaska to California and east of the Cascades, though less frequently, to Montana and Idaho. Occurs in all counties in our area.

Skunk-cabbage is an early blooming, thickly rhizomatous, perennial herb that emits a characteristic skunk-like odor when the leaves or flowers are crushed. Leaves are very large and grow from a basal rosette. Yellow flower spathes (hooded bracts) appear in March, and grow to 20 cm tall. Tiny, yellowish green flowers are clustered on the upright cylindrical spike. Fruits are berry-like, 1- to 2-seeded, and attached to the spike, they persist after the spathe has been shed. Blooms in March.

- leaves to 1.5 m long, simple, smooth-margined, lance-shaped to elliptic, light yellow-green, smooth-surfaced, with net veins
- flowers hidden in showy, bright yellow, lantern-like spathe, often appearing before leaves

Similar Species: False hellebore *(Veratrum californicum* var. *caudatum)* has tall, upright, bluish to light green stems with broad, coarsely-veined, wrapping leaves and flowers borne in a large panicle appearing later in the spring.

Functional Value: The leaves, although eaten by deer, elk, and bear, contain a toxin that causes a temporary paralysis of the salivary glands in humans. The roots are also eaten by wildlife. Insects may use the spathe-cylindrical spike structure for food and as a mating site.

Ethnobotanical Uses: The leaves were used by Native Americans as a surface for food preparation, serving, and storage, and as a liner for food baskets. The sap has been used to treat ringworm and the root is edible when cooked.

Purple loosestrife is a rhizomatous, perennial herb. It is a highly invasive introduced plant that spreads by seed, runners, and stem cuttings. Plants can grow to 2 m tall and are unbranched at the base and highly branched at the top when flowering. Plant stems become woody with age. Stamens are many and occur in three different lengths. Blooms August to September.

- stems more or less square
- leaves mostly opposite, occasionally alternate, attached directly to stem, linear, lance-shaped, pointed, slightly hairy, notched at the base, 3-10 cm long
- inflorescence a dense, elongated terminal spike
- flowers showy magenta, each fused into a tube terminating in 5 lobes, 5-10 mm long
- fruits woody capsules, small and numerous, borne along spike

Habitat: Any damp to very wet habitat, especially along pond and lake margins. Prefers a few inches of inundation much like common cattail *(Typha latifolia)*. Also found in coastal areas where salt influence is present, but not in salt marshes. Found most often with cattail, hardstem bulrush *(Scirpus acutus)* and softstem bulrush *(Scirpus tabernaemontanii)*.

Range: Purple loosestrife is an escaped ornamental which has spread across North America. Occurs in all counties in our area.

Similar Species: Veronicas *(Veronica* species), Watson willowherb *(Epilobium ciliatum)*, and fireweed *(Epilobium angustifolium)* may all be mistaken for young purple loosestrife; however, none become woody and veronica is succulent with round stems. The flowers of each are very different. The flowers of willowherb are few, small, reddish purple and ultimately seated upon a long, reddish seed pod. Fireweed has magenta terminal spikes but the seed pods are long (8 cm), red or scarlet, and release abundant white "fluff." The inflorescences of veronica are usually lateral drooping cymes of tiny, 4-petaled blue flowers.
Another introduced invasive species, tufted loosestrife *(Lysimachia thyrsiflora)*, has begun to appear in the more urbanized areas of the Puget

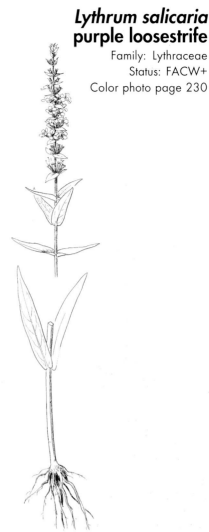

Purple loosestrife has square, woody stems, opposite leaves and showy magenta flowers.

Basin. It has yellow flowers with five unfused petals that are borne laterally or teminally in loose clusters.

Functional Value: This species can provide some erosion control because it grows so densely. Otherwise, its value is negative because of its invasive nature and its ability to fiercely colonize moist habitats and choke out native species.

Ethnobotanical Uses: Formerly used as an ornamental, it is now illegal to buy or sell purple loosestrife in Washington.

HERBS

139

Maianthemum dilatatum
wild lily-of-the-valley; false lily-of-the-valley; beadruby

Family: Liliaceae

Status: FAC

Color photo page 230

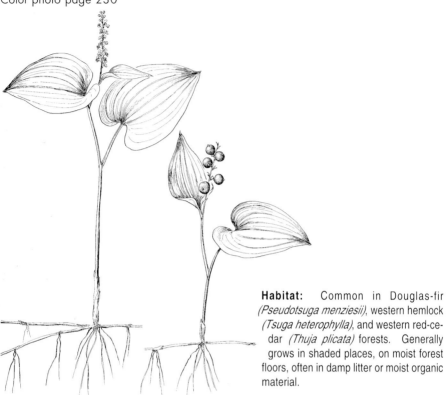

Wild lily-of-the-valley has heart-shaped leaves and beige berries that turn red during the winter.

This perennial herb grows from creeping rootstocks and often forms mats of almost complete groundcover. The tiny, 4-parted flowers are borne in small terminal cylindrical clusters. Berries are about 6 mm long with few brown seeds and are often persistent through the winter.

- flowering stems erect, 15-35 cm tall, smooth without hairs
- leaves medium green, alternate, 2-3 per stem, roughly heart-shaped, 5-11 cm long, with distinct parallel veins
- flowers white, few to many, 2-3 mm long
- berries beige with brown dots early in the summer and fall, turning red during winter

Habitat: Common in Douglas-fir *(Pseudotsuga menziesii)*, western hemlock *(Tsuga heterophylla)*, and western red-cedar *(Thuja plicata)* forests. Generally grows in shaded places, on moist forest floors, often in damp litter or moist organic material.

Range: Native to North America and common in the Pacific Northwest north to British Columbia. Occurs in all counties in our area.

Similar Species: Wild ginger *(Asarum caudatum)* also occurs in moist forest understory habitats, but the heart-shaped leaves of wild ginger have a net-like venation, are dark green, and appear singly or as a clump of a few plants, and flowers are reddish brown, long-sepalled (to 8 cm long), and held just above the forest floor.

Functional Value: The persistent berries are eaten by upland gamebirds, hares (who also eat the foliage), and small rodents.

Ethnobotanical Uses: Native Americans of the Pacific Northwest ate the berries and used the roots to cure sterility and sore eyes.

Genus: *Mentha*
mints
Family: Lamiaceae (Labiatae)

These two "minty" aromatic perennials grow from creeping rhizomes. Typical of all the mint family members, they have square stems. Leaves are opposite and attached directly to the stem or attached by a short stalk (less than 3 mm long). Leaves are 2-8 cm long, 6-40 mm wide, narrow-oval to elliptic-oval, gradually tapering to a pointed tip, and sharply toothed along the margins. The small, irregular flowers have a fused, 5-lobed, tube-shaped calyx and a 4-lobed, tube-shaped corolla. Each have 4 stamens. Bloom June to August.

Similar Species: The bugleweeds *(Lycopus americanus* and *Lycopus uniflorus)*, being in the mint family, also have square stems, but are lacking an obvious odor, and have fewer, smaller flowers (2-4 mm) that are always white and arranged into 2 segments. The stamens of bugleweeds do not extend beyond the petals. Northern bugleweed *(Lycopus uniflorus)* often grows from tubers and has rounded-tipped leaves.

Ethnobotanical Uses: Native Americans of the Pacific Northwest used field mint tea as a cold remedy. Spearmint, highly valued for commercial use, is an ingredient in mint sauces and jellies; flavors chewing gum, candy, liqueurs and baked goods; and is used as an accent and garnish in a variety of dishes. Medicinal interest dates from the first century. It is a foremost remedy for relief of stomach and intestinal gas, and is also used in deodorants.

HERBS

Mentha arvensis var. *villosa*
field mint; corn mint

Status: FACW-
Color photo
page 230

- strong minty aroma
- stems ascending to erect, 20-80 cm tall; stems and leaves hairy
- leaves lance-shaped to lance-oval, 1-8 cm long, dotted with glands, attached by a short stalk
- inflorescence flower compact whorls borne in axils of upper leaves with numerous flowers per whorl
- flowers 4-7 mm long, light pink (occasionally white); stamens longer than petals

Habitat: Moist places, especially along stream banks and shorelines from lowlands to moderate elevations in the mountains. Commonly associated with rushes *(Juncus* species) and veronicas *(Veronica* species).

Range: Field mint is circumboreal, extending south to California, New Mexico, Missouri, and Virginia.

Field mint has a strong minty aroma and flower clusters that are borne in the axils of the upper leaves.

Mint species continued on next page...

Mentha spicata
spearmint

Status: OBL

- distinctive spearmint aroma
- stems erect or creeping, 30-100 cm tall, smooth-surfaced
- leaves irregularly toothed and attached directly to stem
- inflorescence broad, tapering terminal spikes, 3-12 cm long, originating in leaf axils
- flowers 3-5 mm long, lavender; stamens not longer than petals

Habitat: Same as field mint.

Range: Spearmint, native to Europe, is now widespread throughout temperate North America.

These plants have a strong spearmint aroma; flowers are borne in terminal spikes that originate from the leaf axils.

Menyanthes trifoliata var. *trifoliata*
buckbean; bogbean

Family: Menyanthaceae
Status: OBL
Color photo page 231

Buckbean is a succulent, perennial, aquatic to semi-aquatic herb with 3-parted leaves that are held on thick leaf stalks. Each leaflet is between 2-8 cm long, elliptic to oblong, and smooth-margined. Flowers are borne on an erect, stout, leafless stalk. Corolla tubes are funnel-shaped, about 1 cm long, twice the length of the fused sepals, and have five lobes. Fruits are thick-walled capsules with many smooth, shiny, brownish yellow, round to oval seeds. Blooms May to August.

- rhizomes thick, spongy, covered with old basal leaf sheaths
- leaves alternate, 3-parted, attached basally, deep green, on fleshy leaf stalks with sheathing bases
- flowers white, pink, or lilac, covered with long white hairs on the inner surface, borne in racemes 20-45 cm tall

Habitat: Old, acid sphagnum bogs, fens, and lake or pond margins; most common at midelevations, but scattered throughout our range at lower elevations; shade-intolerant.

Range: West of the Cascade crest in Washington and Oregon and into the Sierras of California. Alaska to Greenland, south to Pennsylvania, Indiana, though the Rockies to Colorado, and into northeast Oregon. Also grows in Europe and Asia. Occurs in all counties in our area.

Functional Value: Leaves are eaten by deer.

Similar Species: None.

Ethnobotanical Uses: Contains constituents used to stimulate digestive secretions. Used as a diuretic, to relieve migraine headaches, and for eliminating intestinal worms. Large doses may cause vomiting and diarrhea. The rhizomes were used as a famine food by both northern Alaskan tribes and Finns and Laps who dried and then soaked the stems to remove the bitterness. Dry leaves have been used in beermaking instead of hops.

HERBS

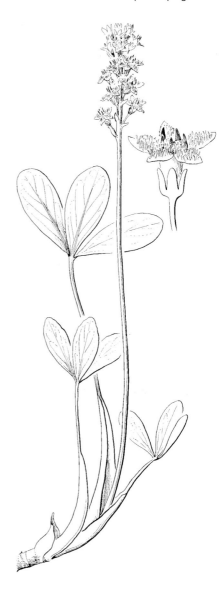

Buckbean plants have thick, spongy rhizomes and succulent, 3-parted leaves.

143

Mimulus guttatus ssp. *guttatus*
common monkeyflower; yellow monkeyflower

Family: Scrophulariaceae

Status: OBL

Color photo page 231

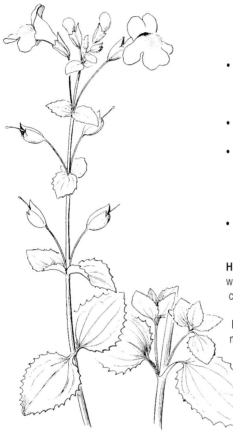

- leaves simple, oval to heart-shaped, fleshy, coarsely and irregularly toothed, arranged along the stem in pairs; lower leaves with leaf stalks, upper leaves clasping
- inflorescence several to many in a terminal cluster with leaf-like bracts
- flowers bright yellow, 1-4 cm long, tubular, 2-lipped, with the upper margin curving back and the lower lip widely flaring, with one or several small, crimson to maroon spots on center lobe of lower lip
- fruit a many-seeded, inflated, papery capsule, 1-2 cm long

Habitat: Predominantly in wet meadows; also in wet ledges, crevices, seepage areas, ditches, clearings, along streams, and near springs.

Range: Common in wet places from sea level to midmontane elevations. Alaska to California, Montana to Mexico. Occurs in all counties in our area.

Similar Species: The bright yellow flowers with maroon markings resemble common ornamental snapdragons. Many other monkeyflowers are present in the Pacific Northwest but none at low elevation. Yellow parentucellia *(Parentucellia viscosa)* is in the same family, but grows in drier sites, and the flowers are smaller (about 2 cm long), light yellow, number to 20 in a sticky, spike-like raceme.

Ethnobotanical Uses: Crushed leaves of common monkeyflower were used by Native Americans as a healing balm for sores. The fleshy leaves can be used in salads. It is a desirable ornamental for moist or wet soils.

Common monkeyflower has opposite leaves and broad, tubular yellow flowers scattered at the tips of the stems.

Common monkeyflower is a highly variable species for which several distinct varieties have been described. It ranges in form from an annual with fibrous roots to a perennial, usually growing from creeping stolons. The hollow, fleshy stems are either erect or trailing, simple or branched, and to 1 m tall. The sepals are fused and the tube formed is strongly 5-angled. Blooms March to September.

Genus: *Myosotis*
forget-me-not
Family: Boraginaceae

The forget-me-nots are creeping, slightly hairy perennials. Stems are long, weak, and leafy to the tips. Leaves are simple, alternate, to 8 cm long, round-tipped, and smooth-margined. The lower leaves may have winged stalks. Numerous blue flowers with yellow centers are borne on terminal racemes. Flowers are 5-lobed, wheel-shaped and spreading, with 5 stamens. Sepals are 3-4 mm long. Fruits are tiny, 4-lobed "nutlets" that are smooth and convex on the top, but angled on the sides.

Similar Species: Water veronica *(Veronica anagallis-aquatica)* has clasping, opposite leaves, smaller flowers (3-4 mm long), and scarcely notched fruits. Marsh veronica *(Veronica scutellata)* has linear to linear-lance-shaped, opposite leaves to 8 cm long, with rather few-flowered racemes, and deeply notched fruits.

Myosotis laxa
small water forget-me-not;
small flower forget-me-not; bay forget-me-not
Status: OBL
Color photo page 231

- plants 10-40 cm tall
- roots only fibrous, no stolons or rhizomes
- leaves oblong to spoon-shaped, 1.5-8 cm long and 3-15 mm wide, with depressed, stiff hairs
- flowers light blue, to 5 mm wide
- petal lobes not overlapping

Habitat: Small water forget-me-not is common in freshwater marshes, ditches, slow-moving water, and shallow pools. It favors saturated soils and can be found in association with many other low-growing obligate freshwater plants, such as water-parsley *(Oenanthe sarmentosa)*, sedges *(Carex* species), and American brooklime *(Veronica americana)*.

Range: Small water forget-me-not is native to North America and common in the Pacific Northwest north to British Columbia.

This forget-me-not species grows from a single clump of fibrous roots; flowers are light blue.

Forget-me-nots continued on next page...

Myosotis scorpioides
water forget-me-not; true forget-me-not; common forget-me-not

Family: Boraginaceae

Status: FACW

- plants 20-60 cm tall
- roots stoloniferous to rhizomatous
- leaves oblong to oblong-lance-shaped, 2.5-8 cm long and 7-20 mm wide, with soft erect hairs
- flowers purple-blue, to 10 mm wide
- petal lobes slightly overlapping

Habitat: Same as small water forget-me-not.

Range: Water forget-me-not is native to Eurasia; it is common in the Pacific Northwest north to British Columbia. Both species occur in all counties in our area.

Water forget-me-not grows from stolons and/ or rhizomes; flowers are purple-blue.

Genus: *Myriophyllum*
water-milfoil

Family: Haloragaceae

These aquatic, perennial plants can be found in large mats either free-floating or along pond and lake shores. Leaves are dissected pinnately into thread-like leaflets, each appearing as a feather, on flexible underwater stems. Leaves are arranged in whorls of 4-6 per node. Leaves that emerge from the waters' surface are opposite. Flowers are minute. Fruits consist of 4 nutlets.

Similar Species: Bladderworts *(Utricularia* species) are aquatic, free-floating plants found in shallow, sluggish water that also have thread-like leaflets; however, leaves are alternate with many bladders attached, and flowers are large (1-2 cm long), yellow, and extending above the water.

Functional Value: Useful in aerating still waters. Plants are eaten by muskrats and moose, and seeds are consumed by birds. Although it provides habitat for aquatic organisms, the dense mats eliminate many native plant communities. Often entangles in boat motors which is a primary mode of dispersal.

Ethnobotanical Uses: Used in freshwater aquaria.

Myriophyllum aquaticum
(Myriophyllum brasiliense)
parrot's feather; South American water-milfoil

Status: OBL

HERBS

This robust water-milfoil has separate male and female flowers that are found on separate plants. Leaves are submerged until plant flowers. Blooms May to July.

- stems 2-4 mm thick, 10-90 cm long, waxy gray-green
- leaves 1.5-3.5 cm long, number 5-6 per whorl; each leaf with 20-30 leaflets
- female flowers lacking petals, male flowers with 4 small petals
- flowers borne in axils of the leaves

Habitat: Occurs in shallow, still, or slow-moving water in ponds and lakes.

Range: Parrot's feather is a commonly grown ornamental plant from South America and is found scattered around the world. Widespread throughout western Washington and Oregon. Occurs in all counties in our area.

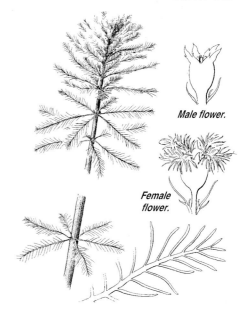

Male flower.

Female flower.

The flowers of parrot's feather are borne in the leaf axils.

Water-milfoils continued on next page...

Myriophyllum spicatum
Eurasian water-milfoil; spiked water-milfoil

Status: OBL

Color photo page 231

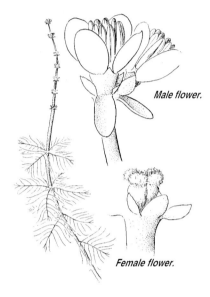

Male flower.

Female flower.

The flowers of Eurasian water-milfoil are borne along a spike that terminates the stem.

This water-milfoil also has separate male and female flowers, but both flower types found on the same plant. Blooms June to August.

- stems 2-4 mm thick, to 2 m long, reddish to olive green when dry
- leaves less than 3 cm long, number 4 per whorl; each leaf with more than 28 leaflets; leaves rarely extending above the water
- petals early deciduous on both male and female flowers
- flowers borne along spike that terminates stem

Habitat: Same as parrot's feather. In addition, Eurasian water-milfoil sometimes occurs in brackish waters.

Range: Eurasian water-milfoil is an escaped Eurasian plant found widespread throughout North America. It occurs from British Columbia south to California, and is widespread throughout western Washington and Oregon. Occurs in all counties in our area.

Nuphar luteum ssp. polysepalum
yellow pond-lily; spatter-dock; yellow cow-lily

Family: Nymphaeaceae
Status: OBL
Color photo page 231

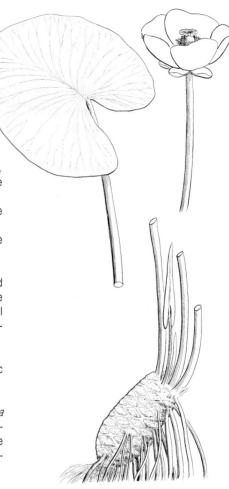

The leaves of this floating, perennial aquatic plant form dense surface coverage in many shallow lakes and ponds, and along shorelines of larger lakes. Plants typically occur in water depths of less than 4 m, and have rhizomes that are thick and club-like. Leaves may float or be found sticking partially out of the water, particularly later in the summer. Blooms June through September.

- leaves large, heart-shaped, stiff, 10-45 cm long, 6-30 cm wide
- leaf stalks attach at notched leaf base
- flowers floating to emergent, yellow with red markings, 6-10 cm in diameter, thick, fleshy, with a thick, flat, round, knob-like stigma
- sepals 7-12, the four outermost green, the remaining yellow
- petals 10-18, small, occurring beneath the multiple purple stamens

Habitat: Common in freshwater ponds, lakes, and sluggish streams where it often forms surface monocultures. Associates include common cattail *(Typha latifolia)*, water-milfoils *(Myriophyllum* species), and bladderworts *(Utricularia* species).

Range: Widely distributed throughout the Pacific Northwest.

Similar Species: White water lily *(Nymphaea odorata)* usually has smaller (5-25 cm in diameter), circular leaves that typically float on the water surface throughout the year, and white flowers with 20-30 petals.

Functional Value: Yellow pond-lily serves as a food source for a variety of animals. The seeds are eaten by waterfowl; the stems, leaves, and flowers are eaten by deer and muskrat; and the roots are commonly consumed by beaver. The floating leaves provide cover for animals and habitat for algae and aquatic insects. In freshwater shallow ponds and lakes, coverage by this species can become quite extensive, crowding out other desirable species, creating low oxygen levels beneath the surface, decreasing fish habitat, and creating other nuisance conditions.

Yellow pond-lily has thick, club-like rhizomes, heart-shaped leaves, and waxy, yellow flowers.

Ethnobotanical Uses: The rootstocks are considered unpalatable and possibly poisonous. Native Americans ate the seeds by either grinding them into flour or roasting them like popcorn.

HERBS

149

Nymphaea odorata var. *odorata*
white water lily; fragrant water lily

Family: Nymphaeaceae

Status: OBL

Color photo page 231

Habitat: Often forms extensive beds in sunny ponds and lake margins in water depths to about 2 m.

Range: Native to eastern North America and widely introduced in our region. Occurs throughout the lowlands in western Washington, but absent from western Oregon.

Similar Species: Pygmy water lily *(Nymphaea tetragona)*, possibly extirpated from Washington State, has smaller leaves and unscented flowers. Anyone sighting this species should report their observations to the Washington Natural Heritage Program at the Washington Department of Natural Resources in Olympia. Watershield *(Brasenia schreberi)*, also a water lily, has small oval leaves that attach to the leaf stalk at the center of the leaf, and the lower leaf surface is covered by a thick, jelly-like coating. The other water lily in our area, yellow pond-lily *(Nuphar luteum)*, has large (6-30 cm wide), heart-shaped leaves that may be partially submerged or emerged, and bright yellow, waxy flowers with 10-18 showy, yellow petal-like sepals and a thick, knob-like stigma at the center.

Ethnobotanical Uses: Water lilies have been used in water gardens and landscape ponds since 1786. Plant breeders have produced many varieties and hybrids that combine white water lily's fragrance with flower colors of other species. Water lily root has been used in folk medicine for dysentery, diarrhea, gonorrhea, tuberculosis, rheumatism, and many other ailments. It has also been recommended as an ingredient in gargles for sore throats, and in lotions for treating skin problems, such as boils, ulcers, tumors, baldness, and inflammations. Water lily (not yellow pond-lily) rhizomes, young leaves, and flowers are edible and have been used as food throughout the world. The leaves and flowers can be boiled as a vegetable, and the seeds can be roasted and eaten whole or ground into flour. Yellow pond-lily is not edible.

White water lily leaves are round with a notched base; flowers are multipetaled and fragrant.

White water lily is a rhizomatous, aquatic perennial. Leaves float horizontally on the surface of water in depths of up to 2.5 m. Flowers open in late morning and close again at sunset. Blooms from June to October.

- leaves circular-rounded, notched at the base, 15-25 cm long
- leaf stalks attached at notched leaf base
- leaves float on the water surface at all times
- flowers white, fragrant, 15 cm in diameter, with 4 green sepals, 20-30 petals, and many petal-like stigmas

Oenanthe sarmentosa
water-parsley

Family: Apiaceae (Umbelliferae)
Status: OBL
Color photo page 232

Water-parsley is a sometimes semi-aquatic soft-stemmed herb that may grow to 1 m or more, but appears shorter because of its reclining, creeping growth; occasionally it may be erect. Water-parsley blooms from June to August.

- stems weak-ribbed hollow tubes, angularly forked, often rooting at nodes
- leaves scattered along stems, parsley-like, twice compound; leaflets oblong to egg-shaped, toothed along margins, lateral veins terminating at teeth tips
- flowers greenish white, on 1-3 cm long stalks, borne in 5-20 compound umbels
- fruits barrel-shaped, 2.5-3.5 mm long, 2 mm wide, with broad ribbing

Habitat: This emergent plant is typically found in low wet places. Water-parsley distribution is usually limited to shallow freshwater marshes that are saturated year-round or during the growing season. Common associates include cattail *(Typha latifolia)*, skunk-cabbage *(Lysichiton americanum)*, and creeping buttercup *(Ranunculus repens)*.

Range: Found in the western Cascades, from Alaskan panhandle to central California, up the Columbia River to west Klickitat County, Washington, and in the Chilliwack Valley, British Columbia.

Similar Species: Water-parsley may be confused with buttercups *(Ranunculus* species) because of the leaf shape; however, those buttercups with compound leaves have 5 leaflets that are not red-tinged at the base, and their flowers are single and yellow. Creeping buttercup leaves are mostly basal and not along the stems, and the leaves have a silver pattern on them. Several other members of the parsley family grow in shallow water or wet marshes, such as angelicas *(Angelica* species)

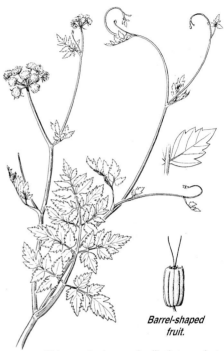

Barrel-shaped fruit.

Water-parsley has parsley-like leaves; plants creep in shallow water.

and poison hemlock *(Conium maculatum)*, both of which are generally taller, more erect, and have flat-topped inflorescences.

Functional Value: Water-parsley produces significant above-ground biomass, growing very densely, and therefore can be useful in slowing water flow to enable sediment settling. It is tolerant of replanting, making it a desirable species for use in wetland restoration plantings in shallow aquatic settings.

Ethnobotanical Uses: This plant is reported to be poisonous, with toxins related to those of western water-hemlock *(Cicuta douglasii)*. Native Americans are purported to have used water-parsley as a laxative, a stomach medicine, and a headache medicine.

HERBS

Orthocarpus castillejoides
owl's-clover; paintbrush owl's-cover; ambiguous owl clover

Family: Scrophulariaceae
Status: FACW+

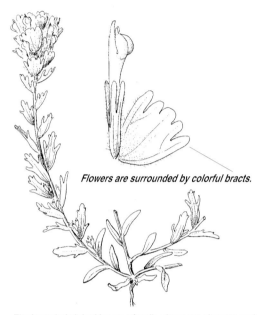

Flowers are surrounded by colorful bracts.

The irregularly lobed leaves of owl's-clover are alternate and attached directly to the stem.

Owl's-clover is an annual herb, 5-35 cm tall, common to coastal salt marshes. Flowers are inconspicuous, but the colorful bracts surrounding the flowers give this plant a showy appearance. Blooms July to September.

- leaves alternate, 1-5 cm long, irregularly 2- to 6-lobed, attached directly to stems
- flowers sac-like, 15-25 mm long, white and yellow, tipped with purple or white, occurring between bracts in a dense spike
- bracts 3- to 7-lobed, yellow-red, tipped with yellow or purple

Habitat: Found in high salt marshes and coastal estuaries of Puget Sound, generally in firm, sandy substrate. It is salt-tolerant. Associated species include marsh cinquefoil *(Potentilla palustris)*, tufted hairgrass *(Deschampsia caespitosa)*, and other high marsh species.

Range: Salt marshes from British Columbia south to Monterey, California.

Functional Value: Grazed by coastal waterfowl.

Similar Species: Many species of owl's-clovers *(Orthocarpus* species) occur in the region, but they are not as common, have purple flowers and bracts, and are not found in salt-influenced habitats.

Ethnobotanical Uses: Aesthetic value derived from attractive appearance. Other species of owl's-clover have been used as dye plants by Native Americans.

Parentucellia viscosa
yellow parentucellia

Family: Scrophulariaceae

Status: FAC-

This attractive annual European pasture herb is now naturalized throughout the Pacific Northwest. Mature plants vary in height between 10-70 cm. Lower leaves are opposite, the upper often alternate. The irregular flowers appear in a compact spike-like raceme, interspersed with many leaf-like bracts. Blooms May through August.

- plant erect, unbranched, covered with leaves that are attached directly to branches
- leaves 1-4 cm long and to 2 cm wide, with coarsely toothed margins and glandular-sticky hairs
- flowers yellow, 15-20 mm long, two-lipped, with shorter hooded upper lip and expanded lower lip divided into 3 lobes, 20 or more per spike

Habitat: Occurs in pastures and other frequently disturbed open sites that are wet during the early growing season and dry out as the season progresses.

Range: Native to the Mediterranean area of Europe. Found throughout the lowlands in our range and south along the coast to northern California; also in western South America. Occurs in all counties in our area.

Similar Species: Common monkeyflower *(Mimulus guttatus)* is in the same family, but it grows only in very wet sites, such as along the banks of flowing streams. In addition, the flowers of the monkeyflower are larger and fewer than those of yellow parentucellia.

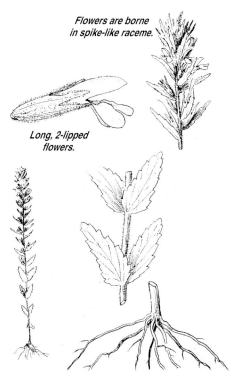

Flowers are borne in spike-like raceme.

Long, 2-lipped flowers.

Yellow parentucellia grow as a single-stemmed plant with many coarsely toothed leaves.

HERBS

Petasites frigidus var. palmatus
sweet coltsfoot; palmate coltsfoot

Family: Asteraceae (Compositae)
Status: FACW-
Color photo page 232

Flower heads appear in flat-topped clusters; achenes have many pappus hairs.

Sweet coltsfoot has thick stems with bract-like leaves; growing on long stalks from base are wide and deeply palmately lobed leaves.

Sweet coltsfoot is a rhizomatous, perennial herb that is one of the earliest species to flower in the spring. Rhizomes are slender, and give rise to many flowering stems and leaves. Flowering stems appear either with or before the leaves,

which are borne independent of the flowering stems. The genus name is derived from a Greek word for a broad-rimmed hat, reflecting its large leaves. Ray flowers are minute with petals only 2-7 mm long. Blooms from March through July.

• flowering stems white woolly, 10-50 cm tall, with broad, bract-like leaves
• basal leaves large, to 40 cm wide, deeply palmately lobed with 5-7 lobes, obviously veined, smooth or sparsely hairy above, white-woolly below, borne on long stalks
• involucre 5-9 mm high, bracts lance-shaped, hairs at base
• flower heads numerous, in large flat-topped clusters, predominantly male or female, with either whitish or pink to purplish ray flowers, or white to purplish disc flowers
• achene white, 5- to 10-ribbed; pappus hairs numerous, 6-13 mm long

Habitat: Occurs in emergent wetlands and moist woods, common in roadside ditches in the foothills of the Cascades.

Range: Native to Pacific Northwest, occurring mostly west of the Cascades. Found from Alaska to California, east to Michigan and Massachusetts.

Similar Species: Sweet coltsfoot is not easily confused with other composites because of its robust form and palmate leaves. *Petasites frigidus* var. *nivalis* occurs only in northwestern Washington, Olympic Mountains, and northern Oregon, and has triangular leaves that are not as deeply lobed, with deeply incised veins.

Ethnobotanical Uses: Native Americans cooked and ate young leaves and stems, and used ashes from burned leaves and stems as a salt substitute. The roots were used as a cough medicine, either boiled or eaten raw. A decoction of roots was also used to treat tuberculosis symptoms or as an emetic. Leaves were warmed and applied to areas afflicted with rheumatism.

Genus: *Plantago*
plantains
Family: Plantaginaceae

The two common plantains found in this region are exotic perennial species with basal rosettes of nonsucculent leaves. A third common plantain, seaside plantain *(Plantago maritima)*, is an estuarine species and is discussed separately. The tiny, inconspicuous flowers are greenish, 4-parted, basally-fused. They are densely clustered at the ends of long, wiry, cylindrical spikes, making them reminiscent of some grasses and sedges. Stamens protrude from the numerous flowers.

Similar Species: Seaside plantain *(Plantago maritima)* is a salt marsh inhabitant which has thin, straight leaves that are fleshy and not obviously veined.

Ethnobotanical Uses: The young plants of these species have a citrus flavor and may be used as a potherb or in salads. Older plants are unpalatably fibrous. Crushed leaves have a cauterizing and "drawing" agent used for removal of toxins in boils, splinters, etc. The leaves have also been used as a cure for dropsy, and chewed for toothache and gum disease. The seeds may be eaten parched or ground into meal. They have reportedly been used as a laxative.

HERBS

Plantago lanceolata var. *lanceolata*
rib plantain; English plantain
Status: FAC
Color photo page 232

Rib plantain is fibrous-rooted. The basal leaves are lance-shaped to narrowly oblong, with 3 - many strongly grooved parallel veins, and can be beige-woolly at the base, and hairless to scattered with hairs above. Blooms between April and August.

- leaves long (10-40 cm) and narrow (1-4 cm wide)
- flowering stems 20-60 cm tall
- flowers with petals 2-2.5 mm long; sepals hairy toward tip; borne in dense spike 2-8 cm long
- seeds 1-2

Habitat: Both rib plantain is common in weedy areas of backyards, along roads, and in other disturbed places. Infrequent in habitants on edges of freshwater emergent wetlands in association with red clover *(Trifolium pratense)*, white clover *(Trifolium repens)*, non-native grasses, and other weedy species.

Range: Common weed most likely introduced from Europe. Occurs in all counties in our area,

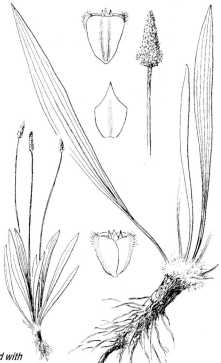

The leaves of rib plantain are lance-shaped with raised parallel veins; flowers are borne in a compact, cone-shaped spike.

Plantains species continued on next page...

155

Plantago major
broadleaf plantain; common plantain

Status: FACU+

Color photo page 232

Broadleaf plantain has apparently parallel-veined leaves, with a well-defined leaf stalk. Flowers from May to August.

- leaves round to broadly elliptic, 4-18 cm long and 3-11 cm wide
- flower stems 5-30 cm long
- flowers with petals 1 mm long, bending backwards
  - seeds 6-30

Habitat: Same as rib plantain.

Range: Same as rib plantain.

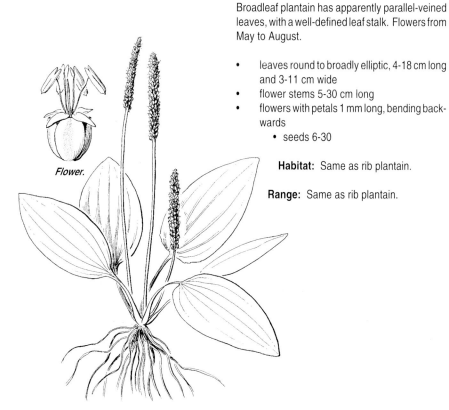

Flower.

The leaves of broadleaf plantain are elliptic with raised parallel veins; flowers are borne in a long, cylindrical spike.

Plantago maritima var. *juncoides*
seaside plantain; salt marsh plantain

Status: FACW+
Color photo page 232

Seaside plantain has a basal rosette of leaves. Flowers are densely borne on a distinctive, cylindrical spike. Stamens protrude from the flowers. Fruits are woody capsules that open like a box revealing 2-4 black seeds. Blooms June to August.

- plant base covered with short, woolly hairs giving it a grayish green color
- leaves basal, erect, long and narrow, succulent, 5-30 cm long, not obviously veined
- flowers green, inconspicuous, with 4 sepals and 4 petals fused into a hairy tube
- inflorescence a cylindrical head 2-10 cm long and less than 1 cm thick, borne on stalks 5-25 cm long

Habitat: This relatively common salt marsh plant is well adapted to saline conditions, but is seldom a dominant species in the marsh. It occurs at all elevations within the marsh and on rocky areas at the edge of salt water. It is often associated with pickleweed *(Salicornia virginica)*, fleshy jaumea *(Jaumea carnosa)*, and seashore saltgrass *(Distichlis spicata)*.

Range: Broadly distributed in maritime regions of the world on saline soils.

Similar Species: Seaside arrowgrass *(Triglochin maritima)* has half-round to triangular leaves that are to 80 cm long, a spike-like inflorescence which normally rises high above the leaves, and a cilantro-like odor when crushed. Seaside plantain is not easily confused with other plantains.

Functional Value: Heavily grazed by waterfowl and other herbivorous birds.

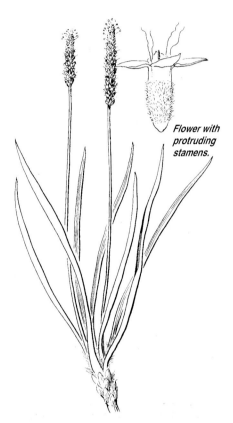

Flower with protruding stamens.

Seaside plantain is an estuary species with thin, succulent leaves.

Ethnobotanical Uses: Native Americans traditionally ate the fresh leaves after mixing them with fish or animal fat. Today, the leaves are canned or dried, and brewed as a tea.

Genus: *Polygonum*
knotweed; smartweed

Family: Polygonaceae

The common wetland species of knotweeds are erect to trailing, leafy-stemmed herbs. Leaves are alternate, generally lance-shaped, with smooth margins and sheathing stipules. Inflorescence is a spike composed of flowers that are tiny, with inconspicous petals that are often white to pinkish.

Key to the Knotweeds

1a. Plants aquatic to moist-soil-terrestrial..2
1b. Plants terrestrial in hardened, parched soils.................prostrate knotweed *(Polygonum aviculare)*

    2a. Flowers white, greenish white or pinkish green, born in several panicles; fruits mostly triangular..3
    2b. Flowers rose to bright pink, born in compact spike inflorescence; fruits lens-shaped..............
    ....water ladysthumb *(Polygonum amphibium)*

        3a. Plant herbaceous...4
        3b. Plants tall, bamboo-like with woody stems and rootstocks..
        ....Japanese knotweed *(Polygonum cuspidatum)*

            4a. Petals without raised glands...5
            4b. Petals with obvious raised glands.................waterpepper *(Polygonum hydropiper)*

                5a. Stipules bristly on the sides and along the top margin; plants without glands; outer pair of petals without veins..6
                5b. Stipules not bristly on the sides and along the top margin, plants glandular to hairy; outer pair of petals with strong, branched veins..
                ....willow smartweed *(Polygonum lapathifolium)*

                    6a. Inflorescence terminal ....
                    ....mild waterpepper *(Polygononum hydropiperoides)*
                    6b. Inflorescence lateral and terminal; leaves with one large purple blotch..ladysthumb *(Polygonum persicaria)*

Polygonum amphibium var. stipulaceum
water ladysthumb

Status: OBL
Color photo page232

Water ladysthumb is a perennial, creeping herb with rhizomes or stolons. Stems freely root at the nodes. Stipules are 1-2 cm long and can be with or without hairs. Leaf stalks are 1/5 to 1/2 as long as the leaf blade. One to two compact, oval flower clusters 1-3 cm long, terminate the erect flower stems. Blooms from June through September.

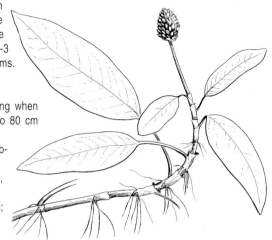

- stems mostly unbranched, floating when aquatic, erect when terrestrial, to 80 cm long
- leaves to 15 cm long, elliptic to ob-long-lance-shaped
- flowers rose-colored to bright pink, 4-5 mm long
- fruits shiny, dark brown, 3 mm long; seeds lens-shaped

Habitat: Occurs in aquatic or semi-aquatic sites in moist, muddy soils.

Flower heads of water ladysthumb are large, oval, and rose-colored to bright pink.

Range: Found on all continents except Australia; water ladysthumb is particularly common in North America.

HERBS

Polygonum aviculare
prostrate knotweed; doorweed
Status: FACW-

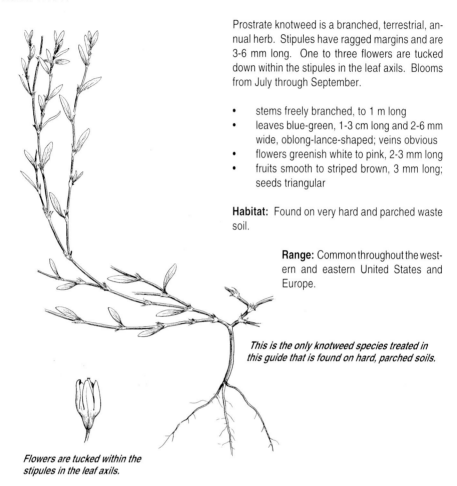

Prostrate knotweed is a branched, terrestrial, an-nual herb. Stipules have ragged margins and are 3-6 mm long. One to three flowers are tucked down within the stipules in the leaf axils. Blooms from July through September.

- stems freely branched, to 1 m long
- leaves blue-green, 1-3 cm long and 2-6 mm wide, oblong-lance-shaped; veins obvious
- flowers greenish white to pink, 2-3 mm long
- fruits smooth to striped brown, 3 mm long; seeds triangular

Habitat: Found on very hard and parched waste soil.

Range: Common throughout the west-ern and eastern United States and Europe.

This is the only knotweed species treated in this guide that is found on hard, parched soils.

Flowers are tucked within the stipules in the leaf axils.

Polygonum cuspidatum
Japanese knotweed

Status: FACU
Color photo page 233

Japanese knotweed is a strongly rhizomatous, woody-stemmed perennial herb. The base of older plants can have a football-sized, woody rootstock. The short, tubular stipules are smooth-margined and usually deciduous – shedding by midsummer. Leaf stalks are 1/4 the length of the leaf blade. Inflorescences are (few) open racemes found in the leaf axils. Male and female flowers on separate plants. Blooms from July through September.

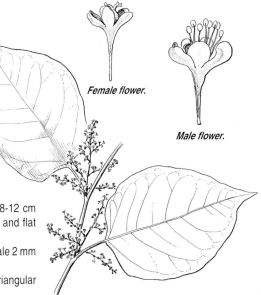

Female flower.

Male flower.

- stems reddish brown and woody (bamboo-like) when mature, erect, freely branching, to 2.5 m tall
- leaves large (10-15 cm long and 8-12 cm wide), round to oval, with straight and flat base; tip abruptly pointed
- flowers greenish white to white, male 2 mm long, female 8-10 mm long
- fruits shiny black, 1mm long; seed triangular

Habitat: Common and very aggressive in moist waste areas or along disturbed stream banks.

Japanese knotweed has woody stems and large leaves that have a flat base, oval body, and pointed tip.

Range: Japanese knotweed is an escaped Asiatic species. Occurs in all counties in our area.

Similar Species: Giant knotweed *(Polygonum sachalinense)*, another invasive knotweed, is up to 3 m tall, has leaves that are 15-35 cm long, more lance-shaped with a heart-shaped base, and green flowers.

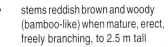

HERBS

Polygonum hydropiper
waterpepper

Status: OBL
Color photo page 233

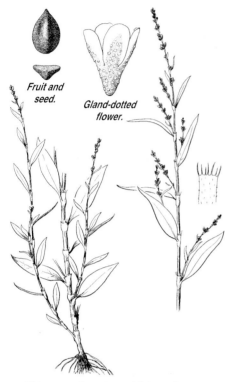

Fruit and seed.

Gland-dotted flower.

Waterpepper is an aquatic to terrestrial annual to occasionally perennial herb. Stems freely root at the nodes. Stipules are 6-15 mm long, with marginal bristles, and rip when they are mature. Stems and leaves have a peppery flavor. Leaf stalks are common at the base of the plant and very short to nonexistent at the top of the plant. Inflorescence consists of several to many contracted panicles that are both terminal and lateral, and 2-7 cm long. Blooms from July through September.

- stem erect, reddish purple, branched or unbranched, smooth to glandular, 8-150 cm long
- leaves lance-shaped to lance-oval, 5-7 cm long, with long-tapered tip and hairy margins
- flowers greenish white, turning red with age, 3-4 mm long, glandular dotted
- fruits dull brown, 3 mm long; seed triangular

Habitat: Found in wet places in lower elevations, especially shallow water areas such as ditches, ponds, and swales.

Range: Common throughout North and South America; native to Europe.

Waterpepper has erect, reddish purple stems; stipules (on right) have bristly margins.

Polygonum hydropiperoides var. *hydropiperoides*
mild waterpepper

Status: OBL

Mild waterpepper is a perennial, semi-aquatic herb. Stems root freely at the nodes. Stipules are 1-2 cm long, hairy, with bristles on the margins. Leaf stalks are absent at the top of the plant, and short below. The inflorescence has two to several interrupted, spike-like panicles. Bloom from July through September.

- stems branched, 30-150 cm tall
- leaves broadly lance-shaped, 5-12 cm long, tapered at the base, smooth to hairy, with hairy margins
- midrib on the underside of leaf hairy
- flowers greenish white to pink, 2.5-3 mm long
- fruits shiny black, 0.5 mm long; seeds triangular

Habitat: Occurs in ponds, marshes, and sites where there are open muddy areas.

Range: Found from Central Alaska to Mexico and South America. Also occurs scattered across the United States.

Mild waterpepper has unbranched stems, leaves with a hairy midvein, and hairy stipules.

HERBS

Polygonum lapathifolium
willow smartweed

Status: FACW

Color photo page 233

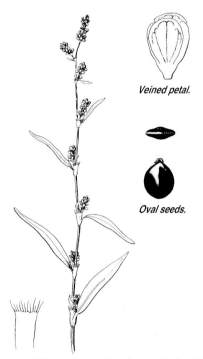

Veined petal.

Oval seeds.

Willow smartweed has brown stipules with a bristly margin.

Willow smartweed is a semi-aquatic, annual herb. Stipules are brown, with a flattened upper margin that is lined with bristles. Leaf stalks are nonexistent at the top of the plant and very short at the bottom. Inflorescence is a group of loose, drooping, spike-like racemes. Blooms from June through September.

- stems many-branched, to 70 cm tall
- leaves broad, lance-shaped to elliptic lance-shaped, 6-20 cm long and 4 cm wide, top smooth, glandular beneath; veins slightly hairy
- flowers white or green to pink, 2.5 mm long, nonglandular with obvious veins that branch at the tips
- fruits shiny dark brown, oval to elliptical, 2-3 mm long

Habitat: Occurs in wet areas where there is shallow standing water.

Range: Naturalized from Europe; introduced in western Washington and Oregon but more common east of the Cascades.

Polygonum persicaria var. *persicaria*
ladysthumb

Status: FACW
Color photo page 233

Ladysthumb is a smooth to sparsely hairy annual herb. Stipules are cylindrical, hairy along the veins, with a bristly margin. Leaf stalks are short and thick. Inflorescence is a crowded, compound raceme. Blooms from March through September.

- stems simple to branched, erect, to 1 m tall
- leaves bright green to olive green with a dark purple blotch in the center of the leaf, 5-12 cm long
- flowers pinkish tinged green, 2-3.5 mm long
- fruits shiny, black round to oval, 2-2.5 mm long

Habitat: Occurs in moist to wet disturbed areas, especially in cultivated wetlands with standing water.

Range: Common throughout North America, although more common west of the Cascade Mountains. Occurs in all counties in our area.

Functional Value: Species which form thick mats in aquatic or semi aquatic habitats are helpful for erosion control. Foliage is edible and is utilized by wildlife.

HERBS

Fruits are
round to oval.

The leaves of ladysthumb have a purple blotch in the center; stipules (above left) are hairy along the veins and have a bristly margin.

165

Genus: *Potamogeton*
pondweeds
Family: Potamogetonaceae

The pondweeds are robust aquatic herbs that emerge from rhizomes and root at the lower nodes. Stems are unbranched or sparingly branched, 1-5 m long, 3 mm thick with a thick mucus-like coating. Plants have both submerged and partially floating leaves, each with their own characteristics (dimorphic). Leaves are alternate or subopposite near the inflorescence. Flowers have 4 petals and are clustered in spikes that attach directly to the stem and emerge erect from the water.

Similar Species: These aquatic weeds are similar to the water smartweeds *(Polygonum* species), except that smartweeds have leaves that are long, linear, lance-shaped, and are not submerged, and sheathing stipules without long, free tips. Watershield *(Brasenia schreberi)* is another floating aquatic, but the stem is attached in the middle of the leaf, and the underneath of the leaves, sheaths, and stems are covered with a gelatinous coating.

Functional Value: Largeleaf pondweed is a reliable indicator of clean water, as it is not very tolerant of pollution, and provides a suitable habitat for aquatic insects. Floating-leaved pondweed transplants well in created open-water wetlands because of its tolerance of poor water quality.

Potamogeton amplifolius
largeleaf pondweed; broad-leaved pondweed
Status: OBL
Color photo page 233

10 cm long around the floating leaves. Inflorescence is less than 5 cm long. Blooms from June to August.

- submerged leaves 8-20 cm long and 2-7 cm wide, olive green to reddish brown, folded along midvein and curved backward, often translucent, 20-40 veins
- floating leaves flat, elliptical, 5-10 cm long and 2-4 cm wide, succulent
- stipules white, sheath-like, occurring on both leaf types
- fruits orange or pink

The floating leaves of this species are flat, whereas the submerged leaves are curved backwards and have wavy margins.

The submerged leaves of largeleaf pondweed emerge from stout rhizomes. The sheath-like stipules that occur on both leaf types can be up to

Habitat: Largeleaf pondweed grows in clean, fresh water up to 6 m deep. Occasionally associated with bladderworts *(Utricularia* species).

Range: Widespread in northern North America.

Potamogeton natans
floating-leaved pondweed

Status: OBL
Color photo page 233

This floating plant emerges from extensive slender rhizomes that produce overwintering tubers. Inflorescence is less than 5 cm long. Blooms May to August.

- submerged leaves 10-30 cm long and 1-2 mm wide, bright green
- floating leaves 6-11 cm long and less than 6 cm wide, oval to broadly elliptic and with sub-parallel veins, copper brown-green, succulent, with stalks longer than leaf blades
- stipules fibrous, only partially wrapped, eventually shredding
- fruits khaki brown, in compact cylindrical clusters, 3 cm long

Habitat: Floating-leaved pondweed *(Potamogeton natans)* occurs in standing, often brackish water that is 1-3 m deep. Most common in sheltered bays and ponds; often found in organic-rich substrates. Associates include milfoils *(Myriophyllum* species), bladderworts, and water starworts *(Callitriche* species).

Range: Same as largeleaf pondweed.

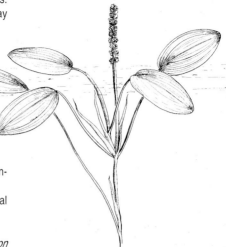

The floating leaves of this plant are broadly elliptical and the submerged leaves are very narrow.

HERBS

Genus: *Potentilla*

Family: Rosaceae

These low-growing perennial herbs spread by creeping stolons and often form dense tangles. Leaves are pinnately compound and alternate. Flowers have 5 petals, 5 sepals, are buttercup-like, with many stamens and pistils.

Functional Value: Their stoloniferous growth habit aids in substrate stabilization and erosion control.

Ethnobotanical Uses: The roots of some cinquefoil species are edible when boiled or roasted to remove the bitter flavor. They taste similar to parsnips! The generic name derives from the Latin "potence," meaning powerful, and refers to the purported potent medicinal properties of certain species. The leaves contain tannin, an astringent, and have been used as a tea to relieve diarrhea, lessen fevers, as a purgative, to ease eye inflamation, and to relieve sore throat.

Potentilla anserina ssp. *pacifica*
Pacific silverweed; common silverweed

Status: OBL
Color photo page 234

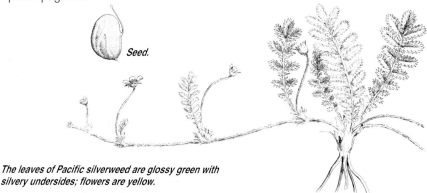

Seed.

The leaves of Pacific silverweed are glossy green with silvery undersides; flowers are yellow.

Pacific silverweed is a coastal, estuarine species. Leaves dry out and become brown, but remain intact and identifiable throughout much of the winter. Flowers are borne singly at the nodes of the stolons. Blooms May to August.

- leaves all basal, glossy green, with silvery, densely hairy undersides; leaflets deeply notched and toothed, 3-50 cm long, 5-10 leaflets per side
- flowers yellow, petals 7-20 mm long
- fruits oval, dark red-brown, flattened, to 2 mm long

Habitat: Pacific silverweed typically occurs in high tidal marshes, at or above the mean high

water, where it is often associated with tufted hairgrass *(Deschampsia caespitosa)* and Lyngby sedge *(Carex lyngbyei)*. It can also be found in nontidal freshwater meadows and marshes. In these situations it is often associated with creeping buttercup *(Ranunculus repens)*, several species of grasses and sedges, as well as reed canarygrass *(Phalaris arundinacea)*. More common in fresh water east of the Cascades than west.

Range: Found throughout the United States.

Potentilla palustris
marsh cinquefoil; purple cinquefoil

Status: OBL

Color photo page 234

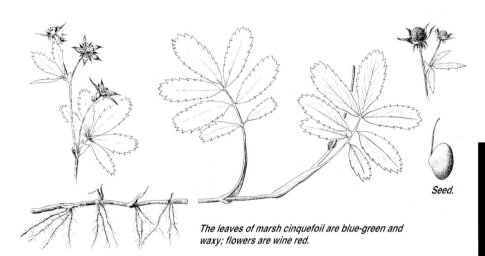

Seed.

The leaves of marsh cinquefoil are blue-green and waxy; flowers are wine red.

The leaves of this invasive freshwater species are deciduous and grow along running stolons which can be 4 m long. Flowers are borne in loose clustered cymes arising from leaf nodes. Blooms June to August.

- leaves blue-green both above and below, waxy to hairy underneath; leaflets sharply toothed, 3-6 cm long, 2-3 leaflets per side
- flowers wine red, petals 2-6 mm long
- fruits broadly oval, glossy light brown, smooth, 1.5 mm long

Habitat: Marsh cinquefoil grows along lake edges, bogs, wet meadows, and streambanks. It can be invasive in bogs that have been disturbed.

Range: Found throughout the United States. Marsh cinquefoil occurs in all counties in our area.

Similar Species: Marsh cinquefoil differs from other cinquefoil species in the Pacific Northwest in having creeping stems that are not cushion-like; waxy, light green leaves; and wine-red flowers, rather than the yellow to white flowers more prevalent in the genus. Largeleaf avens *(Geum macrophyllum)* has similar compound leaves, but the leaflets are irregularly shaped, and plants grow as a clump and are not stoloniferous.

Ranunculus acris
tall buttercup; meadow buttercup

Family: Ranunculaceae
Status: FACW-

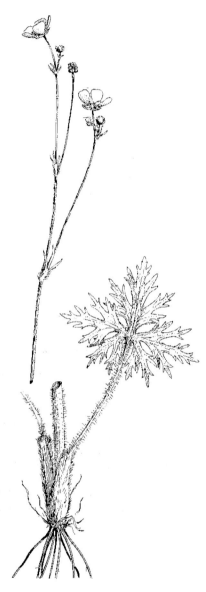

Tall buttercup is a common, erect, perennial herb. It has slender fibrous roots and no stolons. The basal leaves, borne on stalks to 20 cm long, are 3- to 5-lobed, each lobe again being divided nearly to the base. The upper leaves attach directly to the stem and are also highly divided. Blooms May through August.

- plants to 1 m tall, with hairy stems and leaves; stems branched
- leaves palmately divided, lacking light marks on upper surface
- flowers with 5 glossy yellow petals, 10-14 mm long, on erect stalks
- seeds 15-40 per fruit, eye-shaped, 2.5 mm long, smooth with a short (0.5 mm) curved beak

Habitat: Frequent in moist to drained meadows, pastures, and forest clearings. Tall buttercup freely invades seasonally or perennially wet pastures and other disturbed, nonforested wet areas.

Range: Native to Europe. Tall buttercup is widely established from Alaska to California, east to Idaho, Montana, and many other parts of the United States. Present in all counties in our area.

Similar Species: Creeping buttercup *(Ranunculus repens)* has similar hairy basal leaves; however, it has shorter creeping (stoloniferous) stems that root at the nodes forming mats, and leaves that are divided into 3 leaflets which have light markings on the upper surface, and flowering stems that are not erect. Young plants of tall buttercup may be confused with vegetative species of cranesbill *(Geranium* species), but cranesbill species have leaves with stipules, are largely tufted and basal, the leaf stalk hairs (when present) are backward-pointing, and the foliage is often aromatic.

Tall buttercup is an erect plant to 1 m tall with hairy stems.

Ethnobotanical Uses: Many species of buttercup, including all the species described in this guide, contain a toxin that may produce blisters on the skin, and, if ingested, may cause a burning sensation in the mouth and abdominal pain. They are often unpalatable to livestock. Several species of buttercups have been used by Native Americans to poison arrow tips.

Ranunculus aquatilis var. hispidulus
white water buttercup; water crowfoot

Family: Ranunculaceae

Status: OBL

White water buttercup is an aquatic herb with small, white flowers that are held just above the water's surface. It often produces two types of leaves (dimorphic): submerged leaves, and leaves that float on the water's surface. Although white is an unusual flower color for a member of the butter-cup genus, the petals occasionally betray their generic affiliation by having a yellow base. Blooms May to August.

- submerged leaves are divided (repeatedly forked) into thread-like, feathery segments
- floating leaves are shallowly lobed, 5-15 mm long, to 30 mm wide
- flowers with 5 white petals, 5-10 mm long, produced singly in the axils of the leaves on short stalks
- seeds 10-20 per fruit, eye-shaped, 1.5-2 mm long, with a beak that breaks off

Two varieties grow within our range: var. *capillaceus*, in which the floating leaves are dis-sected and resemble the submerged leaves, and var. *hispidulus*, in which the floating leaves are simple and thus dissimilar to the submerged leaves.

Habitat: Submerged in the slow-moving water around the margins of freshwater lakes and ponds, sometimes in mud exposed as water levels recede during the growing season. Also in slow-moving streams and stagnant ditches.

Range: North America from Alaska to Mexico, east to Montana, Wyoming and Utah. Our common variety is *hispidus* which is also found in Europe; var. *capillaceus* occurs locally, but not in Europe. In all counties throughout our area from sea level to the lower mountains.

White water buttercup has thread-like, submerged leaves; white flowers are borne on short stalks from the axils of the leaves.

Similar Species: Eurasian water-milfoil *(Myriophyllum spicatum)* and western water-milfoil *(Myriophyllum hippuroides)* also grow in lake and pond shallows and have leaves that are divided into thread-like segments; however, milfoil leaves are pinnately dissected (similar to a feather), and flowers are tiny and attached directly to the main stem.

HERBS

Ranunculus flammula
small creeping buttercup; spearwort buttercup

Family: Ranunculaceae
Status: FACW
Color photo page 234

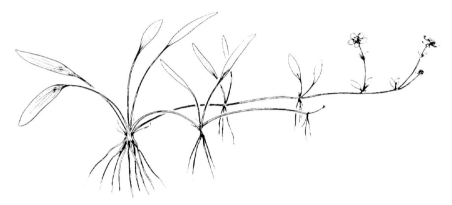

The leaves of small creeping buttercup are narrow and spatula-shaped.

This small, low-growing, perennial herb can be either aquatic or terrestrial. Stem leaves may be attached directly or borne on short stalks. The creeping stems root freely at the nodes forming sparse mats in slow-moving water or stagnant mud pools. Flowers have hairy, greenish sepals. Blooms May to July.

- stems slightly hairy, mostly prostrate, to 50 cm long, mostly unbranched
- leaves simple (not dissected and not lobed), smooth-margined, narrow, spatula-shaped, growing from basal rosette, yellowish green
- flowers yellow, 5-7 mm wide, with varying number of petals (5-11), arising from nodes; flowering stalks often red
- seeds 5-25 per fruit, almost round, 2-3 mm long with a very short (0.5 mm) beak

Habitat: An inhabitant of shorelines and shallow emergent zones of freshwater or brackish swamps and marshes. Small creeping buttercup is most frequent in wet, muddy areas that are shaded for at least part of the day.

Range: Alaska south to California, east to the Rocky Mountain states and through Canada and the north-central states to the Atlantic Coast. A few varieties also found in Europe and Iceland. All counties throughout our area from sea level to the lower mountains.

Similar Species: Young, or nonflowering individuals of small creeping buttercup may be confused with a variety of small emergent herbs. However, on close examination, none of these other plants have the same set of features (i.e., rooting at the nodes and simple basal leaves arising from the nodes, nor do they have yellow-petaled flowers with many achenes on a raised receptacle).

Ranunculus repens var. *repens*
creeping buttercup

Family: Ranunculaceae
Status: FACW
Color photo page 234

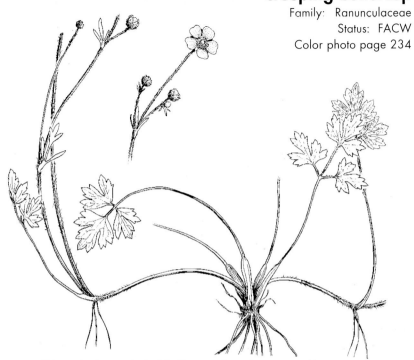

This species is extensively stoloniferous and creeping; compound leaves have 3 leaflets with pale silvery markings on the upper surface.

Creeping buttercup is a common, creeping, stoloniferous perennial herb with shoots that grow to 50 cm long. The mat-forming leaves can be up to 10 cm wide, with leaf stalks to15 cm long. Blooms from May to early August.

- leaves compound, divided into three 3-lobed, triangular leaflets, often densely hairy, dark green, with coarsely and unevenly toothed margins
- leaves often with irregular pale silver marks on upper surface
- flowers yellow, glossy, 10-35 mm wide, on long creeping flower stalks
- seeds 20-50 per fruit, slightly hairy, 2-3 mm long, angular rounded, with a short curved-tipped beak 0.7-1.2 mm long

Habitat: A common inhabitant of almost any moist to wet, disturbed area. Creeping buttercup freely invades wet meadows, roadside ditches, young alder forests, and is a persistent weed in moist gardens. Its associates include soft rush *(Juncus effusus)*, slender bentgrass *(Agrostis capillaris)*, and other native and non-native species.

Range: Creeping buttercup is native to Eurasia; it is extremely common in the Pacific Northwest and east to the Atlantic Coast. Present in all counties in our area.

Similar Species: Largeleaf avens *(Geum macrophyllum)* also has a basal rosette of compound leaves, a tall flowering stalk, and yellow, 5-petaled flowers; however, largeleaf avens has leaflets along the leaf stalks, leaves that are all green with no pale silver markings, and ball-shaped fruits with many "s"-hook-tipped seeds. Tall buttercup *(Ranunculus acris)* has palmately 5-cleft leaves that lack light marks on upper surface, and has and tall, erect stems. Vegetatively, creeping buttercup could be mistaken for water-parsley *(Oenanthe sarmentosa)*, but water-parsley has leaves that are more carrot-like and dissected, and often tinged with red; in addition, the white flowers of water-parsley are arranged in umbels.

Ranunculus sceleratus
celery-leaved buttercup; celery-leaved crowfoot

Family: Ranunculaceae
Status: OBL

Celery-leaved buttercup plants grow as a single erect clump; leaves are highly divided into 3 lobes.

This low-growing to erect annual herb produces a clump of basal leaves with long leaf stalks. It has no stolons, and does not root at the nodes; instead, its roots are a thick, fleshy mass. It grows to 80 cm tall and has waxy stems and leaves. The flowering stems are hollow. Blooms May through September.

- leaves kidney-shaped, highly divided into 3 lobes, each with toothed margins
- flowers set on receptacle (14 mm long) 2-5 mm long, with greenish yellow petals
- seeds 100-250 per fruit, oval, 1 mm long, flattened, with a smooth margin and a corky-ridged central area; beak lacking

Habitat: Found in moist meadows and muddy shorelines along lake margins and stream banks, often where the water is brackish. Celery-leaved buttercup freely invades disturbed ground.

Range: Native to Eurasia. Celery-leaved buttercup is somewhat common in the Pacific Northwest and east to the Atlantic Coast. Occurs in all counties in our area.

Similar Species: Although similar in appearance to other buttercups such as creeping buttercup *(Ranunculus repens)*, celery-leaved buttercup does not produce stolons, and seeds are borne on a long cylindrical, rather than oval, receptacle.

Genus: *Rorippa*
cresses
Family: Brassicaceae (Cruciferae)

These low-growing herbs have diffusely branching stems with deeply divided, variable leaves. The small yellow to white flowers have sepals and petals in groupings of 4 and grow in numerous clusters in leaf axils. Fruits are straight to curved capsules, called siliques, that are typical of other plants in the mustard family. There are six stamens in two groups (4 longer and 2 shorter).

Similar Species: Few other plants with 4 petals, yellow flowers, and silique fruits grow in muddy areas. Marsh yellow cress *(Rorippa islandica)*, and *Rorippa obtusa* are uncommon but could be present. Their siliques are straight, as well as shorter and thicker (2-3 mm wide and less than 8 mm long). Species of *Draba* (and *Cardamine*) also belong to the mustard family and are white-flowered; however, these annual plants are smaller (less than 10 cm tall) and bear a basal rosette of leaves.

Functional Value: Water-cress functions in biofiltration and sedimentation. It is a cover and substrate for amphibians and aquatic insects. The other two species do not grow in thick enough beds to improve water quality.

Ethnobotanical Uses: All three species are edible as a salad green. Water-cress is the most palatable but has been reported to be a carrier of a fluke (parasitic flat-worm) when found in the wild, and should not be consumed.

HERBS

Rorippa calycina
persistent-sepal yellow cress
Status: FACW
Color photo page 234

Persistent-sepal yellow cress is a rhizomatous perennial with weak, often spreading hairy to bristly stems. There are many varieties and the leaves are highly variable with smooth and sinuous to pinnatifid margins. The sepals and petals are about 4 mm long. Blooms from May to August.

This species is rhizomatous with hairy, creeping stems and small yellow flowers.

- stems 10-40 cm tall, freely branching
- leaves 3-7 cm long, borne on stalks near the base or attached directly to upper stem
- flowers light yellow, 4 mm long, lower sepals not sac-like at the base
- siliques erect to ascending, 2-7 mm long, 2-2.5 mm wide, soft hairy, oval to oblong

Habitat: Favors moist areas that are typically dry in late spring and summer, similar to vernal pool conditions. Prefers moist, sandy soils on the margins of seasonally inundated streams and drainages. Can be found in "wallows" typical of abandoned pastures or grazing areas where they form scattered mats, appear clumped, or may form a discontinuous groundcover.

Range: Persistent-sepal yellow cress is common and widespread, scattered sporadically in western North America.

Cresses continued on next page...

175

Rorippa curvisiliqua
western yellow cress, curvepod yellow cress
Status: OBL

Western yellow cress is an annual or biennial herb that lacks rhizomes or stolons. Leaves on spreading stalks 2-7 mm long. Blooms from May through September.

- stems 10-40 cm tall, with many branches, smooth to sparsely bristly
- leaves smooth, 2-7 cm long, deeply pinnately lobed, oblong-lance-shaped and highly variable
- flowers yellow, 1-2 mm long, smaller than sepals
- siliques 6-15 mm long, 1-2 mm wide, slightly curved to straight

Habitat: Same as persistent-sepal yellow cress.

Range: Western yellow cress is native to North America and the north temperate latitudes; it is commonly found in all counties of the Pacific Northwest and north to Canada, south to Baja, and east to Wyoming, Montana, and Colorado.

Western yellow cress grows erect in a single clump and has yellow flowers.

Rorippa nasturtium-aquaticum
(Nasturtium officinale)
water-cress; true water-cress
Status: OBL

Plants have white flowers.

- stems flexible, 10-60 cm long, with erect tip, rooting at nodes
- leaves smooth and waxy, 4-12 cm long, compound with 3-11 oval to lance-shaped leaflets, with terminal lobe being the largest
- petals white to purplish with purplish veins, 3-4 mm long, broadly spoon-shaped
- siliques elongate, 10-30 mm long, about 2 mm wide

Water-cress is a widespread, aquatic perennial best known for its peppery flavor as a salad green. Stems are limp, fleshy, and often floating. The inflorescence is an erect and terminal raceme. There are 4 whitish sepals; the outer pair are sac-like at the base. Flowers are borne on stalks 8-20 mm long that are spreading or bent slightly backwards. Blooms March to October.

Habitat: Water-cress is also commonly found in quiet streams, marshy areas, shallow fresh water, drainage ditches, and pond margins.

Range: Water-cress is a European species that is widely naturalized.

Genus: *Rumex*
docks
Family: Polygonaceae

The following three species of dock are quite similar and are most easily distinguished from one another by leaf margins, flower structure, and fruits as outlined separately below. They are all erect perennial herbs (western dock being the tallest of the three) and have a deep, stout taproot. Stems are large, well-branched, grow to about 1 m, and have sheathing stipules. Leaves are produced both at the base and along the stems; basal leaves are borne on long stalks; and stem leaves are reduced upward and may be attached directly without stalks. Numerous small, reddish brown flowers occur in clumps or whorls along the upper 50-100 cm of the stems. The flowers consist of six inconspicuous petals and sepals (perianth segments). The three inner perianth segments eventually envelop the triangular fruits, which are small and hang from short stalks.

Ethnobotanical Uses: Dock leaves contain oxalic acid, are high in minerals, and have been used for centuries as a potherb and in salads. The roots have been used as a liver tonic. Dock seeds were used by some Native American tribes as flour or meal which is similar to buckwheat. However, consumption of oxalic acid should be kept to a minimum.

Similar Species: These tall docks are most easily confused with each other.

HERBS

Rumex crispus
curly dock
Status: FAC+

Curly dock is common almost everywhere in North America. The flesh of the taproot is yellow. Stems are unbranched below the inflorescence. Leaf stalks are 10-20 cm long and slightly hairy. The small, whorled clusters of inconspicuous flowers alternate with leafy bracts. Blooms from June through September.

- basal leaves lance-shaped to oblong, to 40 cm long and 5 cm wide, with crisped, wavy margins
- flowers green to rusty-brown with outer perianth segments about 5 mm long, smooth-margined to shallowly toothed
- fruits borne on short stalks, 2 mm long, net-veined, with a central swelling and smooth margins

Habitat: Commonly found in disturbed and waste places, wet meadows, and pasture habitats. Because stock frequently do not graze these plants, the tall brownish flowering or fruiting stalks can be seen scattered over wide expanses of open ground. Adapted to areas that dry out completely during the summer.

Range: Curly dock is a naturalized European species. Occurs in all counties in our area.

Curly dock has mostly lance-shaped leaves with wavy margins; seeds (above right) are net-veined with smooth margins.

Docks continued on next page...

Rumex obtusifolius
bitter dock
Status: FAC

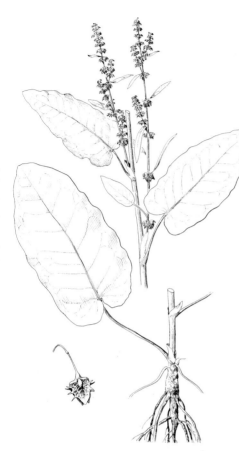

This weedy native is a very robust, perennial herb found primarily in moist, disturbed areas. It grows from a branched root and lacks rhizomes. Stems are 60-120 cm tall. The whorls in the lower inflorescence are spaced further apart than in the upper inflorescence. Blooms from March through September.

- basal leaves oblong-oval or broadly oblong, 10-20 cm long and 15 cm wide, notched at base with undulating, wavy margins at the base
- flowers with inner perianth segments about 5 mm long, outer segments about 3 mm long, strongly 2-4 toothed on each margin
- fruits borne on stalks that are longer than the outer perianth segments, outer edge wrinkled and prickly; inner edge swollen and smooth, 2-3 mm long

Habitat: Same as curly dock.

Range: Bitter dock is found from Alaska to California only west of the Cascade mountains. It is common across Canada and in central, eastern, and southwest United States, Eurasia, Africa, Mexico, and South America.

Bitter dock has oblong basal leaves with heart-shaped bases and only slightly wavy margins; seeds (left) are net-veined with prickly margins.

Rumex occidentalis var. labradoricus
western dock
FACW+

Western dock is the most robust of the weedy docks in our area. Stems are usually single, thick, reddish-tinged, with leafy bracts found only below the flowers. Flowers occur on the stem in clumps, not whorls. Blooms June through August.

- basal leaves oblong-ovate or oblong-lance-shaped, to 40 cm long and 3-15 cm wide, with slightly crinkled margins, and a heart-shaped base
- stem leaves few, reduced upwards
- flowers green-reddish-brown, with inner perianth segments about 3-10 mm long, outer segments about 1.5-3 mm long, smooth-margined to toothed
- fruits borne on stalks 2-3x the length of outer perianth segments, 4 mm long, with prickly margins

Habitat: Same as curly dock.

Range: Western dock is found in the Rocky Mountains, east to Quebec and the Dakotas, and along the coast from British Columbia to central California.

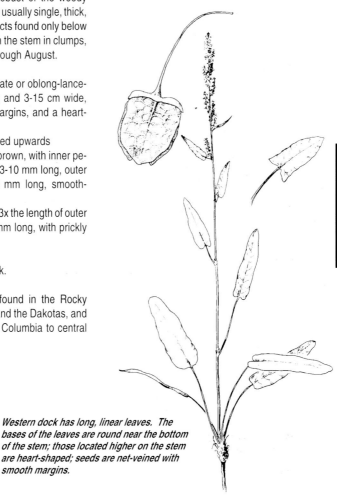

Western dock has long, linear leaves. The bases of the leaves are round near the bottom of the stem; those located higher on the stem are heart-shaped; seeds are net-veined with smooth margins.

HERBS

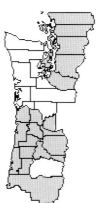

179

Rumex acetosella ssp. *angiocarpus*
sheep sorrel

Family: Polygonaceae
Status: FACU+
Color photo page 234

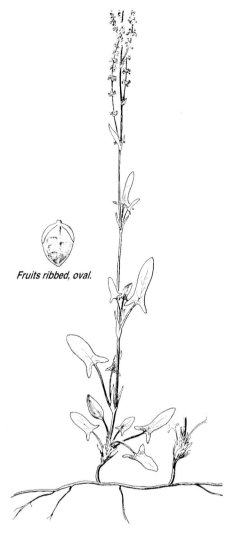

Fruits ribbed, oval.

This small species has arrowhead-shaped leaves.

Sheep sorrel is a strongly rhizomatous, erect, perennial herb. Although plants growing near to one another appear to be isolated individuals, they are often sprouting from a common rhizome. Basal leaves can be 5 cm long and are borne on stalks. The upper leaves are often shorter, with no stalks, and have a straight base. Leaf stipules are large and sheath the stem. Tiny flowers are scattered along elongated, branched panicles to 40 cm long. Male and female flowers are borne on separate plants. Petals, about 1 mm long, largely envelop the fruits. Blooms in May.

- leaves and stems with a lemon-like flavor
- basal leaves small, simple, strongly arrow-head-shaped
- flowering stems thin, 15-50 cm tall, with numerous small, bright, reddish or yellowish globular flowers
- fruits tiny, ribbed, oval

Habitat: Sheep sorrel is common in semi-dry sites along roadsides, in cultivated and abandoned fields, and other disturbed areas. It is common in gravelly soils along roads. This is an upland species, but is common near wetlands.

Range: Native to Europe, sheep sorrel is an extremely common and noxious weed in disturbed and waste places throughout North America. Present in all counties in our area.

Similar Species: With its distinctive basal leaves and reddish yellow flowering stalks, sheep sorrel is not often confused with other weedy herbs.

Functional Value: Sheep sorrel is high in vitamin C and is commonly eaten by wildlife.

Ethnobotanical Uses: The leaves contain oxalic acid; the plant has been used for centuries as a potherb. However, consumption should be limited as oxalic acid is dangerous in large quantities.

Rumex maritimus var. *fueginus*
golden dock; seaside dock

Family: Polygonaceae
Status: FACW+

This hairy, knobby-textured biennial herb has fibrous roots and leaves borne along the stem (unlike other dock species which typically have a tap root and basal leaves). The entire plant is golden in color when the plant is in fruit. The leaves lowest on the main stem are long-stalked. Higher up the stem, leaves are smaller and have shorter stalks. The petals and sepals are inconspicuous. The outer petals are about 2 mm long, the inner about 3 mm long with a sharp tip to 4 mm long. Blooms from late June to September.

* stems well-branched, to 80 cm long, with sheathing stipules
* basal leaves narrowly long and linear or long and oval-shaped to 15 cm long, and about 4 cm broad; margins curled
* flowers small, numerous, typically form greenish brown clumps along the panicle branches, interspersed with many leaves
* fruits triangular, very spiny, hanging from short stalks, 1-2 mm long

Habitat: Golden dock is often found in brackish coastal marshes and in wet meadows.

Range: Native to Eurasia and the Americas. Present in all coastal counties in our area.

Similar Species: With its sheathing stipules, long-tipped inner petals, and habitat of brackish coastal marshes, golden dock is considerably different from other dock species.

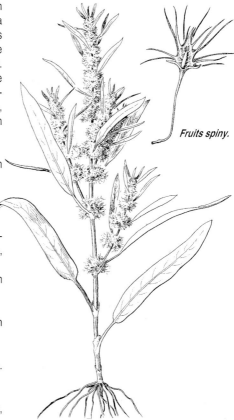

Fruits spiny.

HERBS

Golden dock has sheathing stipules and very spiny fruits.

Ruppia maritima
widgeon-grass; ditch-grass

Family: Ruppiaceae
Status: OBL

Widgeon-grass, a coastal species, has long, thread-like leaves that are all submerged; fruits are borne on coiled stems.

Widgeon-grass is a submersed, perennial herb with delicate, grass-like features. Leaves are 0.5 mm broad and seldom greater than 12.0 cm long. Flowers are minute and inconspicuous, 2 per short terminal "club". Blooms in July and August.

- rhizomatous aquatic with simple or many branched stems, to 80 cm long
- leaves 12 cm long, alternate, thread-like, arising from broadly sheathed stipules
- flowers initially stalkless (although borne on a short club-like structure sheathed by the stipule)
- drupe-like fruits develop a long, loosely coiled stalk 3-30 cm long as the fruit matures

Habitat: Common primarily in brackish marine sloughs, ditches, and tideflats. Tolerates sudden and large fluctuations in salinity concentrations. Transitional species on sandy marine substrates between the eelgrass *(Zostera)* and three-square bulrush-Lyngby sedge *(Scirpus americanus-Carex lyngbyei)* communities. In brackish lagoons with silt substrate and freshwater inputs, it may pioneer with blue-green algae *(Cyanophyta)*.

Range: Cosmopolitan; Pacific Coast from Alaska to Baja California. Inland in fresh to alkaline ditches, ponds, and lakes throughout Canada and United States to Atlantic Coast, South America, and Europe.

Similar Species: Easily confused with many narrow-leaved thread-like aquatic plants especially prior to flowering. Water-milfoils *(Myriophyllum* species) have leaflets arranged in a whorl, tiny inconspicuous flowers, and are found only in fresh water. Bladderworts *(Utricularia* species) have alternate leaves, with thread-like leaflets with bladders attached to them, and flowers that are large, yellow, and emerge as a spike above the water. Eelgrass *(Zostera)* and surfgrass *(Phyllospadix)* grow in more marine environments and have wider leaves (1.5-12 mm), and flowers that are inconspicuous in that they are found inside the leaves.

Functional Value: Sand and beach stabilization. Widgeon-grass is also an important food source for waterfowl and a substrate for aquatic invertebrates.

Genera: *Sagittaria* and *Alisma*
Family: Alismataceae

Habitat: Both of these species are generally found in shallow emergent marshes, ponds, sloughs and ditches, especially in protected waters with depths of 5-15 cm and soft muddy soils. Found along the margins of ponds if standing water remains after May during the growing season. Associated with sedges *(Carex* species), rushes *(Juncus* species), cattails *(Typha* species) and water foxtail *(Alopecurus geniculatus).*

Similar Species: Bogbean *(Menyanthes trifoliata)* is the only common, large, clumped emergent/aquatic plant that is similar to both species. Bogbean has thick rhizomes but no tubers, and the leaves grow along the rhizomes in an alternate pattern, not from a basal rosette of leaves. The leaves are thick and fleshy with 3 lobes. The flowers are white, funnel-shaped with 5 lobes, and the petals have a frilly inner surface.

Functional Value: The tubers of broadleaf arrowhead, imported from the central and eastern United States, are being extensively planted throughout our area to restore or create wetlands. They provide food for many species of waterfowl. Canadian geese are particularly fond of the tubers, and have probably consumed many acres of tubers at wetland restoration or creation sites. Beaver, muskrat, and porcupine eat the entire plant. Broad-leaf arrowhead has been used in wastewater treatment systems, where studies have determined that it effectively removes dissolved nutrients.

Ethnobotanical Uses: Broadleaf arrowhead tubers are edible when roasted or boiled, and have long been an important food item for humans. Many Native North American tribes, including the Chinooks of the lower Columbia River, used the tubers as a staple food. These tubers were also a major article of commerce in that region. Members of the Lewis and Clark expedition ate the tubers as they traveled west, as did many of the early European settlers. The bulbous base of broadleaf water-plaintain has a strong taste when fresh, but after thorough drying it becomes a palatable starchy vegetable.

HERBS

Sagittaria latifolia var. *latifolia*
broadleaf arrowhead; wapato
Status: OBL
Color photo page 235

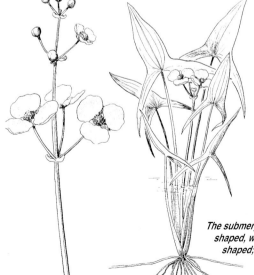

Broadleaf arrowhead is a rooted aquatic to emergent perennial herb that grows from a rosette of basal leaves with numerous stolons and rhizomes. Each plant produces several round tubers on rhizomes and stolons, which in turn produce new plants the following year. In this manner, broadleaf arrowhead spreads, often forming large stands in areas of still or slow-moving water. Blooms from July through September.

The submerged leaves of broadleaf arrowhead are lance-shaped, whereas the above-water leaves are arrowhead-shaped; flowers are 1-2 cm wide.

Contiued on next page...

- above-water leaves arrowhead-shaped, to 25 cm long
- submerged leaves lance-shaped to linear, 4-10 mm wide; leaves growing in a cluster from a single, tuber-like base
- leaf stalks angular but not flattened or channeled
- flowers often either male or female, most often arranged in whorls of 3 (2-8) per node; flowers large (1-2 cm), white, borne in 3's, with numerous stamens and ovaries
- fruits winged, oblong, flattened, with beak 0.5 - 1.5 mm long; borne in a cluster

Range: Broadleaf arrowhead is infrequent throughout most of western Washington from southern Vancouver Island to central California. It is fairly common along the Columbia River west of the Columbia Gorge and south through the Willamette Valley. Restricted to low elevations. It also grows abundantly in the central and eastern United States, south through Mexico and Central America to northern South America, and in the West Indies and Hawaii. Early floras report broadleaf arrowhead was more common in our lakes and ponds before the introduction of the European carp, which eats the tubers.

Alisma plantago-aquatica var. *americanum*
broadleaf water-plaintain; American water-plantain

Status: OBL
color photo page 224

This tall, semi-aquatic perennial herb grows from a rosette of basal leaves. It has no stolons or rhizomes.

- flowering stem to 1 m tall
- leaves from a bulbous base, oval, 3-15 cm wide, borne on flattened, channeled leaf stalks 10-20 cm long
- flowers having both male and female parts, arranged in whorls of 3 terminal panicles per node; individual flowers small (6-9 mm wide), white to slightly purplish, borne in 3's, with 6 stamens and 10-25 separate ovaries
- fruits oblong, unwinged, and grooved but flattened

Range: Broadleaf water-plaintain *(Alisma plantago-aquatica)* is found throughout our area, across the United States, Eurasia, Africa, and Australia.

The leaves of broadleaf water-plaintain are all oval; flowers are 6-9 mm wide.

Salicornia virginica
(Salicornia pacifica)
pickleweed; woody glasswort; Virginia glasswort

Family: Chenopodiaceae
Status: OBL
Color photo page 235

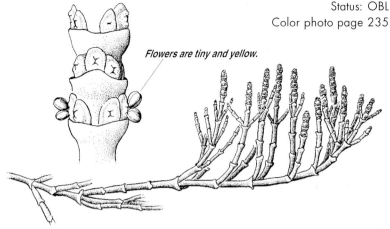

Flowers are tiny and yellow.

The stems of pickleweed are composed of short interlocking segments.

A mat-forming, perennial, this estuarine herb has shallow, fibrous roots. Plants have no obvious leaves and look like chains of segmented stems. New growth is succulent and edible; older stems become woody. In winter, much of the fleshy growth is lost, leaving only a tangle of woody stems. Blooms June to September from depressions at the joints.

- flowering stems green with a reddish or purplish cast, solid, fleshy, jointed, cylindrical, to 5 mm in diameter, 5-30 cm long, either erect or creeping
- flowers tiny, yellow, clustered in 3's at tips of stems

Habitat: Most common in salt marshes throughout Puget Sound and coastal estuaries that receive regular tidal inundation. Usually found on sandy substrate, but also grows in mud or clay. Typical associates include seashore saltgrass *(Distichlis spicata)*, seaside arrowgrass *(Triglochin maritima)*, and fleshy jaumea *(Jaumea*

carnosa). Occasionally infested by thread-like stems of salt-marsh dodder (*Cuscuta salina*).

Range: Along Pacific, Atlantic, and Gulf coasts, and the coasts of Western Europe and the Mediterranean region. Occurs in all coastal counties in our area.

Similar Species: Western lilaeopsis *(Lilaeopsis occidentalis)* also has segmented stems and no obvious leaves but its stems remain succulent when mature and are hollow and green. Seablite *(Suaeda calceoliformis)* is a similar plant which also grows in salt marshes in the Puget Basin; however, seablite has a taproot, and alternate succulent leaves that are narrow and rounded.

Functional Value: Voraciously grazed by waterfowl and other herbivores. Plants trap sediment in lower intertidal areas; its root system helps stabilize tidal beaches.

Ethnobotanical Uses: Provides a field snack called sea asparagus when eaten young and is occasionally pickled or used fresh in salads. When burned, it was used as a source of carbonate of soda for glassmaking before World War II.

Sanguisorba officinalis
great burnet

Family: Rosaceae
Status: FACW+

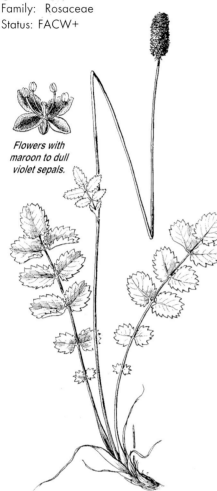

Flowers with
maroon to dull
violet sepals.

Great burnet has pinnately compound leaves
that are bright green above and pale green
below.

- leaves mostly basal, alternate, pinnately compound, 20-40 cm long
- leaflets 9-13, oval to oblong-lance-shaped, 1.5-3 cm long, bright green above and pale green below, with coarsely toothed margins
- flower sepals maroon to dull violet
- stamens round, equal in length to the sepals

Habitat: Grows most often in sphagnum-dominated northern boreal and bog communities, usually along the coast; may also be found in submontane to alpine sites to 1,500 m. Great burnet is shade-intolerant.

Range: Circumboreal; Iceland to much of northern Europe and Asia. In North America, from Alaska and the Yukon along the coast to northwest California, and inland to Mt. Hood, Oregon. Occurs in all counties in our area.

Similar Species: Menzies' burnet *(Sanguisorba menziesii)*, which is found only in the Olympic Peninsula, is virtually indistinguishable; however, it has flattened stamens that are about twice as long as the sepals. Plants without flowers may also be confused with seedlings of Sitka mountain ash *(Sorbus sitchensis)* or European mountain ash *(Sorbus aucuparia)* which are generally woodier and have more elongate leaves. Pacific silverweed *(Potentilla anserina)* has similar compound basal leaves, but they are woolly below, plantlets grow from creeping runners, and flowers are 5-petaled and single from the leaf axils.

Ethnobotanical Uses: No record of use in the Pacific Northwest although *Medieval Medica* indicate plants belonging to this genus were used to staunch bleeding after leeching a patient, hence sanguisorba from *sanguis* (blood), and *sorbere* (to drink or absorb).

Great burnet is a perennial herb that grows from a stout rhizome. Flower stems are mostly leafless and grow to 140 cm tall. The inflorescence is a broad, terminal, cylindrical to oval-egg-shaped spike, 1-2.5 cm long and 1 cm broad. Numerous, minute, petal-less flowers, about 5 mm long, are borne on each spike. Blooms July to August.

Scutellaria lateriflora
mad-dog skullcap; blue skullcap

Family: Lamiaceae (Labiatae)
Status: FACW+
Color photo page 235

Mad-dog skullcap, like other perennial herbs in the mint family, has opposite leaves and an erect square stem arising from slender creeping rhizomes. It grows 20-150 cm tall. Leaves are 3-10 cm long and 1.5-5 cm wide, and are borne on stalks 5-25 mm long. Blooms July to August.

- leaves nonaromatic, oval to broadly lance-shaped; margins blunt-toothed or with spreading pointed teeth.
- inflorescence one-sided racemes, 2-12 cm long, originating in leaf axils and terminating stem; also, 1- several flowers attached directly in leaf axils
- flowers blue to purple, irregular, trumpet shaped, 6-8 mm long
- seeds 4 round, paired nutlets

Habitat: Occurs in freshwater tidal marshes, wet meadows, and along stream banks and lake shores.

Range: Newfoundland to British Columbia, south to Georgia and California. Extensive throughout North America.

Similar Species: Because of its square stems and opposite leaves, mad-dog skullcap is most easily confused with other members of the mint family; however, most other mint species have aromatic leaves and the racemes of flowers do not originate in the leaf axils. Willow-weed *(Scutellaria galericulata)* has single flowers in each axil of the upper leaves and lacks racemes. Stinging nettle *(Urtica dioica)* resembles mad-dog skullcap in growth form, but has hairs, green to reddish flowers, and stinging foliage.

Ethnobotanical Uses:
Widely acclaimed as an effective "nervine" or tranquilizer for nervous disorders ranging from mild anxiety to epilepsy. As a soothing tea it is

Blue to purple flowers are trumpet-like.

This rhizomatous species has square stems and flowers that appear chain-like on stalks from the leaf axils.

used as a sedative and to promote menstruation. The active ingredient is scutellarin, a flavonoid with sedative and antispasmodic properties. Recent pharmocological research indicates significant antifungal and antibacterial activity.

HERBS

Sisyrinchium californicum
golden-eyed grass

Family: Iridaceae
Status: FACW+

Seed capsules.

A delicate member of the iris family, golden-eyed grass is the only yellow-flowered species of an otherwise blue- to purple-flowered genus. The leaves are 5-25 cm long, 2-5 mm broad, and sheathed at the base. The flat, circular, symmetrical flowers have 6 tepals, 8-11 mm long, and are held on slender stalks in clusters of 2-7 flowers. Blooms June and July.

- weakly rhizomatous perennial herb forming dense tufts 5-40 cm tall
- stems 2-6 mm wide, more or less flattened, winged
- flowers yellow, with deep brownish nerves and 2 sheathing, leaf-like bracts
- seed capsules persist after flowering; seeds black with flattened sides

Habitat: Golden-eyed grass is a coastal species, forming dense tufts at edges of wet sites, varying from areas between low sand dunes to bogs or fens to roadside ditches. It is found occasionally in the Puget Sound area and on Vancouver Island around the edges of freshwater lakes and in roadside ditches. This species prefers sandy soils or nutrient-poor systems. Plant associations include: Sitka spruce *(Picea sitchensis)*, coast pine *(Pinus contorta)*, sweetgale *(Myrica gale)*, willows *(Salix* species), slough sedge *(Carex obnupta)*, and cinquefoils *(Potentilla* species).

Range: Occurs from south end of Vancouver Island to southern California. Found exclusively west of the Cascade Mountains in our area.

Similar Species: Grass-widows *(Sisyrinchium douglasii)* inhabits drier areas of the Puget Basin, has reddish purple to magenta flowers, longer leaves, a floral bract exceeding the flowers, and a roundish stem.

The plants of golden-eyed grass are tiny and iris-like with flattened stems and yellow flowers.

Sium suave
water-parsnip; hemlock water-parsnip

Family: Apiaccae (Umbelliferae)
Status: OBL
Color photo page 235

Water-parsnip is an uncommon, erect, terrestrial to semi-aquatic perennial herb with fibrous to thickened roots. Flowering stems are hollow, ridged, leafy, and grow to 120 cm tall. Flowers have a leaf-like involucre that is often bent backwards, with 6-10 bracts. Blooms July and August.

- stems root at all the lower nodes
- leaves once-pinnately compound, tapering to the tip, with the ultimate segments shiny, narrowly sword-shaped to linear; margins toothed with lateral veins not to the tips of the teeth
- leaf stalks sheathing the stem
- flowers white to pinkish, in dense compound umbels with 6-10 involucral bracts
- fruits oval to elliptic and slightly flattened, 2-3 mm long, hairless with deep bony ridges

Habitat: Favors wet, swampy areas such as ponds, edges of lakes, or muddy or sandy stream banks. Water-parsnip occurs most frequently in partially open areas, and often is associated with Douglas spiraea (*Spirea douglasii*), willows (*Salix* species), and redstem dogwood (*Cornus sericea*).

Range: Native to North America and the north temperate latitudes. It is occasionally found on both sides of the Cascades in the Pacific Northwest and east to the Atlantic Coast. Occurs in all counties in our area.

Similar Species: The poisonous western water-hemlock (*Cicuta douglasii*), does not have the obvious involucral bracts of western water-parsnip. In addition, western water-hemlock has a thickened stem base with prominent horizontal partitions and 2-3 times compound leaves with 3 leaflets and lateral veins that go to the tip of the teeth. Water-parsley *(Oenanthe sarmentosa)* shares a similar habitat, but has twice- or thrice-

The leaves of water-parsnip are once-pinnately compound; flowers are borne in dense umbels.

pinnately compound, more dissected leaves, with lateral veins that go to the tip of the teeth.

Ethnobotanical Uses: It is unknown if water-parsnip is poisonous. Reports of poisoning may be caused by misidentification or confusion with western water-hemlock.

HERBS

Solanum dulcamara
bittersweet nightshade; climbing nightshade

Family: Solanaceae
Status: FAC+
Color photo page 235

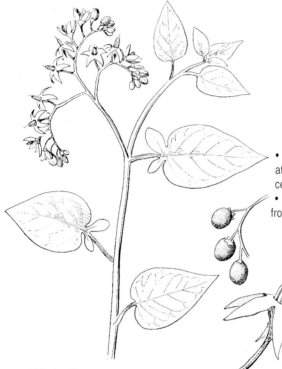

This vine-like and rhizomatous species has blue to violet flowers with fused yellow stamens and oval berries.

• flowers blue to violet, fused into a tube at the base, with yellow stamens in the centers; petals curved back
• berries oval, 2-celled, varying in color from yellow to orange or bright red

Habitat: Found in moist thickets, clearings, open woods, waterways, lake shores, ditches, and along fences; mostly in disturbed sites.

Range: Eurasian species widely introduced across North America. Occurs in all counties in our area.

Climbing to 3 m tall, this vine-like, rhizomatous perennial often covers all vegetation in its path. Five to twenty-five small flowers arise opposite or between leaves in compound branched inflorescences. Blooms in June and July.

- stems semi-woody with persistent woody base, emit a very pungent musky odor when crushed
- leaves of 2 different shapes; some simple, smooth-margined, oval to egg-shaped with a notched base; others with prominent basal lobes or leaflets

Similar Species: The distinctive leaf shape and bright flowers and berries distinguish bittersweet nightshade from the few other vine-like plants common in the Pacific Northwest. Black nightshade *(Solanum nigrum)* is a taprooted woody bush (not vine-like) with white flowers and black fruits. Morning glories *(Convolvulus* species) have regular arrowhead-shaped leaves and large white or red-purple trumpet-shaped flowers.

Functional Value: The berries are eaten by birds.

Ethnobotanical Uses: Although the leaves and berries are reportedly poisonous to humans, toxicity has not been confirmed; bittersweet nightshade has been used for medicinal purposes.

Genus: *Sparganium*
burreeds
Family: Sparganiaceae

Burreeds are rhizomatous, aquatic perennials. The leaves are long, linear, alternate, and with sheathing bases. Petals and sepals are reduced to scales and arranged compactly in a hardened, globe-like flower head. Male and female flowers are borne on the same plant with the male flower heads being smaller and located above the female flower heads. Flower heads on the main stem are carried in the leaf axils, giving the flowering stem a characteristic crooked appearance. Fruits are hardened, top-shaped achenes that fit together compactly within the globular head. Bloom July to August.

Similar Species: There are many subspecies and varieties of narrowleaf burreed. The globular flower heads distinguish them from sedges and grasses.

Functional Value: Both species provide habitat and a food source for wildlife. Great blue herons and other waterfowl feed on the fruits. Leaves and stems are grazed by rodents, deer, and other mammals. Burreeds take up pollutants readily. In addition, they transplant easily, making them desirable species for wetland creation and restoration.

Ethnobotanical Uses: The dried stems of both species are often used for basketry.

HERBS

Sparganium emersum ssp. *emersum*
narrowleaf burreed; simplestem burreed
Status: OBL

Narrowleaf burreed is the most common species of burreed. Plants are highly variable; in the spring leaves are floating and ribbon-like, while later in the season leaves are erect and mostly 20-80 cm long and 5-12 mm wide. Stem and leaves are usually partially submerged. Male and female flower heads each number 1-3. Female flowers have 1 stigma that is less than 2 mm long.

- stems to 80 cm long
- leaves are taller than flowering stem, with roughened margins at base
- flowering stem generally unbranched
- fruits tapering at each end, held on a short stalk

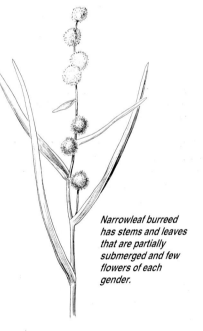

Narrowleaf burreed has stems and leaves that are partially submerged and few flowers of each gender.

Habitat: Narrowleaf burreed grows in shallow standing water, up to 1 m deep, and on the margins of ponds, lakes, and sloughs. Narrowleaf burreed prefers silt and muck substrates that are slightly acidic.

Range: Narrowleaf burreed is circumboreal in distribution. In North

America, varieties of narrowleaf burreed occur from Canada to California.

Burreeds continued on next page...

Sparganium eurycarpum
giant burreed; broadfruited burreed

Status: OBL

Color photo page 235

Giant burreed has 1-2 female flower heads per stem which appear below the more numerous male flower heads.

Giant burreed is more robust than the narrowleaf burreed. It grows in standing water in erect colonies. Leaves are 20-80 cm long and 8-15 mm broad, and triangular in cross section. Male flower heads number 5-12, female heads 1-2 per stem. Female flowers have 2 stigmas that are slightly more than 2 mm long.

- stems to 1.5 m tall
- leaves often shorter than the flowering stem
- flowering stem branched
- fruits pear-shaped, attached directly to stem

Habitat: Giant burreed grows in shallow standing water, up to 1 m deep, and on the margins of ponds, lakes, and sloughs. It is found mostly emersed in meadows and shallow marshes, and around lake margins. It thrives in slightly basic soils, preferring clay-rich, mineral soils.

Range: Giant burreed is widespread in North America from British Coumbia to Baja California, east to Newfoundland, and south to Florida.

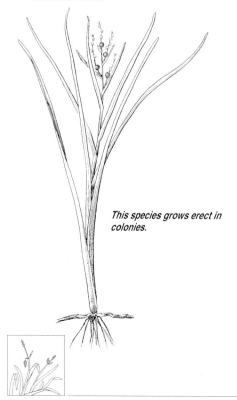

This species grows erect in colonies.

Genus: *Spergularia*
sandspurries
Family: Caryophyllaceae

The sandspurries are low-growing, common salt marsh and seaside herbs. All three species discussed here tolerate rather high salinities in coastal areas and salt marshes on sandy substrates, but can also colonize mud flats. Stems are succulent, erect or prostrate, glandular and sticky, and grow from a many-stemmed, basal clump with tap root. Leaves are opposite, linear, and sharp to the touch after they dry. Stipules are narrowly triangular, paired, and pointed toward the stem ends. All species have small flowers with 5 petals and 5 sepals that quickly turn brown and husk-like after blooming. The white to pink petals can be slightly to much shorter than the sepals. Fruits are a capsule. Seeds are flat, pear-shaped, and usually have papery margins. Characteristics that distinguish them from each other are stem length, leaf arrangement and tip, stipule shape, number of stamens, and whether the seeds have wings. Blooms June to August.

Spergularia canadensis var. *occidentalis*
Canadian sandspurry
Status: OBL

HERBS

Canadian sandspurry is an annual herb. Flowers are often few, but occasionally many, with white to pale pink petals, 6-10 stamens, and are borne on terminal cymes.

- stems somewhat covered with sticky glands, sparsely hairy, to 25 cm long, 1 mm thick
- leaves triangular and fleshy, not sharp-pointed, 4.5 cm long, 1.5 mm wide
- stipules about 1-2.7 mm long
- petals 1-3 mm long, slightly shorter than sepals
- capsules about 3 mm long; seeds brown, 0.8-1.4 mm, smooth, usually winged

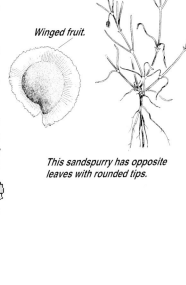

Winged fruit.

Flower.

This sandspurry has opposite leaves with rounded tips.

Habitat: Canadian sandspurry occurs in the high or low salt marsh and is associated with fat-hen saltbush *(Atriplex patula)*, pickleweed *(Salicornia virginica)*, and fleshy jaumea *(Jaumea carnosa)*. It is usually not a dominant plant.

Range: Canadian sandspurry grows along the Pacific Coast from Alaska to northern California. Also grows on the Atlantic Coast from Newfoundland to New York.

Sandspurries continued on next page...

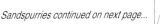

Spergularia macrotheca var. *macrotheca*
beach sandspurry

Status: OBL

The leaves of beach sandspurry are whorled and sharp-pointed; fruits have barely winged margins.

Beach sandspurry is a stout, perennial herb with a thick, woody root. Flowers have dark pink to occasionally white petals with 9-10 stamens, and are borne on terminal cymes, 5-9 mm long.

- stems covered with glands, hairy, to 40 cm long, 1-3 mm thick
- leaves appearing whorled or bundled, fleshy, long-narrow-linear, sharply pointed, 1-4 cm long,
- stipules 4.5-11 mm long
- petals usually much shorter than sepals; sepals covered with glands, hairy
- capsules 3.5-5.5 mm long; seeds smooth, flattened, reddish brown, 0.6-0.9 mm long, barely winged, with ring-like swellings

Habitat: Beach sandspurry is common along coastal beaches, salt marshes, and sea bluffs.

Range: Beach sandspurry is a native of North America. It is found along the coast from British Columbia to Baja California, and inland in the southern portion of the range.

Spergularia marina var. *marina*
saltmarsh sandspurry

Status: OBL

Color photo page 236

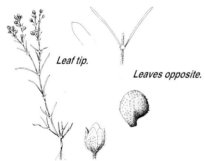

Leaf tip.

Leaves opposite.

Saltmarsh sandspurry has opposite leaves with sharp-pointed tips; fruits lack wings but have a knob at the base.

Saltmarsh sandspurry is a fleshy, many-branched, non-native annual herb. The inflorescence, which is either a terminal cyme or solitary flowers borne

in the leaf axils, is hairy and covered with glands. Flowers have white to pink petals and 2-5 stamens. Blooms May to August.

- stems sprawling, covered with glands, hairy, 5-30 cm long
- leaves fleshy, nearly hairless, with sharp-pointed tips, 2-4 cm long
- stipules triangular, torn-tipped, 1-3 mm long
- petals slightly shorter than sepals
- capsules 2.8-6.4 mm long; seeds brown, 0.3-0.8 mm long, covered with glands, lacking wings, with a small-knobbed base

Habitat: Common along the seashore, in salt marshes, mud flats, and alkaline sites in the interior. Common associates are pickleweed and fleshy jaumea.

Range: Native of Eurasia; grows from southern California to Washington and inland to Rocky Mountain states; also in the eastern United States and South America.

Spiranthes romanzoffiana
hooded ladies'-tresses

Family: Orchidaceae
Status: FACW

Hooded ladies'-tresses is one of two genera of orchids found in wetlands in the Puget Basin. The inflorescence of spiraling rows of flowers resembles braided hair. Leaves are linear with a pointed tip at the base of the plant, then turn into lance-shaped bracts further up the stem. Flowers are borne on the stem directly above the bracts. Blooms June to August.

- roots tuberous
- perennial herb 10-60 cm tall
- 1-4 vertical rows of flowers spiral around the central stem
- flowers waxen, cream-colored, sweetly scented, about 1 cm long

Habitat: Grows in wet meadows and along streams. Also common in disturbed sites.

Range: Across the boreal and northern temperate climate region in North America. Occurring in all counties in our area from sea level to above 1300 m.

Similar Species: The spiraling nature of the white-flowered inflorescence and the stem leaves distinguish hooded ladies'-tresses from the other, rarer orchids found in our area. Two less common species found in the Pacific Northwest are slender bog-orchid *(Platanthera saccata)* and bog candle *(Plantanthera dilatata)*. The flowers of these orchids have a distinct spurred lip that is lacking in hooded ladies'-tresses and do not spiral around the stem. The leaves of slender bog-orchid are elliptical and those of bog candle are round-tipped.

HERBS

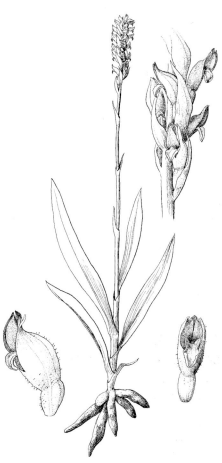

Hooded ladies'-tresses has tuberous roots and cream-colored flowers that are borne in a spiral around a terminal spike.

Spirodela polyrhiza
large duckweed; duckmeat

Family: Lemnaceae

Status: OBL

Large duckweed has flat leaves from which hang many thread-like roots; leaves have a distinctive purple dot in the center of the upper surface.

Large duckweed is an unbranched, small aquatic plant that is occasionally seen floating with other duckweeds, usually where the water is calm and nutrient-rich. It rarely forms dense colonies. Flowers are rare, minute, and sheathed in a pouch on the edge of the plant. When present, flowers are in clusters of 3. Large duckweed usually reproduces vegetatively by growing new "fronds" or forming small aggregates.

- roots 5-16, in cluster on undersides of leaves
- plant flat, disk-like (round to oval), the size of a pencil eraser (5-10 mm long, 6 mm wide), with 5-11 nerves
- upper leaf surface bright green with small purple dot in center; leaf undersides with minute, purplish, warty projections; with 5-11 obvious veins

Habitat: Favors partly shady or sunny ponds, marshes, slow-moving streams, backwaters, sloughs, ditches, canals, and agricultural impoundments. Often found in nutrient-rich waters growing in mats that are a mixture of large duckweed, water-ferns *(Azolla* species), small duckweed *(Lemna minor)*, and water-meals *(Wolffia* species).

Range: A widespread aquatic plant dispersed by currents, waterbirds, and boats. Large duckweed is found from southern Canada to the tropics, and across the continent from the Atlantic to the Pacific. In our area it occurs in freshwater systems from the coast to moderate elevations.

Similar Species: Small duckweed has smaller (2-5 mm), 3-nerved leaves with only one root on the undersides and lacking a purple dot. Water-meals are easily distinguished from large duckweed by their much smaller size. Water-ferns have leaves that are not circular and grow in long chains. Different leaved water-starwort *(Callitriche heterophylla)* can appear to have floating leaves in shallow standing water.

Functional Value: Large duckweed mats can cover the surface of the water, providing food and cover for many invertebrates and other small aquatic creatures. Ducks consume giant duckweed, but it is not as important as the more abundant lesser duckweed. Fish are not known to graze on it.

Ethnobotanical Uses: Rarely cultivated in aquatic settings as a curiosity.

Stachys cooleyae
Cooley hedgenettle; great betony

Family: Lamiaceae (Labiatae)
Status: FACW
Color photo page 236

The simple (unbranched) stem and leaves of this rhizomatous perennial herb are covered with long bristly hairs. An aromatic member of the mint family, Cooley hedgenettle has an "unminty" and, to most noses, a distinctly musky odor when the leaves or stems are crushed. Flowers are borne in terminal spikes to 150 cm tall. Blooms June to August.

- stems unbranched, square, 0.7-1.5 m tall
- leaves opposite, toothed, broadly lance-shaped, covered with bristly hairs on both sides, 6-16 cm long
- flowers deep magenta (purple-red), fused into a 2-lipped, hairy, irregular tube, 2-4 cm long
- sepals fused into a tube with 5 bristly tips

Habitat: Forms small patches in open to semi-shaded, moist, or saturated depressions; usually in forest understories. Prefers muck and highly organic soils to peat soils.

Range: Cooley hedgenettle grows from southern British Columbia to southern Oregon, from the coast up to about 1,300 m elevation in the Cascade Mountains. Occurs from the coast to the base of the east slope of the Cascades in Washington, but is restricted to the west side in Oregon. Found in all counties in our area.

Similar Species: No other mint has such a musky odor, bristly stems, and a terminal spike inflorescence composed of magenta flowers. Stinging nettle *(Urtica dioica)* also has unbranched stems and opposite leaves that are covered with bristly hairs; however, the tiny, greenish flowers are clustered on stems that grow from the axils of the leaves, and the hairs are stinging. In addition, stinging nettle generally grows on drier sites and is more common.

Functional Value: Cooley hedgenettle has attractive foliage and flowers. It transplants well and is tolerant of disturbance, making it useful for wetland creation, enhancement, and restoration. The purple-red flowers attract hummingbirds.

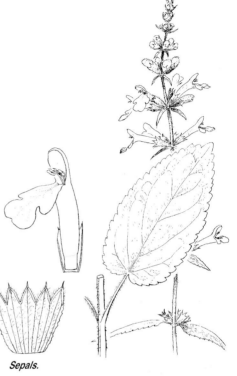

Sepals.

Cooley hedgenettle has square, bristly stems, and fused, 2-lipped flowers that are borne in a terminal spike.

Ethnobotanical Uses: Pojar and McKinnon (1994) report the Saanich Indians made a spring tonic by steeping crushed rhizomes in hot water, and local Puget Sound Native American groups used the plant for healing boils. Although Haida children on the Queen Charlotte Islands used to chew the stems, sucking the juice and spitting out the fiber, other groups did not consider Cooley hedgenettle edible. Several groups regard it as the half-brother of stinging nettle, referring to their resemblance to one another.

HERBS

Genus: *Stellaria*
chickweeds
Family: Caryophyllaceae

Chickweeds are succulent, spreading, perennial herbs with slender rhizomes. Leaves are opposite and attached directly to long trailing stems. Flowers appear singly in leaf axils or are arranged in a cyme and held on slender stalks of varying lengths. Flowers are white and very small (1-2 mm long); they often lack petals, but have 5 sepals that are 3-nerved with dry margins. Fruits are an oval to cylindrical capsule.

Similar Species: Sea-milkwort *(Glaux maritima)* is similar to saltmarsh chickweed, but the flowers of sea-milkwort are attached directly to the stalk.

Ethnobotanical Uses: The chickweeds are reportedly excellent in salads and widely used for such in Europe. You'll not need to add salt to saltmarsh chickweed salads.

Stellaria crispa
curly chickweed, crisp starwort
Status: FAC

Curly chickweed has leaves with curly margins.

at tip, 10-20 mm long, with transparent, wavy margins
* flower stalks 5-20 mm long, emerging from leaf axils and stem tips
* sepals lance-shaped, 2.5-4 cm long; petals lacking
* capsule oval and nearly 2x as long as sepals; seeds very lightly wrinkled and warty

Curly chickweed plants have spreading stems that often form dense mats. Lower leaves are held on short stalks. Flowers are borne singly. Sepals are lance-shaped and 2.5-3.5 mm long. Blooms late May and early August.

* stems hairless and weak, seldom branched, 10-50 cm long
* leaves lance-shaped to oval, sharply pointed

Habitat: Curly chickweed occurs in moist areas, mostly in lowlands or lower montane woods. It prefers very moist to wet nitrogen-rich soils, and is found sporadically to plentifully on water-collecting sites in broad-leaved forests, and occasionally inhabits disturbed sites; ranges from shade-tolerant to shade-intolerant.

Range: Curly chickweed occurs from Alaska to California, east to Alberta, Montana, and Wyoming.

Stellaria humifusa
saltmarsh chickweed
Status: OBL

Any small, delicate plant with tiny chickweed-like flowers found in a salt marsh will most likely be saltmarsh chickweed. Flowers are usually borne singly in the leaf axils.

- stems normally less than 5-40 cm long, yellow-green, hairless
- leaves attached directly to stem, lance-shaped to oblong, slightly fleshy, 6-12 mm long
- flower stalks 5-15 mm long, stout
- petals slightly longer than sepals (4-5 mm)
- capsule egg-shaped, as long as sepals; seeds very lightly wrinkled and warty

Habitat: Saltmarsh chickweed is quite common in high salt marshes, but never as a dominant plant. It may be found nestled among many other species, such as the bentgrasses *(Agrostis* species), Pacific silverweed *(Potentilla anserina)*, and tufted hairgrass *(Deschampsia caespitosa)*.

Range: Saltmarsh chickweed is circumpolar; Alaska to Labrador and south along the west coast to Oregon.

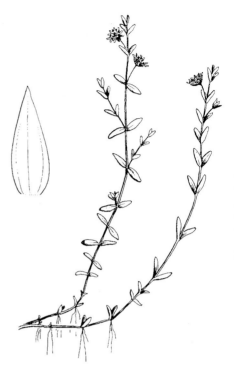

Saltmarsh chickweed has yellow-green stems and grows in salt marshes; leaves are oblong to lance-shaped.

HERBS

chickweeds continued on next page...

Stellaria longifolia
longleaf chickweed, longleaf starwort
Status: FACW

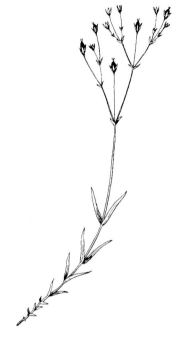

Longleaf chickweed has square stems, linear leaves, and terminal flowers.

Longleaf chickweed bears few to many flowers in terminal cymes that originate at the bracts and are membranous to somewhat leafy. Flowers from May to August.

- stems 60 cm long, 4-angled, hairless
- leaves 15-35 cm long, linear to lance-shaped to linear, sharply pointed at each end, hairless or with a few basal tufts
- flower stalks 5-20 mm long, spreading
- 5-petals, 3-4.5 mm long, usually equaling or slightly exceeding the sepals
- sepals 3-4 mm long, smooth-surfaced, narrowly elliptic-lance-shaped
- capsule greenish yellow, oval, slightly shorter than sepals; seeds smooth

Habitat: Longleaf chickweed occurs along stream banks and in meadows.

Range: Longleaf chickweed is found from Alaska to Newfoundland, south to California, New Mexico, and South Carolina; also found in Eurasia.

Genus: *Streptopus*
twisted-stalks
Family: Liliaceae

The twisted-stalk species are erect, somewhat succulent, rhizomatous, perennial herbs. Leaves are alternate, have parallel veins, and are attached directly to the stem. Flowers are bell-shaped, composed of 6 small tepals (petals + sepals), and hang under the leaves from slender stalks that attach to the stem at the leaf axils.

Similar Species: False solomon's seal *(Smilacina* species) also has a similar leaf arrangement but the inflorescence is a terminal panicle or raceme. Fairybells *(Disporum* species) have alternate, heart-shaped leaves that are strongly oblique at the base. The flowers of fairybells are also solitary on drooping, short stalks, but they are borne at the ends of the branches and the entire plant is sparse to very hairy.

Streptopus amplexifolius var. *americanus*
claspleaf twisted-stalk
Status: FAC-
Color photo page 236

HERBS

Stems are 50-120 cm long and very succulent. Leaves are 5-14 cm long, oval to oblong-lance-shaped, clasping around the stem, with veins that are not obvious. The slender flower stalks are 1- to 2-flowered. Blooms May to July.

- stems twisted in a distinctly zig-zag pattern, freely branching, coarsely hairy below on the first branches
- flowers hanging on thin, sharply bent, gland-bearing stalks 9-15 mm long
- tepals white- to green-tinged, 9-15 mm long, tips flaring and bending back
- berries yellow-red or dark purple, oval to oblong, 10-15 mm long, also on sharply bent stalks

Habitat: Grows in moist forests, along stream banks, in clearings and mountain thickets, mostly at 1000-2000 m. Common lowland associates include fir *(Abies* species), lady fern *(Athyrium filix-femina)*, oak fern *(Gymnocarpium dryopteris)*, thimbleberry *(Rubus parviflorus)*, salmonberry *(Rubus spectabilis)*, and three-leaf foamflower *(Tiarella trifoliata)*.

This species has branching flowering stalks that are bent in a zig-zag pattern; leaves are clasping and succulent.

Range: Occurs from Alaska south in the Cascade and Olympic mountains of Washington to the north Cascade and coastal mountains of Oregon. Claspleaf twisted-stalk is found east in northern Canada to the Great Lakes region, and most of eastern United States.

Ethnobotanical Uses: Whole plants and roots of claspleaf twisted-stalk were used by Native Americans as a scent and applied to fishing nets to improve fish catch.

Twisted-stalks continued on next page...

Streptopus roseus var. *curvipes*
rosy twisted-stalk
Status: not listed (facu-)

Stems are 15-30 cm tall. Leaves are 5-9 cm long, oval to elliptic, and not clasping around the stem. The thin flower stalks, which are hidden by the leaves, are 1-flowered or occasionally 2-flowered, 9-20 mm long, not bent, and sparsely hairy. Blooms in June and July.

- stems single, unbranched, straight, with sparse hairs at nodes
- leaves shiny below
- flowers hanging on thin, straight (nonbending), sparsely hairy stalks
- tepals white to rose or reddish purple
- berries red, bulbous and oblong, 5 mm long

Habitat: Same as claspleaf twisted-stalk.

Range: Occurs from Alaska south in the Cascade and Olympic mountains of Washington to the north Cascade and coastal mountains of Oregon. Rosy twisted-stalk is found only east to southeast British Columbia.

Rosy twisted-stalk has straight, unbranched flowering stems; leaves are shiny and nonclasping.

Tiarella trifoliata
three-leaf foamflower, coolwort; false mitrewort; lace flower

Family: Saxifragaceae
Status: FAC-
Color photo page 236

Three-leaf foamflower is a rhizomatous, perennial herb that grows 15-60 cm tall. Stems are erect, hairy, and covered with glands. Small leaves occur on the lower half of the stem and are held on long stalks. The inflorescence is a long, delicate, terminal spike. Flowers have 5 petals and 10 stamens. Blooms from May through August.

- leaves bright green, compound with 3 leaflets (trifoliate); leaflets irregular and deeply toothed, 2-7 cm long, with sparse hairs
- flowers white, tiny (2 mm long), narrowly-tube shaped, several to many along the stalk
- fruits small capsules that split to form 2 scoop-shaped halves; seeds black, shiny

Habitat: Grows in damp woods, especially along stream banks and forested roads.

Range: Aleutian Islands south through Alaska to northern Oregon. From coast to 1,000 m in the Cascades. East in British Columbia to the Rockies, south through Montana, western Idaho. Not found in eastern Washington or Oregon. Throughout all counties in our area.

Similar Species: Three-leaf foamflower has three distinct varieties. The common variety, which occurs at low elevation, is described above. A second variety is found at higher elevations and has simple, maple-shaped leaves. The third variety has leaves that are both lobed and deeply cleft and appear much more dissected than the common variety. Piggy-back plant *(Tolmiea menziesii)* has a similar basal growth form and terminal flower cluster, but leaves are shallowly 5- to 7-lobed, and flowers are larger (9-14 mm long) and chocolate-colored. Fringecup *(Tellima grandiflora)* also has a similar basal growth form, bright green leaves, and terminal, spike-like flower cluster, but flowers are yellow-green (sometimes pinkish), 6-8 mm long, cup-shaped, and with lace-like petals that are curved backwards. In addition, fringecup is an upland species.

These plants form a basal, rhizomatous clump. They have compound leaves with 3 leaflets and tiny, white flowers.

HERBS

Tolmiea menziesii
piggy-back plant; youth-on-age; thousand mothers

Family: Saxifragaceae
Status: FAC
Color photo page 236

This species has coarsely toothed, heart-shaped leaves and small, purple to brown flowers. Plantlets emerge from the leaf base.

Inflorescence is a terminal, spike-like cluster, bearing tube-shaped flowers. Blooms from May through August.

- leaves bright green, shallowly 5- to 7-lobed, heart-shaped
- flowers green-purple to chocolate-colored, medium-sized (9-14 mm long), with 4 petals and 3 stamens
- fruits a 2-beaked capsule longer than the sepals

Habitat: Piggyback-plant is found in moist dark woods, especially on the muddy banks of shallow streams.

Range: Southern Alaska along the west coast to Santa Cruz, California. Found only rarely east of the Cascades. Occurs in all counties in our area.

Similar Species: Three-leaf foamflower *(Tiarella trifoliata)* has a similar basal growth form, bright green leaves, and terminal, spike-like flower cluster, but leaves are compound with 3 leaflets and flowers are minute and white. White fringecup *(Tellima grandiflora)* has similar basal, bright green, lobed leaves, and erect terminal spikes, the leaves are round, flowers are yellow-green (sometimes pinkish), large (6-8 mm), cup-shaped with lace-like petals that curve backwards, and it grows in drier areas.

Piggyback-plant is a hairy, rhizomatous, perennial herb. Flower stems emerge from a basal grouping of leaves, grow to 80 cm tall, and are covered with glands in addition to being hairy. Leaves are palmately veined, 10 cm wide, 8 cm long, with margins once or twice shallowly toothed. They are borne on long (7-20 cm) stalks. Plants reproduce vegetatively by developing buds at base of the leaf blade where the leaf stalk emerges. These little plantlets can root if the leaf touches the ground.

Trientalis arctica
(Trientalis europaea ssp. arctica)
arctic starflower

Family: Primulaceae
Status: OBL
Color photo page 236

Arctic starflower is a hairless, perennial, rhizomatous herb commonly found in forested areas. Small tubers (less than 1 cm long) develop on the roots. Plants are low-growing (5-20 cm tall), occurring either singly or in small groups, and occasionally forming a mat or carpet on the forest floor. Leaves are oval to elliptical with both ends rounded, 4-8 cm long, and 2.5-5 cm wide. Stems are slender with terminal 6-petaled flowers. Blooms from May through August.

- leaves indistinctly whorled in one grouping of 4-6, borne on 1-4 mm long stalks; there are a few, alternate, reduced leaves at base of stem below whorled leaves
- flowers few, star-like, white (occasionally pink-tinged), 12-16 mm wide, borne on short, slender stalks, petals fused at the base
- fruits dry, 5-chambered capsules, with few globose seeds

Habitat: Arctic starflower is common in bogs and emergent shrub and forested wetlands.

Range: A native North America species, arctic starflower occurs from Alaska to Alberta, British Columbia to northern Idaho; also in the Cascade Mountains. Arctic starflower is common along the coast in Washington and Oregon; present in all counties in our area.

Similar Species: Broad-leafed starflower *(Trientalis latifolia)* has no reduced leaves below an obviously whorled set of leaves, flowers that are 8-12 mm broad and pink to rose-colored, and larger tubers (1-2 cm long) on the roots. In addi-

The flowers of this delicate plant are borne on two stalks that emerge from the whorled leaves.

tion, this species inhabits drier open forests, thickets, and meadows, and is commonly found throughout our drier western Cascade forests.

Ethnobotanical Uses: The broad tubers that form on the roots of broad-leafed starflower were reportedly collected and eaten by some Northwest native groups, but it is not known if the small tubers of arctic starflower were consumed.

HERBS

Genus: *Trifolium*
clover

Family: Fabaceae (Leguminosae)

Clovers are perennial herbs that have palmately compound, bright green leaves with three leaflets (trifoliate). All species have the distinctive, round flower heads composed of many, small, pea-like flowers. Fruits are inconspicuous pods containing a few, small, pea-like seeds. Species are distinguished from each other by their growth habit, root type, leaf shape and size, and flower head color and size.

Similar Species: Birdsfoot trefoil *(Lotus corniculatus)*, another herb belonging to the pea family, has 5 leaflets, yellow flowers, and the fruits resembling a bird's foot which expel their seeds when dry.

Functional Value: All clovers have nitrogen-fixing bacteria in root nodules that enrich the soil. Because clovers establish quickly, they are a good species for erosion prevention and are often used in hydroseed mixes. Small rodents eat the blossoms and leaves, and hummingbirds feed on the nectar.

Ethnobotanical Uses: Cooked clover roots and leaves are edible (soaking in salt water aids digestibility), and a tea may be brewed from dried flowers. Red and white clover are cultivated for hay and silage, especially in soils too wet or acid for alfalfa, and are included in many pasture seed mixes. Red clover is the Vermont State flower. Marsh clover rhizomes when steamed or dried were an important food for some coastal Native Americans.

Trifolium pratense
red clover

Status: FACU

Color photo page 237

Red clover has erect, hairy stems that emerge from a tap root; leaves are elliptical and pointed; flowers are pink to purple.

Red clover is taprooted and short-lived. It has upright stems and is quite common in waste areas. The inflorescence is terminal above a pair of reduced leaves. The fruits are small, 2-seeded pods.

- plants hairy, erect, 20-60 cm tall, with several stems
- leaflets 1.5-3.5 cm long, narrowly oval to elliptical, with pale V marks across the base; tips are round
- flower heads large, 2-3 cm in diameter, on very short stems
- flowers pink to purple, 11-15 mm long, 50-200 per flower head

Habitat: Red clover grows in fields, pastures, along roadsides, and in disturbed areas. It thrives in soils that are well drained and frequently watered, but does not tolerate prolonged inundation.

Range: Red clover, a native of Europe, is found throughout our region and much of North America. Present in all counties in our area.

Trifolium repens
white clover
Status: FAC
Color photo page 237

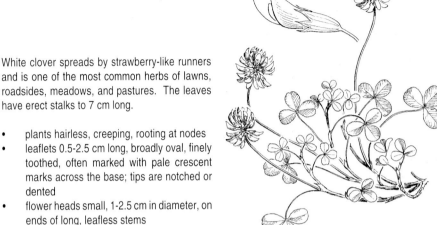

White clover spreads by strawberry-like runners and is one of the most common herbs of lawns, roadsides, meadows, and pastures. The leaves have erect stalks to 7 cm long.

- plants hairless, creeping, rooting at nodes
- leaflets 0.5-2.5 cm long, broadly oval, finely toothed, often marked with pale crescent marks across the base; tips are notched or dented
- flower heads small, 1-2.5 cm in diameter, on ends of long, leafless stems
- flowers white or light pink, 7-11 mm long, 20-40 per flower head

Habitat: White clover flourishes in relatively moist soils in full sun or part shade, where it often grows in extensive patches. Although it survives trampling, grazing, and mild drought, it will not tolerate prolonged saturation or inundation during the growing season. Associates of the red and white clovers include grasses and weedy herbs (dandelion, plantain).

White clover is stoloniferous with hairless stalks and oval leaves that have notched tips; flowers are white.

Range: White clover, a Eurasian native, is now established throughout our region and in North America from Alaska and Canada to Mexico. It is the most common and widespread clover in the Northwest. Present in all counties in our area.

HERBS

Clovers continued on next page...

Trifolium wormskjoldii
marsh clover; springbank clover
Status: FACW+
Color photo page 237

*Marsh clover is stoloniferous with hairless
stalks and long-oblong leaves with red
margins; flowers are red-purple.*

Marsh clover is a native coastal species with creeping roots and branched, creeping stems. Flower heads are held by saucer-shaped involucres with 8-12 toothed bracts. The fruits are small pods containing 2-6 seeds.

- plants hairless, low-growing, leafy-stemmed, 10-80 cm long
- leaflets 1-3 cm long, narrowly oval to lance-shaped, pointed-tipped, finely toothed, with red margins
- flower heads large, 2-3 cm in diameter, on short side stems
- flowers reddish purple or magenta, mostly white-tipped, 12-16 mm long, 2- to 5-flowered

Habitat: Marsh clover is found in wet and periodically inundated places, such as high salt and brackish marshes, coastal dunes, wet meadows, and stream banks. It is commonly associated with Pacific silverweed *(Potentilla anserina)*.

Range: Marsh clover is found from British Columbia to California and Mexico, and east to the Rocky Mountains; from coastal lowlands to lower montane.

Triglochin maritima
seaside arrowgrass

Family: Juncaginaceae
Status: OBL
Color photo page 237

The fleshy, succulent leaves of this perennial, coastal marsh herb are round to triangular in cross section, and grow in tufts from the root mat or from short rhizomes. Each leaf has a sheath that encircles the inner, older, and usually shorter leaves. Numerous, tiny, greenish or purple flowers are clustered along the upper third of the flowering stem. Blooms May to August.

- leaves basal, 10-80 cm long, half-round above base, with sheath extending to 1/3 of leaf length
- inflorescence an erect, spike-like, terminal cluster, 30-120 cm tall, extending well above leaves
- flowers small on short stalks, greenish with wine-red blush; stigmas red
- fruits dry, woody, splitting length-wise to reveal 6 seeds
- plants, when crushed, emitting a strong odor similar to cilantro

Habitat: Common in low salt or brackish tidal marshes, seaside arrowgrass is a mudflat colonizer. Persists as a minor component of high marshes. In salt marshes, it is frequently associated with pickleweed *(Salicornia virginica)*, fleshy jaumea *(Jaumea carnosa)* and Lyngby sedge *(Carex lyngbyei)*. In lower intertidal areas plants do not persist in winter as the aboveground portion is removed by tidal waters.

Range: Occurs along entire West Coast of the United States, and throughout Eurasia.

Similar Species: Seaside arrowgrass is much more common than other arrowgrass species in our area. Marsh arrowgrass *(Triglochin palustre)* and graceful arrowgrass *(Triglochin concinnum)* are generally less than 30 cm tall (although both can exceed that) and have leaves that remain round above the base. Seaside plantain *(Plantago maritima)* grows from a taproot, has shorter leaves, to 30 cm, and a

Seaside arrowgrass is a tufted, estuarine plant with triangular stems and tiny, greenish flowers that are scattered along a tall spike.

flowering spike that is shorter than the leaves (to 10 cm tall).

Functional Value: Heavily grazed by waterfowl. Traps sediment to prevent erosion of salt marsh edges, which helps salt marsh expansion.

Ethnobotanical Uses: The inner leaf bases were consumed by Native coastal peoples as a spring food. The seeds were parched and used for flour. It is now known the plants contain hydrocyanic acid, a toxin, and should not be eaten. Livestock have died after consuming seaside arrowgrass. European settlers roasted the seeds as a substitute for coffee. It was wise of them to roast the seeds because the toxin is volatilized on heating.

HERBS

Genus: *Typha*
cattails
Family: Typhaceae

Cattails are herbaceous perennials that grow to 3 m tall in standing water. The stems are erect, cylindrical, pithy, and to 5 cm thick in common cattail *(Typha latifolia)*. Leaves are alternate, linear, flat, and convex on the outer surface. Plants have separate male and female flowers that are borne on the characteristic cylindrical, spike-like "cat tails" terminating the flowering stems. Male flowers occur above the female flowers but the male flowers and spike wither shortly after flowering. The female inflorescence turns brown at maturity and is shed as a brown-tipped fluff that blows away in the wind. Fruits are about 1 mm long and elliptical, and carried on long slender hairs. Blooms June to July.

Similar Species: When not in flower, the emergent vegetation of yellow iris *(Iris pseudacorus)* looks very similar to both common and narrowleaf cattail. Yellow iris leaves have a flattened leaf sheath, grow only to 1 m long, are wider (25-35 mm), and have leaf tips that are more rounded.

Ethnobotanical Uses: An important component in the culture of indigenous people around the world. To the Coast Salish of the Pacific Northwest, cattail provided the most important mat-making material beside tule *(Scirpus acutus)*. Stems were sewn together with nettle or typha twine to form kneeling pads and mats for insulating walls of winter houses. Leaves were woven either into mats for sitting, door and window coverings, or into baskets, bags, capes, hats, and headdresses. Cattail fluff (female flowers) was collected and used as pillow stuffing, spun with dog wool into blankets, or used as absorbent material in diapers. The large rhizomes were considered a delicacy and eaten raw, but caution should be taken not to confuse it with the toxic rhizomes of yellow iris.

Typha angustifolia
narrowleaf cattail; lesser cattail
Status: OBL

- stems to 1.5 m tall
- leaves 5 mm broad, 60 cm long, and deep green
- male flowers separated from female flowers by a bare 0.5-4 cm stalk
- female inflorescence to 15 mm thick, with a thin bract attached below

Habitat: Narrowleaf cattail occurs in shallow, quiet to slow-moving, fresh to brackish waters of marshes, bays, and lagoons. It often forms extensive, almost exclusive, stands. When growing with common cattail, narrowleaf cattail moves into deeper water.

Range: Narrowleaf cattail is found along the Atlantic Coast, west to Colorado, Nebraska, Missouri and occasionally to Wyoming, Montana and eastern Washington. It is currently migrating into the Southwest and along the Pacific Coast with isolated populations in Arizona, Utah, Nevada, California, and Oregon. Recent sightings at the lower Columbia River estuary and in coastal counties, especially Thurston and Pierce in southwest Washington.

The male flowers of narrowleaf cattail are divided from the female flowers by a section of naked stem.

Typha latifolia
common cattail; broad-leaf cattail

Status: OBL

Color photo page 237

- stems 1-3 m tall, growing from extensive creeping rhizomes
- leaves mostly 8-20 mm broad, 1.5 m long, rather spongy, sheathing, grayish green
- male flowers borne directly above female flowers without an intervening bare stalk
- female inflorescence 12-30 mm thick

Habitat: Common cattail is widespread in predominantly freshwater communities including shallow bays, sloughs, marshes, springy places, ditches, and swales. Common cattail frequently produces extensive single-species stands.

Range: Common cattail, a native, occurs from Alaska to Mexico, east in most of southern Canada, and throughout the United States, Mexico, Eurasia, and northern Africa. It may be found in all counties in our area.

The male flowers of common cattail are attached to the stalk directly above the female flowers.

HERBS

Urtica dioica ssp. *gracilis* var. *lyallii*
stinging nettle

Family: Urticaceae
Status: FAC+
Color photo page 237

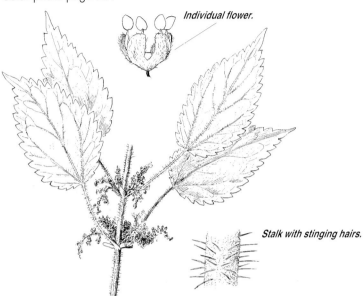

Individual flower.

Stalk with stinging hairs.

Stinging nettle has square stems and tiny flowers that are borne in clusters from the leaf axils.

Although stinging nettle grows to 3 m tall, it is most often felt before it is seen. Hairs on the leaves and stem inject formic acid into the skin, causing a stinging sensation that may last from hours to several days. It is a perennial herb that spreads rapidly from shallow rhizomes.

* stems usually unbranched, square, and with many stinging hairs
* leaves opposite, lance-shaped to oval or with a notched base, to 15 cm long, with stipules 5-15 mm long, toothed along margins, with stinging hairs mostly on the bottom surface
* flowers small, green to reddish, borne in drooping clusters at leaf axils

Habitat: Grows in moist, nitrogen-rich areas from deep woods to sagebrush desert. Though it prefers open, rich forests, this plant is often found in disturbed sites and can dominate large areas.

Range: Native of North America, it is found in much of the United States and Canada. This variety occurs in all counties on our area.

Similar Species: Cooley hedgenettle *(Stachys cooleyae)* also has unbranched, square stems and opposite leaves; however, hedgenettle species (members of the mint family) are unpleasantly aromatic, have large, tubular, purple flowers that are borne in a terminal spike, and, although the plant is covered with bristly hairs, they are not stinging. Cooley hedgenettle is less common than stinging nettle and does not grow in some of the drier habitat conditions that the nettle can tolerate. Mad-dog skullcap *(Scutellaria lateriflora)* resembles stinging nettle in growth form, but lacks hairs, has blue to purple, tubular flowers, and is not as common as stinging nettle.

Ethnobotanical Uses: Young leaves of this plant have been steamed and eaten as a vegetable or pureed and used as a soup. The leaves can be used in herbal teas. The fibrous stems have been used to make a strong cord for weaving fishing gear and basketry by Native Americans.

Genus: *Utricularia*
bladderworts
Family: Lentibulariaceae

Both of these bladderworts are small, freshwater, aquatic perennial herbs that are free-floating and lack visible roots. The unique air sacs or bladder-like structures, found on the leaves and scattered along the stem, provide buoyancy and act as traps to capture small aquatic invertebrates. Leaves are alternate, thin, and finely divided. The tubular, yellow, 2-lipped flowers are clustered on a single stalk that emerges from the water.

Similar Species: May be confused with marestails *(Hippuris* species) or milfoils *(Myriophyllum* species) because of the finely divided leaves, but the bladders attached to the leaves distinguish bladderworts from all other aquatic plants.

Functional Value: Bladderwort is sometimes listed as wildlife food, but is generally considered to have little or no food value. The surface of the plant is utilized as habitat for animals and other plants.

Utricularia minor
small bladderwort; lesser bladderwort
Status: OBL

HERBS

Small bladderwort blooms June to September.

- stems less than 1 mm wide
- leaves 3-branched at the base
- bladders grow on leaf ends, but not on all leaves
- 2-9 flowers, each 4-12 mm long

Habitat: Small bladderwort occurs in bogs and shallow water. Associates include common cattail *(Typha latifolia)*, yellow pond-lily *(Nuphar luteum)*, and small duckweed *(Lemna minor)*.

Range: Circumboreal.

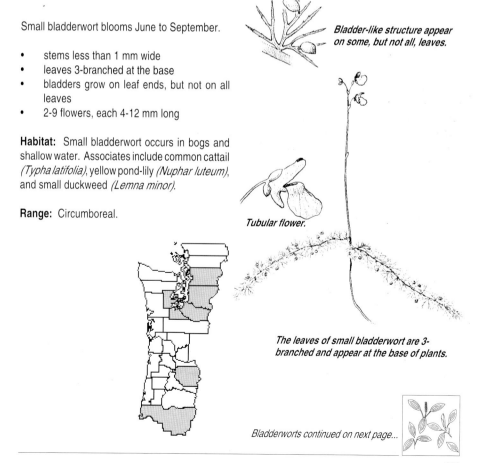

Bladder-like structure appear on some, but not all, leaves.

Tubular flower.

The leaves of small bladderwort are 3-branched and appear at the base of plants.

Bladderworts continued on next page...

213

Utricularia vulgaris ssp. *macrorhiza*
common bladderwort

Status: OBL color
photo page 238

The leaves of common bladderwort are 2-branched with bladder-like structure that grow along the center of the leaf segments.

Common bladderwort blooms June to August.

- stems about 1 mm wide
- leaves 2-branched at the base
- bladders grow along center of leaf segments
- 6-20 flowers, each 1-2 cm long

Habitat: Common bladderwort is commonly found in ponds and slow-moving streams. Associates include common cattail *(Typha latifolia)*, yellow pond-lily *(Nuphar luteum)*, and small duckweed *(Lemna minor)*.

Range: Circumboreal.

Vallisneria americana
American wild-celery, American tapegrass

Family: Hydrocharitaceae
Status: OBL

American wild-celery is a submerged, rhizomatous perennial herb. Stems are flexible and horizontal. The length of the stems and leaves is dependent on the water depth; leaves are variable; stems grow to 20 cm long. Male and female flowers occur on separate plants. Male flowers are tiny and have 1-3 petals, 3 sepals, and 2 stamens. Several hundred are borne on spathes at the base of the plant. Female flowers are white, solitary, with all parts in 3's (including stigmas). They are borne on the surface of the water on a spiraled stalk. Blooms from July to September.

- floating leaves, 10-50 cm long (sometimes longer), flat, ribbon-like, round-tipped, clustered in thick mats
- submerged leaves often reddish, finely toothed, with cross-walls visible as horizontal lines, 3-10 mm wide, with 1-3 parallel light-colored veins
- flowers free-floating when mature, on coiled stalks 1-2 m long
- fruits 5-10 cm long, cylindric

Habitat: Found from shore level to deep water of freshwater lakes and slow-moving streams; tolerates brackish water in its native range.

Range: Native from Quebec and Nova Scotia south to Texas and Florida; introduced in Dry Falls Coulee, Grant County and several lakes west of the Cascades.

Similar Species: The floating leaves of the burreed *(Sparganium* species) and Northern mannagrass *(Glyceria borealis)* lack prominent veins and cross-walls. In addition, the inflorescence of burreed is a globular head composed of hardened top-shaped achenes that fit together compactly, and mannagrass has a delicate, open, grass panicle.

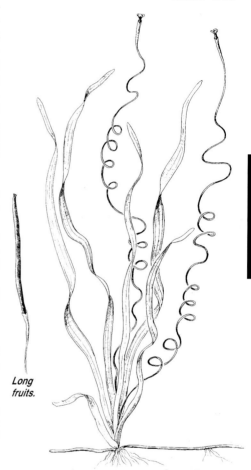

Long fruits.

The floating leaves of this species are ribbon-like; solitary, white, female flowers are borne on coiled stalks.

Functional Value: Protects the bottom of lakes and streams from currents and serves to stabilize the shore, as well as providing excellent food for waterfowl and cover for fish.

HERBS

215

Genus: *Veronica*
Family: Scrophulariaceae

These three veronicas are low-growing, perennial, rhizomatous, creeping herbs. They have stems that are more or less succulent and often tinged with red throughout the life of the plant. Leaves are simple, opposite, either on a short stalk or attached directly to the stem. The inflorescence is a raceme of few to numerous flowers that emerge from the leaf axils. Petals form saucer-shaped flowers, to 1 cm wide, on short stalks to 12 mm long, with sepals to 3 mm long. Flowers are violet-blue to lilac, 4-lobed, with 2 spreading stamens. Fruits are round capsules with many tiny seeds.

Similar Species: Young plants of Watson willowherb *(Epilobium ciliatum)* may appear similar to the speedwells, but the willowherb differs in having reddish green leaves and stems only when young, while the stems of the speedwells can remain red into maturity. Vegetative plants of water-purslane *(Ludwigia palustris)* also have reddish succulent stems and grow in shallow emergent wetlands, but the stems are erect, leaves are long-stemmed, mostly irregular in shape, to 2.5 cm long, and an olive-red color. Additionally, the flowers of water-purslane lack petals, and have 1-2 mm long sepals.

Veronica americana
American brooklime; American speedwell
Status: OBL
Color photo page 238

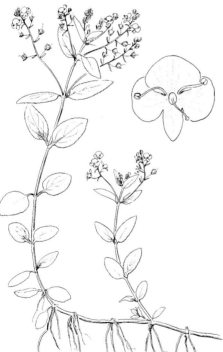

American brooklime is the most robust of the common veronicas with stems that are usually creeping and to 80 cm long. The fruits are generally shorter or nearly equal to the sepals. Blooms May to July.

- leaves oval to lance-shaped, 0.5-5 cm long and 1.5-8 cm wide, tapering and pointed, with finely toothed margins, borne on short stalks
- flowers bluish violet without white centers, 7-10 mm wide on 5-10 mm long stalks
- fruits heart-shaped to round capsules, 2-lobed, notched, 3-4 mm long

Habitat: Common in shallowly inundated freshwater wetlands (one to four inches deep), ditches, slow-moving water and shallow pools (palustrine emergent marsh). Favors saturated soils and can be found in association with many other low-growing, obligate freshwater plants, such as water-parsley *(Oenanthe sarmentosa)*, sedges, and rushes.

Range: Native to North America; common in western United States to Alaska. Present in all counties in our area.

The leaves of American brooklime are mostly oval to lance-shaped and borne on short stalks.

Veronica anagallis-aquatica
water veronica; water speedwell

Status: OBL

Water veronica is the least common and smallest of the wetland veronicas. Plants typically have stems that grow to 60 cm long. The fruits are shorter than the sepals. Blooms June to September.

- leaves lance-shaped to lance-oblong, 2-8 cm long, sharp-pointed, with smooth to finely toothed margins, attached directly to the stem and clasping
- flowers 5-10 mm wide
- fruits egg-shaped capsule, slightly 2-lobed, scarcely notched, 2.5-4 mm long and wide

Habitat: Same as American brooklime.

Range: Native to North America; common in western United States to Alaska.

Water veronica has lance-shaped leaves that attach directly to the stem.

Veronica species continued on next page.

HERBS

217

Veronica scutellata
marsh speedwell

Status: OBL

Color photo page 238

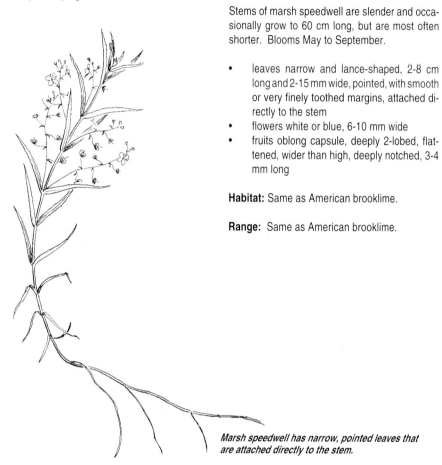

Stems of marsh speedwell are slender and occasionally grow to 60 cm long, but are most often shorter. Blooms May to September.

- leaves narrow and lance-shaped, 2-8 cm long and 2-15 mm wide, pointed, with smooth or very finely toothed margins, attached directly to the stem
- flowers white or blue, 6-10 mm wide
- fruits oblong capsule, deeply 2-lobed, flattened, wider than high, deeply notched, 3-4 mm long

Habitat: Same as American brooklime.

Range: Same as American brooklime.

Marsh speedwell has narrow, pointed leaves that are attached directly to the stem.

Genus: *Viola*
violets
Family: Violaceae

The wetland violets of the Pacific Northwest are small perennial herbs with stems that arise in clumps from rhizomes. Leaves are alternate, heart-shaped, simple, smooth (almost waxy), and have scalloped magins. Flowers are small and irregularly shaped with 5 sepals, 5 petals, and 5 stamens. The lowermost petal is spurred, larger than the others, and sac-like.

Similar Species: There are many species of violet in the region: most are found in moist forests and are not wetland species; many are found predominantly at midmontane to higher elevations. There are relatively few white-flowered species that are smooth-surfaced and stoloniferous, with leaves greater than 2.5 cm long, and flowers 8-10 mm long similar to marsh violet. Other yellow-flowered violets are either not rhizomatous, or have purple blotches beneath the leaf, such as redwood violet *(Viola sempervirens)*.

Ethnobotanical Uses: Young leaves and flower buds can be eaten raw in salads or used as potherbs. Slowly dried leaves can be used as a tea. The leaves and flowers were eaten as a possible prevention or cure of bronchial disorders.

HERBS

Viola glabella
stream violet
Status: FACW+
Color photo page 238

This yellow violet is one of the tallest violets in the region. Flowering stems have only one set of leaves, which occur at the top of the stem, near the flower. Basal leaves are borne on stalks 10-20 cm long. Blooms from March through July.

- rhizomes thick and scaly
- stems 5-30 cm tall
- stipules membranous, 5-10 mm long, oval
- leaves heart-shaped with a notched base and pointed tip, commonly hairy, with sharply toothed margins
- flowers yellow, 8-15 mm long, lower 3 petals with purple lines on the throat

Habitat: Stream violet grows in moist forests, in clearings, or along streams. It is found at all elevations.

Range: Stream violet is found from southeast Alaska to California, in the coastal ranges and the Sierra Nevada Mountains.

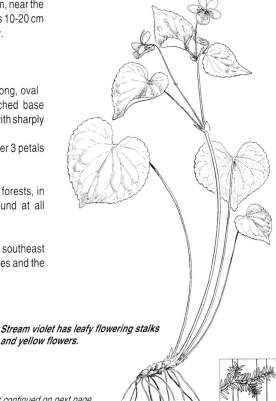

Stream violet has leafy flowering stalks and yellow flowers.

Violets continued on next page...

Viola palustris
marsh violet

Status: OBL

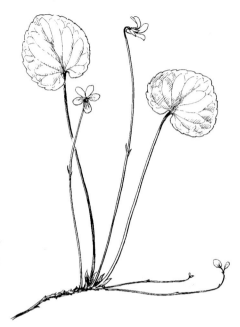

The flowering stalks of marsh violet are leafless and the flowers are white to violet.

- flowers and leaves arising independently from rhizomes
- stipules lance-shaped, smooth-margined, attached directly to the rhizomes
- leaves round with a heart-shaped base, 2.5-3.5 cm wide
- flowers white to lavender, 10-13 mm long, the lower 3 petals lilac-tinged with purple lines

Marsh violet grows from slender, widespread rhizomes and creeping stolons, but has no aerial stems. Basal leaves are borne on stalks to 15 cm long. Blooms from May through July.

Habitat: Marsh violet is common in sphagnum communities and also occurs in moist meadows, and along streams, in wet to very wet soils within boreal, wet temperate and cool temperate climates; intolerant of shade. Found at low to subalpine elevations.

Range: Marsh violet is found from British Columbia to California, east to the Rockies and northerly to Labrador and Maine. Both species occur in all counties in our area.

Xerophyllum tenax
beargrass

Family: Liliaceae
Status: Not listed (fac-)
Color photo page 238

Beargrass is an evergreen, perennial herb that forms dense clumps of persistent, wiry, basal leaves. Flowers are borne on long, slender stalks, and have six petal-like, persistent sepals and six stamens that exceed the length of the sepals.

- leaves grass-like, long (to 60 cm), 1.5-4 mm wide, minutely barbed on the margin
- flower stems erect, unbranched, with a dense tuft of leaves, to 150 cm tall
- inflorescence densely flowered terminal cluster with nipple-like top; bulb-shaped when immature, elongating to 50 cm when mature
- flowers cream-colored, saucer-shaped

Habitat: Grows in open woods and clearings from near sea level to over 2,300 m. Beargrass occurs in a variety of soil types ranging from well-drained pumice soil to clay and peat. It is somewhat dependent on fire for maximum flowering.

Range: British Columbia south to California, east to the Rocky Mountains, south to Montana and Idaho. Occurs in all counties in our area.

Similar Species: The densely clumped, evergreen, barbed-edged leaves and distinctive flowers are not like any other species.

Functional Value: Forage for large mammals (such as its namesake bear, elk, or mountain goats) and for smaller mammals.

Ethnobotanical Uses: The tough leaves are used in Northwest Native American basketry, especially for fine imbrication, trimming, and ornamentation. In addition, it is used as the weft in finely woven baskets and in making mats. Historically, beargrass leaves were a valuble trade item to tribes outside its growing range. It is being overcollected in mountainous areas for use in flower arrangements.

Flower cluster with nipple-like top.

HERBS

Beargrass leaves are grass-like with barbed margins.

221

Genus: *Zostera*
eelgrass

Family: Zosteraceae

Eelgrass *(Zostera marina)* and dwarf eelgrass *(Zostera nana)* are perennial herbs that grow submerged or partially floating in salt water. Both species grow well in sandy or muddy substrates throughout Puget Sound. They are often found associated with algae. They have upright stems that originate from a slender rhizone. Flowers are enclosed in a sheath that appears similar to the leaves. Seeds are enclosed in elongated, membranous, and translucent packets. Blooms June to August.

Similar Species: These eelgrass species may be confused with Scouler's surf-grass *(Phyllospadix scouleri)*, an uncommon marine plant, that has fleshy leaves that grow off a stout-woody rhizome, and has long, obvious inflorescences. In addition, surf-grass typically grows in high wave energy, rocky intertidal areas.

Functional Value: An argument could be made that eelgrass is the most important plant species of Northwest marine environments. Eelgrass communities are considered to be among the highest value habitats of any in the Pacific Northwest. Eelgrass leaves are a preferred substrate for deposition of herring eggs, which are the basis of a significant commercial industry in the Northwest. Eelgrass also constitutes the principal forage for black brant and other herbivorous waterfowl. Eelgrass communities provide refuge for marine animals and substrate for epiphytes and epifauna.

Ethnobotanical Uses: Extensive recreational crabbing occurs in and adjacent to eelgrass beds. Harvested leaves have been used as packing material for shipping fishery products.

Zostera marina
eelgrass

Status: OBL
Color photo page 238

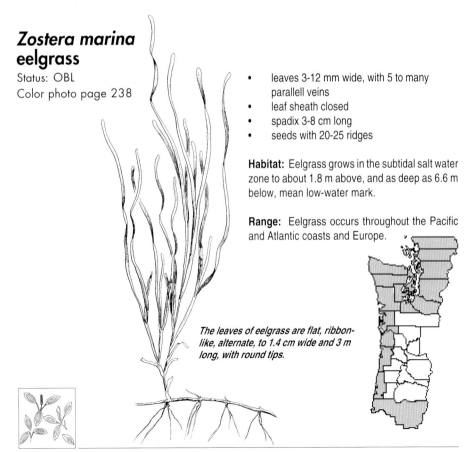

- leaves 3-12 mm wide, with 5 to many parallell veins
- leaf sheath closed
- spadix 3-8 cm long
- seeds with 20-25 ridges

Habitat: Eelgrass grows in the subtidal salt water zone to about 1.8 m above, and as deep as 6.6 m below, mean low-water mark.

Range: Eelgrass occurs throughout the Pacific and Atlantic coasts and Europe.

The leaves of eelgrass are flat, ribbon-like, alternate, to 1.4 cm wide and 3 m long, with round tips.

Zostera nana
dwarf eelgrass

Status: OBL
Color photo page 238

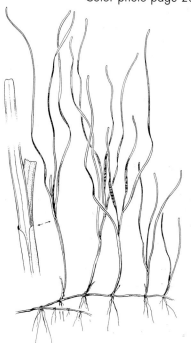

- leaves 1.5 mm wide with 3 parallel veins
- leaf sheath open to base
- spadix 3-6 cm
- seeds mostly smooth to slightly few-ridged

Habitat: Dwarf eelgrass occurs on mud flats between low and semi-high (1.0-2.4 m) tide.

Range: Dwarf eelgrass was introduced from Europe and is now common throughout Puget Sound and Pacific Northwest coastal estuaries. Particularly luxuriant communities exist in Padilla Bay, Willapa Bay, and Grays Harbor, Washington.

The leaves of dwarf eelgrass are 1.5 mm wide and do not exceed 15 cm long.

HERBS

Alisma plantago-aquatica (broadleaf water-plaintain)
Photo by Sarah Spear Cooke

Angelica genuflexa (kneeling angelica)
Photo by Binda Colebrook

Asarum caudatum (wild ginger)
Photo by Fred Weinmann

Aster subspicatus (Douglas aster)
Photo by Fred Weinmann

Bidens cernua (nodding beggarticks)
Photo by Al Hanners

Atriplex patula (fat-hen saltbush)
Photo by Dyanne Sheldon

Brasenia schreberi (watershield)
Photo by Sarah Spear Cooke

Cakile edentula (American searocket)
Photo by Clayton Antieau

Callitriche heterophylla (different leaved water-starwort)
Photo by Sarah Spear Cooke

Camassia quamash ssp. breviflora (common camas)
Photo by Binda Colebrook

Camassia quamash ssp. quamash (great camas)
Photo by Ron Vanbianchi

**Cirsium arvense & Cirsium Vulgare
(Canada thistle and common thistle)**
Photo by Sarah Spear Cooke

Cicuta douglasii (western water-hemlock)
Photo by Binda Colebrook

Conium maculatum (poison-hemlock)
Photo by Sarah Spear Cooke

Conium maculatum (poison-hemlock)
Photo by Sarah Spear Cooke

Cuscuta salina (salt-marsh dodder)
Photo by Clayton Antieau

Cotula coronopifolia (brassbuttons)
Photo by Fred Weinmann

Drosera rotundifolia (roundleaf sundew)
Photo by Al Hanners

Epilobium ciliatum ssp. watsonii (Watson willowherb)
Photo by Fred Weinmann

Galium aparine (cleavers bedstraw)
Photo by Sarah Spear Cooke

Galium trifidum (small bedstraw)
Photo by Binda Colebrook

Geum macrophyllum (largeleaf avens)
Photo by Sarah Spear Cooke

Glaux maritima (sea-milkwort)
Photo by Fred Weinmann

Gnaphalium uliginosum (marsh cudweed)
Photo by Sarah Spear Cooke

Grindelia integrifolia (Puget-Sound gumweed)
Photo by Fred Weinmann

Hippuris vulgaris (common marestail)
Photo by Sarah Spear Cooke

Honckenya peploides (seabeach sandwort)
Photo by Clayton Antieau

Hypericum anagalloides (bog St John's wort)
Photo by Sarah Spear Cooke

Impatiens capensis (spotted touch-me-not)
Photo by Sarah Spear Cooke

Impatiens noli-tangere (yellow touch-me-not)
Photo by Fred Weinmann

Iris pseudacorus (yellow iris)
Photo by Fred Weinmann

Jaumea carnosa (fleshy jaumea)
Photo by Fred Weinmann

Lemna minor (small duckweed)
Photo by Fred Weinmann

Lilaeopsis occidentalis (western lilaeopsis)
Photo by Vic Yoshino

Lotus corniculatus (birdsfoot trefoil)
Photo by Clayton Antieau

Ludwigia palustris (water-purslane)
Photo by Sarah Spear Cooke

Lycopus americanus (American bugleweed)
Photo by Fred Weinmann

Lysichiton americanum (skunk-cabbage)
Photo by Rick Pratt

Lythrum salicaria (purple loosestrife)
Photo by Vic Yoshino

Maianthemum dilatatum (wild lily-of-the-valley)
Photo by Sarah Spear Cooke

Mentha arvensis (field mint)
Photo by Binda Colebrook

Menyanthes trifoliata (buckbean)
Photo by Sarah Spear Cooke

Mimulus guttatus (common monkeyflower)
Photo by Fred Weinmann

Myosotis laxa (small water forget-me-not)
Photo by Fred Weinmann

Myriophyllum spicatum (Eurasian water-milfoil)
Photo by Fred Weinmann

Nuphar luteum (yellow pond-lily)
Photo by Ron Vanbianchi

Nymphaea odorata (white water lily)
Photo by Fred Weinmann

Oenanthe sarmentosa (water-parsley)
Photo by Sarah Spear Cooke

Petasites frigidus (sweet coltsfoot)
Photo by Sarah Spear Cooke

Plantago lanceolata (rib plantain)
Photo by Fred Weinmann

Plantago major (broadleaf plantain)
Photo by Fred Weinmann

Plantago maritima (seaside plantain)
Photo by Fred Weinmann

Polygonum amphibium (water ladysthumb)
Photo by Binda Colebrook

Polygonum cuspidatum (Japanese knotweed)
Photo by Al Hanners

Polygonum hydropiper (waterpepper)
Photo by Sarah Spear Cooke

Polygonum lapathifolium (willow smartweed)
Photo by Mike Zierke

Polygonum persicaria (ladysthumb)
Photo by Al Hanners

Potamogeton amplifolius (largeleaf pondweed)
Photo by Sarah Spear Cooke

Potamogeton
crispus
invasive
non-native
(introduced)

wrong

dyanne.sheldon
e otak . com

pondweed)

233

Potentilla anserina (Pacific silverweed)
Photo by Rick Pratt

Potentilla palustris (marsh cinquefoil)
Photo by Binda Colebrook

Ranunculus flammula (small creeping buttercup)
Photo by Sarah Spear Cooke

Ranunculus repens (creeping buttercup)
Photo by Fred Weinmann

Rorippa calycina (persistent-sepal yellow-cress)
Photo by Clayton Antieau

Rumex acetosella (sheep sorrel)
Photo by Fred Weinmann

Polygonum cuspidatum (Japanese knotweed)
Photo by Al Hanners

Polygonum hydropiper (waterpepper)
Photo by Sarah Spear Cooke

Polygonum lapathifolium (willow smartweed)
Photo by Mike Zierke

Polygonum persicaria (ladysthumb)
Photo by Al Hanners

Potamogeton amplifolius (largeleaf pondweed)
Photo by Sarah Spear Cooke

Potamogeton natans (floating-leaved pondweed)
Photo by Ron Vanbianchi

Potentilla palustris (marsh cinquefoil)
Photo by Binda Colebrook

Potentilla anserina (Pacific silverweed)
Photo by Rick Pratt

Ranunculus flammula (small creeping buttercup)
Photo by Sarah Spear Cooke

Ranunculus repens (creeping buttercup)
Photo by Fred Weinmann

Rorippa calycina (persistent-sepal yellow-cress)
Photo by Clayton Antieau

Rumex acetosella (sheep sorrel)
Photo by Fred Weinmann

Sagittaria latifolia (broadleaf arrowhead)
Photo by Al Hanners

Salicornia virginica (pickleweed)
Photo by Dyanne Sheldon

Scutellaria lateriflora (mad-dog skullcap)
Photo by Clayton Antieau

Sium suave (water-parsnip)
Photo by Binda Colebrook

Solanum dulcamara (bittersweet nightshade)
Photo by Fred Weinmann

Sparganium eurycarpum (giant burreed)
Photo by Marty Chaney

Spergularia marina (saltmarsh sandspurry)
Photo by Fred Weinmann

Stachys cooleyae (Cooley hedgenettle)
Photo by Sarah Spear Cooke

Tiarella trifoliata (three-leaf foamflower)
Photo by Ken Brunner

Streptopus amplexifolius (claspleaf twisted-stalk)
Photo by Fred Weinmann

Trientalis europaea (northern starflower)
Photo by Clayton Antieau

Tolmiea menziesii (piggy-back plant)
Photo by Al Hanners

Trifolium pratense (red clover)
Photo by Fred Weinmann

Trifolium repens (white clover)
Photo by Al Hanners

Trifolium wormskjoldii (marsh clover)
Photo by Fred Weinmann

Triglochin maritima (seaside arrowgrass)
Photo by Fred Weinmann

Typha latifolia (common cattail)
Photo by Dyanne Sheldon

Urtica dioica ssp. gracilis (stinging nettle)
Photo by Fred Weinmann

Utricularia vulgaris (common bladderwort)
Photo by Clayton Antieau

Veronica americana (American brooklime)
Photo by Binda Colebrook

Veronica scutellata (marsh speedwell)
Photo by Sarah Spear Cooke

Viola glabella (stream violet)
Photo by Fred Weinmann

Xerophyllum tenax (beargrass)
Photo by Clayton Antieau

*Zostera marina & Zostera japonica
(eelgrass & dwarf eelgrass)*
Photo by Fred Weinmann

Guide to Identifying the Rushes

Rushes are grass-like, mostly perennial herbs that usually grow in clumps in moist to wet areas. There are two genera of rushes discussed here – *Juncus* and *Luzula*. The few annual rushes are small and have very little root mass. Some rushes have green, thick, and straw-like stems with basal sheaths, and others have more grass-like blades that are flat, often hollow and filled with pith, or have visible cross partitions or darker green lines, called *septae*, across the width of the blade. *Leaf sheaths* are open at the base. *Leaves* are singly arranged or occasionally occur in alternate pairs; occasionally they are *equitant*, (sidewise-flattened and arranged in a fan-like manner), with the leaf margins turned toward the stem, as in iris. Often the leaves have transparent margins and prolonged, thin, and upward (not outward) appendages called *auricles* at the leaf/sheath junction. *Stems* are round to flattened. Each stem bears either a terminal or lateral-appearing inflorescence. The *inflorescence* is generally composed of *flower clusters*, which vary in number and consist of a few to many individual flowers. Some inflorescences are few-flowered and open or diffuse, while others are many-flowered and compact. Attached to the base or along the side of each inflorescence is an *involucral bract*, an appendage that appears to be either scale-like, leaf-like, or can extend stem-like beyond the inflorescence. Plants that appear to have a lateral inflorescence actually have a stem-like involucral bract. Flowers are small, have organs of both sexes, and are greenish or purplish to brown-black. The flower petals and sepals look the same and are called *tepals*. which number 6 in two groups of three. The inner 3 are often shorter than the outer 3, and the shape and the length of the tepals overall are helpful in distinguishing between species. Stamens number 1, 2, 3, or 6. The *style* is single with a 3-branched stigma. The size and shape of the *capsule* in relation to the tepals is another identifying feature. Each capsule contains many *(Juncus)* or 3 *(Luzula)* seeds per flower; the small seeds often have a long appendage on at least one end.

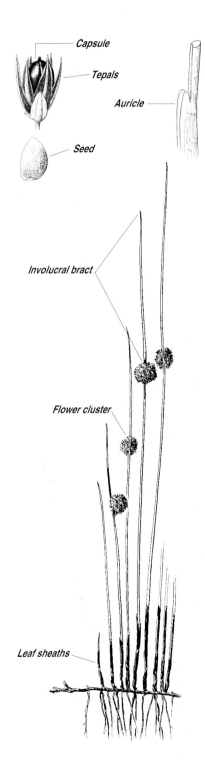

Capsule

Tepals

Auricle

Seed

Involucral bract

Flower cluster

Leaf sheaths

RUSHES

Functional Value: Rushes are used for nesting material, food, and shelter by many insects, birds, and small mammals. They are highly productive plants and can be responsible for a considerable amount of wetland plant material. They are believed to be valuable for removing excess nutrients and heavy metals from urban stormwater; as a result, they are often incorporated in wetland and bio-swale designs. Those species that are widely spreading and form continuous mats or thick clumps are especially useful for slowing surface water flows, allowing for settling of sediments.

Ethnobotanical Uses: The leaves of many rush species were used as thread by Native Americans and sewn into hide garments as decoration. They are still being used today for basketry.

Key to Identifying the *Juncus* Species

1a. Plants annual with very little root mass; generally less than 30 cm tall; leaves generally less than 1 mm wide; 1-3 flowers per flower cluster..2
1b. Plants perennial; often greater than 30 cm tall; leaves generally greater than 1 mm wide; flowers more than 3 per flower cluster...3

    2a. Plants less than 4 cm tall; 1-3 flowers per flower cluster................inch-high rush *(Juncus uncialis)*
    2b. Plants often greater than 4 cm tall; flowers single and scattered on inflorescence branches ....toad rush *(Juncus bufonius)*

    3a. Inflorescence apparently lateral; lowest involucral bract round in cross section, seemingly a continuation of the main stem..4
    3b. Inflorescence apparently terminal; lowest involucral bract flattened and channeled; shorter than or longer than inflorescence..7

        4a. Plants strongly tufted and rhizomatous; stems to 3 mm thick; tepals less than 3.5 mm..5
        4b. Plants strongly rhizomatous; stems often wiry, thin or to 5 mm thick; tepals often greater than 3.5 mm...6

            5a. Stamens usually 3; lowest involucral bract usually less than 1/3 length of stem; very common almost everywhere..soft rush *(Juncus effusus)*
            5b. Stamens usually 6; lowest involucral bract generally greater than 1/3 length of stem; found west of the Cascades in Oregon........................grooved rush *(Juncus patens)*

            6a. Plants of coastal dunes (interdunal swales); flowers congested into tight, 1-3 cm, round, head-like clusters; lowest involucral bract equal to the length of stem (i.e., flower clusters appear to be in the middle of the stem); tepals greater than 5 mm..salt rush *(Juncus lesueurii)*
            6b. Plants not restricted to coastal dunes, although common in brackish marshes near the coast; inflorescence more diffuse, open; involucral bracts often less than 1/2 length of stem (i.e., inflorescence appears higher up along the stem); tepals to 5 mm..Baltic rush *(Juncus balticus)*

        7a. Leaves flattened, equitant...8
        7b. Leaves rounded or flattened in cross section, not equitant...9

8a. Inflorescence compact; fewer than 10 flower clusters per inflorescence, each greater than 8 mm broad, appearing as black or dark brown balls...daggerleaf rush *(Juncus ensifolius)*

8b. Inflorescence open, diffuse; more than 10 flower clusters per inflorescence each less than 6 mm broad ....pointed rush *(Juncus oxymeris)*

9a. Leaves septate, round in cross section...10

9b. Leaves not septate, with flat/grooved surface facing stem...14

10a. Plants rooting at nodes (strawberry-like), forming a continuous carpet; leaves and stems thin..spreading rush *(Juncus supiniformis)*

10b. Plants rhizomatous or tufted, but not as above...11

11a. Plants very rhizomatous; tepals longer than capsule; stamens 6...Sierra rush *(Juncus nevadensis)*

11b. Plants tufted; rhizomes, if present, very short; tepals generally longer than capsule; stamens 3 or 6...12

12a. Tepals much smaller than capsule; less than 3 mm; stamens 6...jointed rush *(Juncus articulatus)*

12b. Tepals equal to or greater than capsule; more than 3 mm long; stamens 3 or 6...13

13a. Inflorescence open, diffuse; stamens 3................................... ....tapertip rush *(Juncus acuminatus)*

13b. Inflorescence round; stamens 6... ....Mertens' rush *(Juncus mertensianus)*

14a. Plants tufted; not restricted to coastal areas, common in disturbed sites......... ....slender rush *(Juncus tenuis)*

14b. Plants rhizomatous; coastal (salt marsh or sandy substrates)......................15

15a. Plants of coastal salt marshes; 30-70 cm tall; flower clusters usually many, in a diffuse inflorescence..............................mud rush *(Juncus gerardii)*

15b. Plants of sandy substrates (interdunal swales); generally less than 30 cm tall; flower cluster usually few, appearing as large rounded balls...sickleleaf rush *(Juncus falcatus)*

RUSHES

Juncus acuminatus
tapertip rush

Family: Juncaceae
Status: OBL
Color photo page 356

*bright
orange
Thioscales*

Tepals are equal in
length to capsule.

- leaves half-round in cross section, septate
- auricles present on leaf sheaths
- inflorescences diffuse with 3-30 flower clusters 5-8 mm long, each 5- to 20-flowered, obviously terminal, erect to ascending
- tepals straw-colored or greenish brown, 3-3.5 mm long, sharp-pointed
- stamens 3, occasionally 6
- capsules equal in length to the tepals, 3-angled, egg-shaped, tapering uniformly to a sharp tip
- seeds oblong, long-tapered, each end sharp-pointed

Habitat: In wet places such as ditches, lake margins, and meadows. The tapertip rush grows in open emergent systems that generally remain wet throughout the year. Associates include American brooklime *(Veronica americana)*, water-starwort *(Callitriche* species), toad rush *(Juncus bufonius)*, soft rush *(Juncus effusus)*, and sedges *(Carex* species).

Range: From southwest British Columbia south, mostly west of the Cascades, to California, east to southwest Idaho and Arizona, and throughout much of eastern North America from Minnesota to Texas and New Mexico, and from Nova Scotia to Florida.

Similar Species: The small inflorescences of pointed rush *(Juncus oxymeris)* are more diffuse and have 10-70 small flower clusters of 3-12 flowers. In addition, pointed rush is highly rhizomatous and has flattened leaf blades that lack obvious, continuous septae. The inflorescence of Sierra rush *(Juncus nevadensis)* is also diffuse, but bears fewer than 20 flower clusters, each in a tight clump, and tepals that are long and lance-shaped. Sierra rush is strongly rhizomatous, not tufted. Jointed rush *(Juncus articulatus)* has an inflorescence with more spreading branches, 6 stamens, and a round to oval capsule with a short, tapering, pointed tip that well exceeds the tepals. Mud rush *(Juncus gerardii)* also has a diffuse inflorescence, but tepal tips curl over, capsules are oval, seeds are oval and flat-topped, the leaves are not septate, and it is found only in salt marshes.

Tepertip rush is tufted and has leaves with
obvious auricles.

Tapertip rush is a 40-80 cm tall perennial that is mostly tufted, though it may have very short rhizomes and appear mat-like. Plants often have a reddish cast. The involucral bract is rather conspicuous, very short, and appears as a leafy spur at the base of each group of flower clusters. Blooms late May through August.

Juncus articulatus
jointed rush

Family: Juncaceae
Status: OBL
Color photo page 356

This tufted, grass-like perennial rush grows 15-50 cm tall from stout rhizomes and also roots from the lower leaf nodes. The involucral bract is shorter than the inflorescence and appears as a leafy spur at the base of the two lowest flower clusters. Blooms late June to August.

- leaves 1-3 per stem, round in cross section, septate; no leaf blades
- auricles rounded
- inflorescences spreading, with 10-20 small, 6- to 12-flowered clusters of tiny flowers, appearing terminal
- tepals to 3 mm long, deep brown, occasionally pale, linear and long-pointed
- stamens 6
- capsules exceeding the tepals, ovoid and conical, slightly 3-angled, uniformly tapered, with short, pointed beak
- seeds oval, one end sharp-pointed, other end with flat, blunt tip

Habitat: Wet sites near the coastline, such as brackish marshes on sand dunes, to lake margins and stream edges. In swales between sand dunes, jointed rush may form a discontinuous ground cover in saturated soils.

Range: Native to north temperate latitudes, jointed rush is found over much of the continental United States and into south British Columbia.

Similar Species: The inflorescence of Sierra rush *(Juncus nevadensis)* is also diffuse, but does not bear as many flower clusters (fewer than 20), each cluster has fewer than 12 flowers, and clusters are spaced further apart; in addition, the capsule is smaller than the tepals. Sierra rush is also strongly rhizomatous, but not tufted. Tapertip rush *(Juncus acuminatus)* has 5-20 flowers per flower cluster and typically 3 sta-

Jointed rush grows from stout rhizomes and has leaves with obvious auricles. The tepals are shorter than the capsule; the seeds have a flat, blunt tip.

mens, and the tepals are greater than 3 mm. Pointed rush *(Juncus oxymeris)* again is highly rhizomatous, but the capsule barely exceeds the tepals, uniformly tapered to tip; leaves are flat, incompletely septate, and lack auricles. Mud rush *(Juncus gerardii)* also has a diffuse inflorescence, but tepal tips curl, capsule is smaller than tepals, seeds are blunt-tipped, leaves are not septate, and it is found only in salt marshes. Slender rush *(Juncus tenuis)* has a more compact (less spreading) inflorescence, and an oval, nontapering capsule that is shorter than the tepals.

RUSHES

243

Juncus balticus
Baltic rush
Family: Juncaceae
Status: FACW+

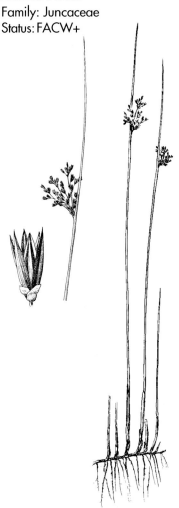

- stems thin (1-2 mm), wiry, flat to only slightly flattened, spiral along length; basal sheaths, no leaf blades
- inflorescences diffuse, appearing lateral; involucral bract rises stem-like above the flowers
- tepals purplish brown, often with a green center, 3.5-6 mm long, long-pointed
- stamens 6
- capsules oval, about as long as inner tepals
- seeds very small and indistinct

Habitat: Soils that remain damp year-round, often where there are saline or alkaline conditions, just inland of mudflats along the coast. Baltic rush can be found with tufted hairgrass *(Deschampsia cespitosa)*, seashore saltgrass *(Distichlis spicata)*, alkali grass *(Puccinellia pumila)*, three-square bulrush *(Scirpus americanus)*, and soft rush *(Juncus effusus)*.

Range: Much of temperate and subarctic North America, Eurasia, and South America. Common in all coastal counties in our area.

Similar Species: Salt rush *(Juncus lesueurii)* has flower clusters that are tight and globular; mud rush *(Juncus gerardii)* is also a salt-adapted rush, but the inflorescence is terminal and stems are clumped. Soft rush *(Juncus effusus)* is strongly tufted and more robust with stout sharp stems, flowers having only 3 stamens, and tepals typically 3.5 mm or less in length. Grooved rush *(Juncus patens)* also has a lateral inflorescence and apparently leafless stems that are 3-5 mm wide.

Baltic rush spreads from mat-forming rhizomes; tepals are equal in length to the capsule.

Baltic rush grows 20-70 cm tall and is a strongly rhizomatous perennial that forms uniform, loose carpets in suitable habitats. The involucral bract is stem-like, 2-7 cm long, and ascends above the inflorescence. Blooms June through August.

Functional Value: Erosion prevention and sediment retention. Baltic rush is also reported to have nitrogen-fixing capabilities.

Juncus bufonius
toad rush

Family: Juncaceae
Status: FACW
Color photo page 356

Toad rush is a finely fibrous-rooted, tufted annual, 5-20 cm tall, with several to many branching stems. Plants are light green when young and turn brown with age. It is the only annual rush with a terminal inflorescence that has 6 stamens; all others have 3 stamens. The lower involucral bract is needle-like and very small. Blooms June through September.

- roots very fine and few; lacks rhizomes
- leaves narrow (less than 1 mm), 1-3 per stem, flattened to inrolled, mostly basal; no leaf blades
- inflorescences branching, lateral as well as terminal; flowers usually borne singly
- tepals light green, 3-8 mm long, narrowly lance-shaped, pointed
- stamens 6
- capsules shorter than tepals, oblong-elliptic, round-tipped
- seeds oval, flat-tipped, with small, pointed ends

Toad rush tepals are longer than the capsule; seeds have pointed ends.

Habitat: Disturbed, moist sites and open ground, often in lawns and well-watered gardens, in gravel fills, on edges of vernal pools and streams, and on tidelands throughout much of our area. Found from near sea level to midmontane.

Range: Found across much of North America and Eurasia; occurs in all counties in our area.

Similar Species: Inch-high rush *(Juncus uncialis)* is also an annual, but rarely exceeds 4 cm in height, and like all other annual rushes, except toad rush, has a terminal inflorescence and 3 stamens.

Toad rush has finely fibrous roots and is lacking rhizomes.

Functional Value: Sediment retention and erosion prevention on newly disturbed surfaces.

RUSHES

Juncus effusus
soft rush

Family: Juncaceae
Status: FACW
Color photo page 356

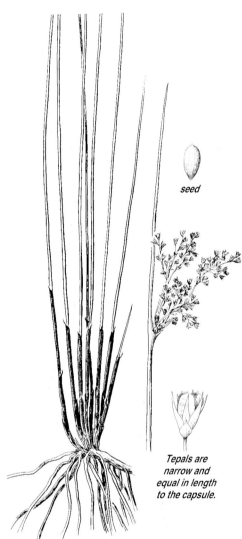

seed

Tepals are narrow and equal in length to the capsule.

Soft rush has lance-like basal sheaths, stem-like involucral bracts, and is strongly rhizomatous.

Soft rush is the most common tufted rush in the Pacific Northwest. It is a perennial, 20-100 cm tall, with stout rhizomes. It has lance-like basal sheaths that are 15 cm long and wrap around the base of

the flowering stem. The involucral bract is round, 7-20 cm long, erect, much longer than the inflorescence, and appears to be a continuation of the stem. Blooms June through August.

- stems round, stout and sharp; leaves basal, appearing only as brown sheaths; no leaf blades
- inflorescences diffuse to tight, 3-15 cm long, appearing lateral
- tepals greenish or brown, 2.5-3.5 mm long, needle-like
- capsules oval, flat-topped, equaling tepals, thin, soft, light brown to olive brown, strongly 3-angled
- stamens 3
- seeds elliptical

Habitat: In wet lowland pastures to montane meadows and ridges, also occurs in freshwater or saltwater coastal tideflats. Invasive in swamps, marshes, and wet meadows. Just inland of mudflats along the coast, soft rush can be found with tufted hairgrass *(Deschampsia cespitosa)*, seashore saltgrass *(Distichlis spicata)*, three-square bulrush *(Scirpus americanus)*, and Baltic rush *(Juncus balticus)*.

Range: Alaska to Baja California, east through Canada to Manitoba and Newfoundland, south to Idaho and to most of central and eastern United States. Also found in temperate regions of other continents. Occurs in all counties in our area.

Similar Species: Baltic rush *(Juncus balticus)*, a more delicate rush with nontufted rhizomatous growth, has flowers with 6 stamens and tepals that are typically 3.5-5 mm long. Grooved rush *(Juncus patens)* has flowers with 6 stamens, tepals that are narrow, long, and tapered, with transparent margins, and a swollen round seed, with a lengthwise ridge.

Functional Value: Muskrats feed on the rootstalks, and various wetland wading birds find shelter among the stems.

Ethnobotanical Use: Soft rush, also called candle rush by the Japanese, is used for tatami mats.

Juncus ensifolius
daggerleaf rush
Family: Juncaceae
Status: FACW
Color photo page 356

Daggerleaf rush is a leafy, strongly rhizomatous perennial, 20-60 cm tall, with stems arising singly or a few together. The involucral bract is a flattened short spur and is wrapped around the stem at the lowest flower cluster. Blooms June through August.

- leaf blades strongly equitant flattened, partially septate, 7-15 cm long, 2-5 mm wide
- inflorescences of 1-10 globose flower clusters, each 4- to 25-flowered, 3-4 cm long, tightly clumped, black to brownish purple; terminal
- stamens 3 or 6
- tepals pale greenish brown to deep purplish brown, 3-3.5 mm long, lance-shaped
- capsules shorter or longer than tepals, oblong, dark brown, rounded above but abruptly contracted to a sharply 3-angled pointed tip
- seeds oblong with pointed tips

Habitat: In moist sites, but not primarily around standing water; shade-intolerant. Occurs from sea level to montane meadows. Associates include veronica *(Veronica* species) and foxtail *(Alopecurus* species).

Range: Alaska to southern California, and east to the Rocky Mountains from Alberta to New Mexico. Occurs in all counties in our area.

Similar Species: Pointed rush *(Juncus oxymeris)* also has flattened blades, but the flower clusters are light to medium brown, large, loose, more than 10 and often more than 50. While sickleleaf rush *(Juncus falcatus)* has a globose inflorescence, it has flat, nonequitant-bladed leaves, involucral bracts longer than the inflorescence, and flat paddle-shaped achenes. Mertens' rush *(Juncus mertensianus)* also has a similar dark globular flower cluster, but the clusters are usually borne singly and the tepals are equal to the capsule. In addition, Mertens' rush has round, fully septate stems, and no leaf blades. Salt rush *(Juncus lesueurii)*, a saltmarsh species, has a similar flower clusters, but again the globular inflorescence is borne singly. Salt rush is further distinguished by its round stems and no septa.

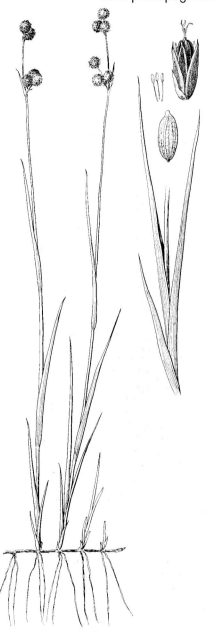

Daggerleaf rush has long spreading rhizomes and equitant leaves; tepals are equal in length to the capsules.

RUSHES

247

Juncus falcatus var. *sitchensis*
sickleleaf rush

Family: Juncaceae
Status: FACW-
Color photo page 357

Sickleleaf rush has scaly rhizomes, flat leaf blades, and an inflorescence with 2 long involucral bracts.

Sickleleaf rush is a somewhat tufted, rhizomatous perennial, 5-20 cm tall. Rhizomes are scaly. The lower involucral bract extends well beyond the inflorescence. Blooms from late May to July.

- leaf blades flat, grass-like, to 3 mm broad
- inflorescences terminal, numerous, half-round clusters, each with more than 7 flowers

- tepals dark chocolate-brown, usually with a broad, greenish midstripe that is minutely roughened, 4-6 mm long, extending as a pointed tip past tepal end
- stamens 6
- capsules shorter than tepals, egg-shaped, leathery, rounded and dimpled at the tip
- seeds flattened, paddle-shaped

Sickleleaf rush has wide tepals that are longer than the capsule, and paddle-shaped seeds.

Habitat: In coastal swamps, tideflats, and back into the sand dune area.

Range: Along the Pacific Coast, from Alaska to southern California, and in Asia.

Similar Species: Pointed rush *(Juncus oxymeris)* also has flattened leaf blades, but the inflorescences are light to medium brown, large, and loose. Daggerleaf rush *(Juncus ensifolius)* has flat, equitant, partially septate leaves, a short involucral bract on the lowest inflorescence, and oblong capsules. Mertens' rush *(Juncus mertensianus)* has a similar dark globular inflorescence, but with only a single flower cluster, half-round stems that are septate, and no leaf blades. Salt rush *(Juncus lesueurii)*, a salt marsh species, is very rhizomatous, but lacks leaf blades, and the tight, globular flower clusters are borne about midlength on the stem.

Functional Value: Erosion control and sediment retention.

Juncus gerardii var. *gerardii*
mud rush

Family: Juncaceae
Status: FACW+

Mud rush is a rhizomatous, tufted perennial, 30-70 cm tall. Each tuft has many stems and leaf sheaths arising along the rhizome. The involucral bracts, a few of which are shorter than the inflorescence, are conspicuous, needle-like, and are borne at the base of each flower cluster. Blooms June through September.

- leaf blades flat, grass-like, less than 3 mm broad
- inflorescences diffuse, flowers appear single or in 3s, usually more than 5 clusters; terminal
- tepals dark brown with a greenish midstripe, round tips curled over or hooded
- stamens 6
- capsules equal to tepals, oval to elliptical, round-tipped
- seeds oval, flat-topped, and blunt-tipped

Habitat: Predominantly coastal freshwater marshes with marine influence and coastal salt marshes.

Range: Vancouver Island, British Columbia, south into the Puget Basin; along the Atlantic Coast of North America; in Eurasia. Occurs in all counties in our area.

Similar Species: Pointed rush *(Juncus oxymeris)* is more highly rhizomatous, and has a more diffuse inflorescence with 10-70 small flower clusters of 3-12 flowers. Sierra rush *(Juncus nevadensis)* also has a diffuse inflorescence but with fewer than 20 tight, few-flowered, flower clusters, and tepals that are not curled over. Jointed rush *(Juncus articulatus)* has a larger, more spreading inflorescence of many, few-flowered clusters. The tepals are shorter than the pointed capsule. Tapertip rush *(Juncus acuminatus)* is tufted or with short rhizomes, the plants are reddish in color, the stems and round leaves are septate, and the diffuse inflorescence consists of many flower clusters, each having less than 10 flowers. Slender rush *(Juncus tenuis)* is not found in salt water, its leaves are not flattened, and the tepals are straight and sharp-pointed. Baltic rush *(Juncus balticus)* is found in salt water areas but the apparently lateral inflorescence is not branched and is very small.

Mud rush is tufted with narrow leaf blades; tepal ends curl over the capsule.

RUSHES

Juncus lesueurii
salt rush
Family: Juncaceae
Status: FACW

Salt rush has bladeless stems and globular inflorescences that appear lateral; tepals are longer than the capsule; seeds are flat with blunt tips.

Salt rush is a stout perennial, 20-60 cm tall, with thick, elongate rhizomes. The involucral bract is round and sharp-pointed, almost as long as the stem, and appears as a continuation of the stem. Blooms June through July.

- stems round, lacking septae, basal sheaths dark brown; no leaf blades
- inflorescences tight, globular, borne singly, appearing lateral; involucral bract extends beyond inflorescence
- tepals green in the center and purplish brown along the membranous margins, 5-6 mm long, lance-shaped
- stamens 6
- capsules equal to the inner tepals, oval to rounded, sharp-tipped
- seeds flat, irregularly shaped, with flat or blunt ends

Habitat: Coastal marshes and dunes. Associates include bighead sedge *(Carex macrocephala)*, Pacific reedgrass *(Calamagrostis nutkaensis)*, American dunegrass *(Elymus mollis)*, and seaside plantain *(Plantago maritima)*.

Range: Southern British Columbia south to San Luis Obispo, California.

Similar Species: Soft rush *(Juncus effusus)* also has rounded stems with no leaf blades and an apparently lateral infloresence, but is strongly tufted, and even more robust, with a diffuse inflorescence; rarely occurs in coastal dunes. Baltic rush *(Juncus balticus)* is also a rhizomatous coastal dune species, but has thinner, spiraled, usually single stems, and a diffuse, few-flowered inflorescence. Mud rush *(Juncus gerardii)* is also a salt-adapted rush, but the inflorescence is terminal and plants are tufted. Sickleleaf rush *(Juncus falcatus)* and Mertens' rush *(Juncus mertensianus)* also have globular inflorescences but they are terminal.

Family: Juncaceae
Status: OBL

Mertens' rush is a tufted, rhizomatous perennial, 5-30 cm tall. The involucral bract is leaf-like and as long as or slightly longer than the inflorescence. Blooms July to September.

- stems half-rounded; leaves 1-4 and basal, septate, thin, weak, rounded; sheaths brown to purple; no leaf blades
- auricles membranous and rounded
- inflorescences 1, occasionally 2, dark, tight, globose, terminal, to 2 cm in diameter, with many flowers
- tepals dark brown to purple-black, 3-4 mm long, sharp-pointed, lance-shaped
- stamens 6
- capsules shorter than tepals, oblong, dark brown to purple-brown, rounded abruptly at the tip
- seeds long, tapered at each end, with sharp-pointed tip

Habitat: In meadows along seeps, stream banks, and pond edges, and in drainage swales and ditches. From lowlands to above timberline.

Range: Alaska to Alberta, south to California, and east to New Mexico.

Similar Species: Daggerleaf rush *(Juncus ensifolius)* has a similar inflorescence, but flattened, equitant leaves. Sickleleaf rush *(Juncus falcatus)* has similar half-round flower clusters, but they are numerous. In addition, sickleleaf rush has flat leaves, involucral bracts that are clearly longer than the inflorescence, and flat paddle-shaped seeds. Salt rush *(Juncus lesueurii)*, a salt-marsh species, has a similar globular inflorescence, but is apparently lateral; stems are round, also with no leaf blades, and lack septa.

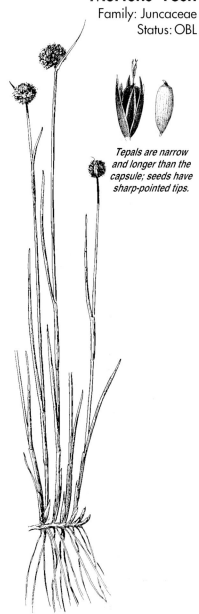

Tepals are narrow and longer than the capsule; seeds have sharp-pointed tips.

Mertens' rush has narrow, septate leaves.

RUSHES

Juncus nevadensis var. *nevadensis*
Sierra rush

Family: Juncaceae
Status: FACW

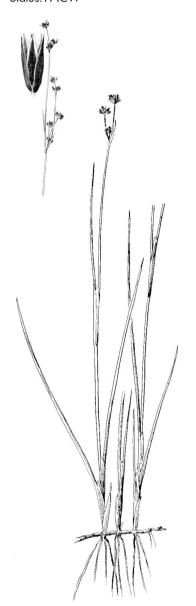

Sierra rush is a strongly rhizomatous perennial, 10-70 cm tall. Stems are round and arise singly. Involucral bracts are short, needle-like, and are borne at the base of the lowest flower cluster. Blooms July through August.

- leaves 5-20 cm long, semi-flat, septate
- auricles pointed, 1-3 mm long
- inflorescences diffuse, terminal, branched, with 2- to many clusters per branch, each cluster fewer than 12-flowered
- tepals light brown to dark purple-brown, 3-5 mm long, lance-shaped, not curling over
- stamens 6
- capsules shorter than tepals, dark brown, ovoid-elliptic, abruptly tapering to the tip
- seeds oval with bluntly pointed tips

Habitat: Wet areas at the margin of streams and lakes, from near sea level to lower elevations in the mountains.

Range: Southern British Columbia south to southern California; east to the Rocky Mountains, from Montana to New Mexico.

Similar Species: Tapertip rush *(Juncus acuminatus)* is also diffuse-flowered with septate, half-round leaves, but is nonrhizomatous typically with 3 stamens. Pointed rush *(Juncus oxymeris)* is also rhizomatous, but has flattened leaf blades that are incompletely septate, have a larger, more diffuse inflorescence, and capsules slightly longer than the tepals. Jointed rush *(Juncus articulatus)* has an inflorescence that is more spreading, a capsule longer than the tepals, and 6 stamens. Mud rush *(Juncus gerardii)* also has a diffuse inflorescence, but the tepal tips curl over the blunt-tipped capsule, the leaves are not septate, and is found only in salt marshes.

Sierra rush has long rhizomes and narrow, flat, septate leaves; tepals are longer than the capsule.

Juncus oxymeris
pointed rush
Family: Juncaceae
Status: FACW+
Color photo page 357

Pointed rush is a stoloniferous and widely rhizomatous perennial that grows 40-90 cm tall. The lower involucral bract is obvious, but much shorter than the inflorescence, and only found on the major inflorescence branches. Blooms May to August.

- leaf blades equitant-flattened, incompletely septate
- inflorescences of 10-70 large, loose flower clusters 2-5 cm long, each 3- to 12-flowered; terminal
- tepals greenish yellow to brown, 3-4 mm long, lance-shaped, not curling over
- stamens 6
- capsules slightly longer than tepals, long, tapering uniformly to the tip
- seeds oval with bluntly pointed tips

The tepals of pointed rush are shorter than the capsule.

Habitat: Wet meadows and lake shores in lowlands west of the Cascades.

Range: Southwestern British Columbia south to California.

Similar Species: Daggerleaf rush *(Juncus ensifolius)* also has flattened-equitant leaf blades and the flower clusters are fewer than 10 and tightly compressed. Tapertip rush *(Juncus acuminatus)* has similar, but smaller, diffuse inflorescences, and is strongly tufted with short rhizomes. Sierra rush *(Juncus nevadensis)* has round stems, no leaf blades, smaller more compact inflorescences with fewer than 20 flower

Pointed rush plant has a diffuse inflorescence and incompletely septate stems.

clusters per inflorescence, and tepals that are equal to or longer than the capsule. Jointed rush *(Juncus articulatus)* has round leaves with auricles, no leaf blades, an inflorescence that is less spreading, and a pointed capsule that well exceeds the tepals. Mud rush *(Juncus gerardii)* also has a diffuse inflorescence, but tepal tips curl over, capsules are blunt-tipped, leaves are not septate, and it is found only in salt marshes.

RUSHES

253

Juncus patens
grooved rush
Family: Juncaceae
Status: FACW

This perennial rush grows from short, stout, and creeping rhizomes. It is strongly tufted and 30-90 cm tall. The involucral bract, which extends beyond the inflorescence, is generally one-third as long as the stem and sharp-pointed. Blooms June through August.

- stems blue-green and round, bearing brownish, loose, pointed sheaths; leaves reduced and bristle-like if present
- inflorescences 2.5-9 cm long, open, with more than 20 flowers; appearing lateral
- tepals greenish to light brown, 2.5-3 mm long, narrowed, tapered, stiff, with transparent margins, spreading away from capsule
- stamens 6
- capsules almost as long as tepals, swollen-round
- seeds oval with distinct ridge along entire length

Habitat: In saturated soil conditions from lowland valleys upwards into the lower elevation montane forest on the west side of the Cascades in Oregon.

Distribution: Willamette Valley and Cascade Mountains, Oregon, south to Santa Barbara County in California.

Similar Species: Soft rush *(Juncus effusus)* also has round stems with an apparently lateral inflorescence and is strongly tufted, but it is more robust, with stout and sharp stems, flowers that have only 3 stamens, needle-like tepals, and a flat-topped capsule. Baltic rush *(Juncus balticus)* is not tufted, has thin, wiry stems that arise singly, and usually occurs in more coastal areas.

Grooved rush is strongly tufted and has an inflorescence that appears lateral; tepals are longer than the wide capsule.

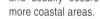

Juncus supiniformis
spreading rush
Family: Juncaceae
Status: OBL
Color photo page 357

The tufted stems of spreading rush appear along slender, creeping rhizomes. Rooting occurs at each of these individual tufts, similar to strawberry plants. This perennial species often forms uniform, nonflowering, continuous mats on both estuarine and freshwater mud flats. Stems are 10-30 cm tall. The lower involucral bract is shorter than the inflorescence. Blooms July to September.

- leaves half-round, septate, very thin, needle-like, floating in water, 2-4 per stem; no leaf blades
- inflorescences loose, branched, with 2-6 few-flowered clusters; terminal
- small plantlets often sprout within inflorescence clusters
- tepals brown, 3-4.5 mm long, narrowly lance-shaped, pointed
- stamens 3 or 6
- capsules longer than tepals, cylindrical, abruptly narrowing to a sharp beak
- seeds oblong with bluntly pointed tips

Habitat: In marshes, ponds, ditches, and tidal estuarine and freshwater mud flats; often grows where plants will be submerged early in the season.

Range: From Alaska south, along the coast west of the Cascades, to Mendocino County, California.

Spreading rush is stoloniferous; plantlets sprout from the inflorescence.

Similar Species: European spreading rush *(Juncus supinus)* is also a tufted perennial, but has no rhizomes, stems are prostrate and rooting, tepals are blunt, and the capsule is longer than the tepals. It is an exotic species common only in Snohomish, Skagit and north King counties, Washington.

RUSHES

Juncus tenuis var. tenuis
slender rush
Family: Juncaceae
Status: FACW-
Color photo page 357

The tepals of slender rush are longer than the capsule.

The terminal inflorescence of slender rush has two, long involucral bracts.

Slender rush is a tufted perennial, with fibrous roots and grows 15-70 cm tall. The two involucral bracts are longer than the inflorescence. The lower bract can appear to be a continuation of the stem. Blooms June to September.

- stems slender, rounded, bright green; leaves borne on the lower 1/5 of the stem, 1 mm wide, flat; no leaf blades
- auricles membranous, white, 1-3.5 mm long, rounded, overlapping, appearing as a continuation of the leaf sheath
- inflorescences diffuse, 1-7 cm long, branched, terminal, with 10-50 singly borne flowers; involucral bract usually longer than flowers
- tepals green to straw-colored, 4-5 mm long, with a green midrib and white margins; sharp-tipped, tips not curling over
- stamens 6
- capsules subequal to or shorter than tepals, straw-colored, oblong to oval; tip abruptly rounded and dimpled
- seeds elliptical, small, with a ridge along entire length on both sides

Habitat: Freshwater sites with saturated soil conditions during the winter and dry conditions during the summer. Disturbed areas with seeps and springs, such as meadows, shaded roads, and ditches.

Range: From Alaska south to Mexico, east over most of southern Canada and the United States. Also known from South America, Europe, and Australia. Distribution spotty throughout our area.

Similar Species: Mud rush *(Juncus gerardii)* has similar stems, leaves, and auricles, but has a diffuse inflorescence, with tepal tips that curl over, blunt-tipped capsules, and it is found only in salt marshes. Pointed rush *(Juncus oxymeris)* has a much larger and more diffuse inflorescence with 10-70 small flower clusters of 3-12 flowers. In addition, pointed rush is long-spreading, not tufted, and has flattened leaf blades. Sierra rush *(Juncus nevadensis)* has a few-flowered, open inflorescence, but has long auricles and is rhizomatous. Jointed rush *(Juncus articulatus)* has an inflorescence that is more spreading, a pointed capsule that well exceeds the tepals, tall rounded auricles, and septate leaves.

Juncus uncialis
inch-high rush
Family: Juncaceae
Status: FACW+

This rush is a fibrous-rooted, diminutive annual less than 4 cm in height. A single inflorescence bract, scarcely 0.5 mm, nearly surrounds the base of the single flowers.

- leaves longitudinally channeled or grooved, often inrolled, 0.8-1.0 cm long
- inflorescences 2-3 mm wide, 1-3 flowers terminate naked stem
- tepals 3 mm long, with thin, transparent margins, and broad, green midribs
- stamens 3

Habitat: Damp soils that are not inundated all year.

Range: Usually from Lane County, Oregon, south; may occur in Washington.

Similar Species: Toad rush *(Juncus bufonius)* is also a small (or large) annual rush, but has 6 stamens, and inflorescences that are both lateral and terminal on the stems.

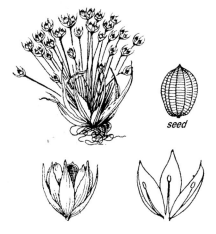

seed

This fibrous-rooted annual rush is less than 4 cm tall.

RUSHES

Luzula multiflora
(Luzula campestris)
field woodrush; many flowered woodrush

Family: Juncaceae
Status: FACU

*Tepals are longer
than the capsule.*

Field woodrush is the only perennial woodrush common in moist to dry meadows in the Puget Basin. It grows in dense tufts, and can be 10-60 cm tall with stem leaves 2-4 cm long. The inflorescence is terminal, erect, with few to many tight clumps of 8-15 flowers. Blooms April through July.

- leaves 2-6 mm wide, flat, with long white hairs on the margins and at the leaf nodes, midvein lacking; stem leaves brown, blunt-tipped
- tepals green to deep chestnut brown, 2-4.5 mm long, with abruptly long-pointed tips and transparent margins
- stamens 6, 0.5-2 mm long
- capsules egg-shaped, shorter than tepals, brown, round-tipped
- seeds 3, brown, egg-shaped with a roundish spongy growth at the base

Habitat: In dry to moist, nitrogen-poor, open gravelly meadows, coastal bluffs, beaches, and shores from low to midmontane elevations.

Range: Across the northern hemisphere in cool to moist temperate climates. Alaska to Southern California. Also found in temperate regions of other continents.

Similar Species: Small-flowered woodrush *(Luzula parviflora)*, a more delicate woodrush common to forest hummocks, has an open inflorescence with flowers arising singly or in pairs, green to brown tepals, typically 2 mm long, and stamens 0.3-0.6 mm long.

Field woodrush is nonrhizomatous; leaves have tufts of white hairs on the margins.

Luzula parviflora
small-flowered woodrush

Family: Juncaceae
Status: FAC-

Small-flowered woodrush is the most common woodrush in the Pacific Northwest. It grows singly or in small tufts to 80 cm tall with at least four leaves. The inflorescence is terminal, nodding, open to tightly clumped, with flowers on branch tips arising singly or in pairs. Blooms May through August.

- basal leaf sheaths purple brown
- leaves 3-10 mm wide, flat, with white hairs on the margins, midvein lacking
- tepals green to purplish brown, 2 mm long, pointed-tipped; 2 bottom bracts long, torn-edged
- stamens 6, 0.3-0.6 mm long
- capsule spherical to egg-shaped, equal to or exceeding the tepals, thin, green to deep purple-brown, round-tipped,
- seeds 3, yellow to brown, cylindrical, with a ridge on one side

Habitat: In moist forests on hummocks from lowlands to subalpine elevations in the Cascades. Small-flowered woodrush can be found with deer fern *(Blechnum spicant)*, oak fern *(Gymnocarpium dryopteris)*, spreading wood fern *(Dryopteris expansa)*, and sword fern *(Polystichum munitum)*.

Range: A naturalized Eurasian species found across North America in Boreal to moist temperate climates. Also found in temperate regions of other continents. Occurs in all counties in our area.

Similar Species: Field woodrush *(Luzula multiflora)*, a more robust woodrush common to open wet meadows, has many erect, tightly clumped, dark brown inflorescences with flower heads 8-15 per clump, green to deep chestnut brown tepals, typically 2-4.5 mm long, and stamens 0.5 to 2 mm long.

Small-flowered woodrush has wide, flat leaves.

RUSHES

Guide to Identifying the Sedges
Family: Cyperaceae

Species in the sedge family are grass-like, perennial herbs that grow in clumps (tufted) or have stems growing laterally underground (rhizomatous) or above ground (stoloniferous and mat-forming). *Leaves* are 3-ranked (3 whorled leaves attached at the same point) and have closed *sheaths*, i.e., the leaf bases are fused around the stem. Some species have a *ligule*, a notched appendage at the juncture of the leaf and leaf sheath. *Stems* are triangular, round, or occasionally flat in cross section, and all are solid. Each stem bears 1 to many *flower spikes* or *spikelets* (smaller secondary spikes) that are either attached directly to the stems or are borne on a side stalk. Flower spikes usually have a leaf-like *involucral bract*, attached to the spike base, that varies from large and leafy to small and inconspicuous or absent. Bracts may or may not be sheathing (wrapped around the stem) at the base. Individual flowers are attached directly to the flower spikes and have small bracts called *scales*, attached at the base. The scales of the female flowers are helpful in distinguishing between species. Non-*Carex* species in the sedge family have a perianth, a group of *bristles* positioned below the achene.

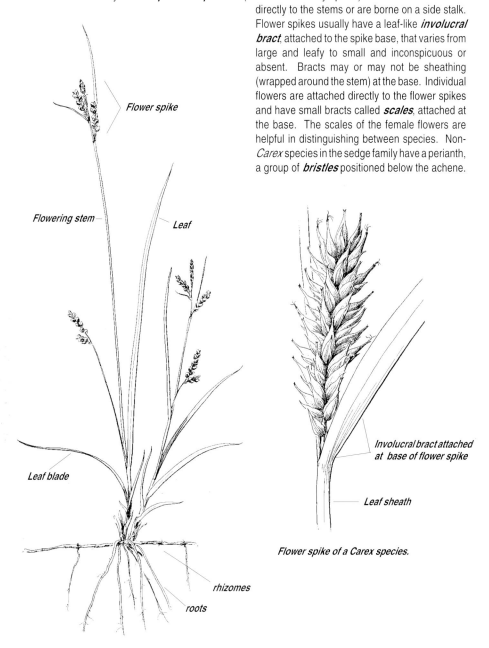

Flower spike

Flowering stem

Leaf

Leaf blade

rhizomes

roots

Involucral bract attached at base of flower spike

Leaf sheath

Flower spike of a Carex species.

The *achene* (fruit) is either 2-sided with convex sides (lens-shaped) or 3-sided (triangular). The non-*Carex* genera often have a large cap-like appendage on the end of the achene called a *tubercle*.

In *Carex*, the largest genus within the sedge family, plants have both male and female organs or occasionally are unisexual. Flower spikes or spikelets can have all male flowers or all female flowers, or be mixed with either sex flower above the other. Female flowers are enclosed by a fused sac called the *perigynium (peri)* with an apical opening through which the style or stigmas protrude. A *beak* (neck) on the peri may also be evident. The size and shape of the mature peri is often essential for identification. Stigmas usually number 2 but occasionally will be 3, in which case the achene is triangular. Male flowers often have 2 stamens but can have 3 or 1.

Functional Value: Most sedge species produce a large crop of water-dispersed fruits. These are eaten by a variety of animals, such as insects, waterbirds, finches, and some mammals. The leaves are often used as nesting material, and some mat-forming species provide shelter and nesting sites.

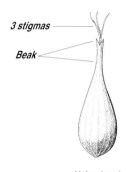

3 stigmas

Beak

Veined peri.

Ethnobotanical Uses: The leaves of many sedge species were used as thread by Native Americans and sewn into hide garments as decoration. The leaves and stems of many sedge family species are still used today for basketry.

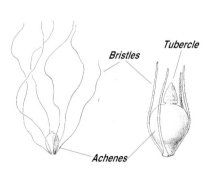

Tubercle

Bristles

Achenes

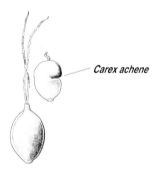

Carex achene

Peri lacking veins, with short beak and 2 stigmas.

Many of the non-Carex sedge species have bristles, which are reduced petals, surrounding the achene.

The Carex species have a peri, a fused sac, which encloses the female flower.

SEDGES

Key to Identifying the *Carex* Species

Note: Plants with mature peri and achenes are necessary for precise identification. Immature specimens may not offer accurate information.

1a. Plants bearing both female and male flowers (though male flowers may be difficult to find) 2
1b. Plants generally unisexual; peri 10-15 mm long, thick, leathery, shiny, long-beaked; stigmas 3 ; male heads 3.5-5 cm long & 1-1.5 cm thick, female head 3.5-8 cm long & 2.5-5 cm thick; estuaries, sandy beaches, and sand dunes along the coast; June-July ....
....big-head sedge *(Carex macrocephala* var. *macrocephala)*

    2a. Stigmas 2; achenes two-sided (lens-shaped) 3
    2b. Stigmas 3; achenes three-sided (triangular) 18

Stigmas 2 and Achenes Lens-Shaped

3a. Lateral inflorescence attached directly to stem 4
3b. Lateral inflorescence with stalks, or if attached directly to stem, spikes elongate 14

    4a. Male flowers above female flowers in same spike 5
    4b. Female flowers above male flowers in same spike 8

        5a. Peri with body tapering into a beak; leaf sheaths cross-wrinkled on front face of blade......6
        5b. Peri with body abruptly contracted into a beak; leaf sheaths not cross-wrinkled on front face of blade, unless found only in Willamette Valley, then sheaths cross-wrinkled 7

            6a. Leaves yellow-green, shorter than inflorescence; involucral bract only on lowest spike; peri swollen at base with long cleft beak..
....sawbeak sedge *(Carex stipata* var. *stipata)*
            6b. Leaves longer than inflorescence; involucral bract short on each spike; peri round with short tapered cleft beak, leaf sheath with red spots on neck..
....fox sedge *(Carex vulpinoidea)*

            7a. Spikes generally 10 or less, often greenish; leaf sheaths not cross-wrinkled on front face of blade; leaf blade 1.5-2.5 mm wide; peri 3.8-5.0 mm long; inflorescence 1.5-3.5 cm long ....foothill sedge *(Carex tumulicola)*
            7b. Spikes more than 10, brownish or straw-colored; leaf sheaths cross-wrinkled on front face of blade; leaf blade 2-5 mm wide; peri 2.0-4.0 mm long; inflorescence 5-10 cm long; Willamette River Valley – Columbia River.............dense sedge *(Carex densa)*

        8a. Margin of peri winged, the wing narrow or broad; peri planoconvex or flattened
....9
        8b. Margin of peri rounded or sharp-edged, at most thin edged, but not winged; peri planoconvex
....12

            9a. Lowermost involucral bract(s) conspicuously exceeding the inflorescence, 2-15 cm long..10
            9b. Lowermost involucral bract(s) short/inconspicuous 11

10a. Lowest inflorescence bract leaf-like, longer than the inflorescence, not erect; beak gently round or slightly flattened and smooth-margined in the distal 1 mm or so; peri flattened to planoconvex; stem triangular..
....slenderbeak sedge *(Carex athrostachya)*

10b. Lowest involucral bract long, erect, leaf-like, looks like a continuation of the round stem; peri beak tip minutely 2-toothed, flat, and sometimes reddish brown; peri planoconvex.. one-sided sedge *(Carex unilateralis)*

11a. Female scale light brown with green midrib, nearly as long and wide as the flattened peri, concealing it from the back; spikes easily distinguished; peri base protruding as a knob..harefoot sedge *(Carex leporina)*

11b. Female scale red-brown with green midrib, shorter and narrower than the planoconvex peri, exposing the beak and distal margin; peri base not protruding beyond round body; spikes crowded in inflorescence and not easily distinguished; open, often rather dry slopes.................thick-head sedge *(Carex pachystachya)*

12a. Spikes 4-8; peri usually fewer than 25 per spike 13

12b. Spikes 7-15; peri usually 20-40 per spike; lower leaf sheaths dotted with purple opposite the blade; beak top reddish brown tinged.........northern clustered sedge *(Carex arcta)*

13a. Peri usually 5-10 per spike, 2.5-3.8 mm long, 1.5 mm wide; beak 0.5-1.0 mm; leaves 1-2.5 mm wide; peri tapering into a barely toothed beak; lowest spike with long bract; stems weak, often bent...............smooth-stem sedge *(Carex laeviculmis)*

13b. Peri mostly 10-25 per longest spike; peri 3.5-5 mm long, 2 mm wide; beak 1-2 mm; leaves generally 2-5 mm wide; peri tapering into a toothed, shallow 2-toothed beak; lowest two spikes with long bract; stems typically erect ....
....Dewey sedge *(Carex deweyana* var. *deweyana)*

14a. Lowest involucral bract long-sheathing, leaf-like; peri beakless; peri dusty-white-green becoming golden-orange at maturity (drying pale) ....golden sedge *(Carex aurea)*

14b. Lowest involucral bract sheathless or nearly so, the blade bract-like or leaf-like; peri beaked but the beak usually very short 15

15a. Peri very firm and thick-walled; upper 1-3 spikes staminate...16

15b. Peri thinner-walled and more or less membranous; generally only the terminal spike staminate...17

16a. Female spikes (5-12 cm long) seldom with conspicuous stalk though generally with bent and nodding tip; achene often with a more or less deep median constriction; peri nerveless, smooth and shining; fresh water ....slough sedge *(Carex obnupta)*

16b. Female spikes slender (1.5-5 cm long), generally nodding on slender elongate stalks; female scale with red-green midrib, pointed tip; achene occasionally with median constriction; coastal marshes and tidal flats ....Lyngby sedge *(Carex lyngbyei)*

17a. Peri conspicuously veined or ribbed on both faces as well as on the margins; female bract with dark red-brown midrib, round tip; wet meadows, stream banks, lakeshores, from sea level to near timberline ....lenticular sedge *(Carex lenticularis)*

17b. Peri nerveless or nearly so on both faces, or occasionally some with 1-2 irregular nerves; female scale very narrow, blunt-tipped ....water sedge *(Carex aquatilis* var. *dives)*

Carex species key continued on next page...

SEDGES

Stigmas 3 and Achenes Triangular

18a. Peri velvety-hairy; achenes with concave sides and blunt angles, slenderly hair-tipped, and the tip bent; leaf blade 1-2 mm and in-folded .... slender wetland sedge *(Carex lasiocarpa* var. *lasiocarpa)*

18b. Peri without hairs 19

    19a. Peri 10-15 mm long; 2-toothed beak about as long as the oval body of peri; leaf blade with spiny-toothed margins; spikes densely aggregated; plant typically unisexual; strictly marine .... bighead sedge *(Carex macrocephala* var. *macrocephala)*

    19b. Peri generally 8 mm or less in length; spikes not tightly aggregated; fresh water 20

        20a. Style jointed (not continuous) with the achene; the style withering, deciduous 21

        20b. Style and achene continuous; style not withering, tending to bend inside the peri after achene is mature 22

            21a. Involucral bracts subtending lower spikes sheathing (1) 1.5-7 cm; peri length 4-7 mm; male spike length 1.5-3 cm; female spike length 1-4 cm; leaf margin smooth.............. .... Henderson sedge *(Carex hendersonii)*

            21b. Involucral bracts subtending any spikes nearly or quite sheathless; peri length 2.5-3.5 mm; male spike length 4-9 cm; female spike length 3.5-14 cm; leaf margin rough.. bigleaf sedge *(Carex amplifolia)*

            22a. Female spikes on slender nodding stalks; female scales short with a long (2-6 mm) awn.. bearded sedge *(Carex comosa)*

            22b. Female spikes erect, attached to stem or only short-stalked but still erect; female scales without awn or short-awned.. 23

                23a. Peri inflated, ascending along the spike axis when young, spreading outward at right angles to down bending in fruit, closely arranged in numerous rows; dry leaves 2-15 mm wide with conspicuous septate, knobby nodes .... beaked sedge *(Carex utriculata)*

                23b. Peri ascending along the spike axis even in fruit, loosely arranged in the spikes in a few rows; peri tapering gradually from the body to the often poorly defined beak; dry leaves 1-7 mm wide without septate, knobby node.......................... .... inflated sedge *(Carex vesicaria* var. *major)*

Carex amplifolia
bigleaf sedge
Family: Cyperaceae
Status: FACW+
Color photo page 357

Bigleaf sedge is a mat-forming species with stout rhizomes. Stems are sharply triangular and grow 50-100 cm tall. Leaves are flat, rough-margined, 50 cm long, and 8-20 mm wide. The lowest leaves are very short or are reduced to sheaths around the base of the stem. On each stem, there are several stalked, erect, cylindrical flower spikes, 4-10 cm long. The lowest spike is subtended by a nonsheathing involucral bract that is long, leafy, and purplish. Blooms late May through July.

- male flower spikes terminal; female spikes lateral
- female scales narrow, red or brown with pale green midrib, equal to or longer than peri, with a short red awn
- peri smooth, light-colored, 3 mm long, inflated around the achene, with a beak 1 mm long; style deciduous; more than 60 peris per spikelet
- stigmas 3; achene triangular, 1-2 mm long

Habitat: Emergent wetlands and bogs from low to midmontane elevations.

Similar Species: Water sedge *(Carex aquatilis)*; see key.

Bigleaf sedge has sharply triangular stems, two types of flower spikes, and a smooth peri with a long beak.

SEDGES

Carex aquatilis var. dives
(Carex sitchensis)
water sedge
Family: Cyperaceae
Status: OBL
Color photo page 359

Narrow female scale.

Water sedge is usually mat-forming but some-times tufted, with stout, deeply rooted rhizomes and many fibrous roots on each basal clump. Stems are round and 30-150 cm tall. Leaves are flat, 30-40 cm long, and narrow (5-8 mm wide). There are 3-7 erect, cylindrical flower spikes, 5-11 cm long, that are all attached directly to the stem; or the lowest borne on long stalks and the upper attached directly or nearly so. The lowest spike is subtended by leafy, nonsheathing involucral bracts, 7-25 cm long. Blooms late June through August.

- male flower spikes terminal, female spikes lateral; or male flowers above female flowers on same spike
- female scales narrow, blunt-tipped, reddish brown to purple-black with a pale brown midrib and tip, equal to or longer than the peri
- peri flat, elliptic, red-brown speckled on pale green, lacking nerves, 2-3 mm long, with a thin-walled, notched-tip beak 0.2 mm long
- stigmas 2; achene lens-shaped, 1 mm long, shiny

Habitat: Shallow water or very wet soil, often in swampy places or at the margins of ponds and lakes. Occurs from foothills to near timberline.

Similar Species: Bigleaf sedge *(Carex amplifolia)*; see key.

Water sedge has round stems, two types of flower spikes, and an involucral bract that is longer than the inflorescence.

Carex arcta
northern clustered sedge

Family: Cyperaceae
Status: OBL

Northern clustered sedge is a tufted sedge that grows 30-60 cm tall and has stout, deeply rooted rhizomes. Stems are sharply triangular. Leaves are flat, longer than the stems, 30-40 cm long, 1.5-4 mm wide, and borne on the lower part of the stem. There are 5-15 erect flower spikes, 5-10 cm long, attached directly to the stem, each with 25-40 flowers. Most of the spikes are closely aggregated into a single oblong, 1.5-4 cm long, pale green to brown-green head. Involucral bracts are short and narrow. Blooms late June through August.

- lower leaf sheaths dotted with purple on the inside of the blade
- flower spikes 5 cm long, number 7-15, with female flowers above male flowers, lowest spike subtended by leafy, nonsheathing involucral bracts
- female scales shorter than the peri, colorless to pale brown with a dark greenish midrib and transparent margins
- peri egg-shaped, light green to greenish brown, 2-3 mm long, with obvious and very short veins, and beak with sharply toothed margins
- stigmas 2, achene lens-shaped, 1-2 mm long

Habitat: Wet places in lowland to near timberline elevations. Occasionally found in sphagum bogs.

Similar Species: Slenderbeak sedge *(Carex athrostachya)*, sawbeak sedge *(Carex stipata)*, thick-head sedge *(Carex pachystachya)*, harefoot sedge *(Carex leporina)*, fox sedge *(Carex vulpinoidea)*; see key.

Flower spike, scale, and peri.

Northern clustered sedge has sharply triangular stems; flower spikes have short involucral bracts.

SEDGES

Carex athrostachya
slenderbeak sedge

Family: Cyperaceae
Status: FACW

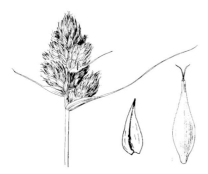

Flower spike, scale, and peri with tapering beak.

Slenderbeak sedge is a thickly tufted species with no rhizomes. Stems are sharply triangular and grow 15-100 cm tall. Leaves are shorter than the stems, flat, 30-40 cm long, 2-4 mm wide, and borne on the lower part of the stem. The lowest leaves are very short or are reduced to sheaths around the base of the stem. There are several erect flower spikes, 6-10 mm long, that are attached directly to the stem, and closely aggregated into a single, straw-colored to light-brown, egg-shaped head, 1-2 cm long. Flower spikes are subtended by leafy, nonsheathing involucral bracts that are longer than the inflorescence, but not erect. Blooms May through August.

- flower spikes each with female flowers above male flowers
- female scales tan to brown, transparent-margined with a firm midvein, short awn-pointed, broad at the base, shorter and narrower than the peri
- peri flat-elongate 3-5 mm long, pale green to tan with a brown dorsal midvein, and toothed, thin, transparent wing margins; body of peri tapering to an obliquely cleft beak, to 1 mm long
- stigmas 2; achene lens-shaped, to 1.5 mm long

Habitat: Seasonally wet meadows in lowland to moderate elevations.

Similar Species: Thick-head sedge *(Carex pachystachya)*, harefoot sedge *(Carex leporina)*, fox sedge *(Carex vulpinoidea)*, and one-sided sedge *(Carex unilateralis)*, see key.

Slenderbeak sedge has triangular stems and flower spikes that are subtended by long involucral bracts.

Carex aurea
golden sedge
Family: Cyperaceae
Status: FACW+
Color photo page 358

Golden sedge is a small plant with only a few slender stems that grow 3-40 cm tall. Rhizomes are well developed. Stems and leaves are light brown at the base. Leaves are flat, 1.5-4 mm wide, and longer than the stems. The erect, stalked flower spikes are few-flowered (4-10 peris per spikelet), 2-20 mm long, and located all along the stem. Upper spikes are subtended by a leafy involucral bract, 3-12 mm long, the longest of which is long-sheathing and leaf-like. Spikes fall over when mature. Blooms late April through August.

- male flower spikes terminal; occasionally spikes with female flowers above male flowers
- female scales straw-colored to brown with a greenish midrib and white, with transparent margins, shorter than or equal to (and narrower than) the peri
- peri egg-shaped, 2-3 mm long, moderately spreading, light green when young, greenish brown when mature, with barely visible veins along body; (golden orange with age); beak lacking
- stigmas 2, occasionally 3; achene usually lens-shaped (though triangular if there are 3 stigmas); 1-2 mm long, filling the peri

Habitat: Wet places from lowland to near timberline elevations. Prefers gravelly soils, usually on the margins of lakes and streams.

Similar Species: Slender wetland sedge *(Carex lasiocarpa)*, see key.

Scale and beakless, golden peri with 2 stigmas.

SEDGES

Golden sedge has separate male and female flower spikes.

Carex comosa
bearded sedge; bristly sedge

Family: Cyperaceae
Status: OBL
Color photo page 358

Bearded sedge is a densely tufted, coarse-stemmed plant with stout rhizomes. It grows 50-100 cm tall. Stems are thick and round. Leaves are smooth, 4-11 mm wide, with ligules and knobby partitions, especially on the sheath; the leaf below the lowest female spike is sheathless, but very long – surpassing the entire inflorescence. Leaf-like involucral bracts are found on all spikes except the terminal, male spike, and may be sheathing. Female spikes number 3-6, and are loosely aggregated at the tip. Each female spike has many peris, densely crowded in a cylinder. Blooms May through July.

- male flower spikes 1 (may have a few female flowers at either end), terminal, up to 6 cm long; female spikes lateral on slender and bending stalks, 2-7 cm long and 1.5 cm thick
- female scales 1-2 mm long, thin and translucent walled, awn-tipped, 2-6 mm long, with reddish vein
- peri thin, long lance-shaped, pale greenish gold, smooth, 5-8 mm long, gradually tapering to a long divided beak, 15-20 obvious veins
- stigmas 3; achene triangular, 1-2 mm long, in the lower 1/2 of the peri sac; style bony and persistent, straight or wavy-bent

Habitat: In fresh water; in marshes, along lakeshores, and in wet meadows. Bearded sedge is a sensitive species in Washington.

Similar Species: Beaked sedge *(Carex utriculata);* see key.

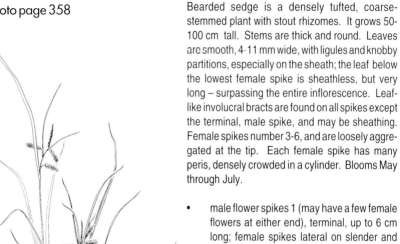

Peri is long and thin, with cleft beak.

Male flower spike.

Bearded sedge has round stems and large, cylindrical female flower spikes.

Female flower spikes.

270

tolerant of low quality water → outcompetes RC6

Carex densa
(Carex breviligulata; Carex vicaria)
dense sedge
Family: Cyperaceae
Status: OBL

Dense sedge is a flat-stemmed, densely tufted species that grows 30-100 cm tall. Leaf sheaths are pale on the inside or front stem surface opposing the blade and distinctively puckered. Leaves are longer than the stems and 2-7 mm wide. The lowest leaves are very short or reduced to sheaths around the base. Leaf sheaths are wrinkled across the front and red-dotted. Flower spikes are small, 6-10 mm long, few-flowered, and attached directly to the stem. Ten or more spikes are densely clustered in an oblong, terminal head, 5-10 cm long, giving the appearance of a single spike. All spikes are subtended by a short, leafy, nonsheathing involucral bract, the lowest of which is 5 cm long. Blooms May through August.

Peri with short, notched beak and obvious veins.

- male flowers above female flowers on same flower spike
- female scales narrower but equal or greater in length to peri, brown or golden, with a firm midvein, sometimes with a short (1.5 mm long) awn
- peri round, flattened, 2-4 mm long, straw-colored to light brown to gold, green toward the margins; body of peri with many obvious veins, abruptly contracted to a clefted beak 1-2 mm long
- stigmas 2; achene lens-shaped, 1-2 mm long

Habitat: Mostly found in the sunny floodplains of the Willamette River Valley. Dense sedge can dominate seasonal wetlands and wet prairies; it often grows in scattered to adjoining clumps around the edges of pools, in shallow marshes and ditches. Always occurs at low elevations. Most common associates are other sedges, rushes *(Juncus* species), and tufted hairgrass *(Deschampsia cespitosa).* This is a sensitive plant in Washington.

Similar Species: Fox sedge *(Carex vulpinoidea)*, northern clustered sedge *(Carex arcta)*, sawbeak sedge *(Carex stipata)*, thick-head sedge *(Carex pachystachya)*, and harefoot sedge *(Carex leporina)*; see key.

Dense sedge has a dense inflorescence of 10 or more compact flower spikes.

SEDGES

271

Carex deweyana var. *deweyana*
Dewey sedge

Family: Cyperaceae
Status: FAC+

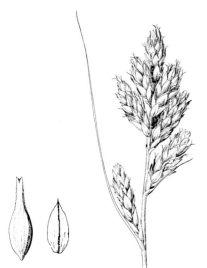

Peri with long, notched beak, and awn-tipped scale.

Inflorescence with one long involucral bract at base of inflorescence.

Dewey sedge forms dense tufts from short roots; it is lacking rhizomes. Stems are 20-100 cm tall. The many flat, grass-like leaves are 2-5 mm wide and shorter than the stems. Leaves occur mainly on the lower part of the stem with the lowest leaves either short or reduced to sheaths around the base. Each stem with 4-8 flower spikes per stem that are erect, cylindrical, light green or greenish tan, loosely aggregated, 7-20 mm long, and attached directly to the stem. The lowest two spikes are subtended by a long, leafy, nonsheathing involucral bract. Blooms late May through July.

- flower spikes with female flowers above male flowers
- female scales white to light brown with a pale green, firm midrib, short awn-tipped, equal to or shorter than the peri
- peri 10-25 per spike, narrow, elongate, 3-5 mm long, thin-walled, green to tan with many obvious veins, lacking wings; body of peri inflated around the achene, tapering to a notched beak, 1-2 mm long
- stigmas 2; achene lens-shaped 1-2 mm long

Habitat: A common, mostly upland, species, Dewey sedge grows on hummocks, along stream banks, and in moist woodlands or forest openings from near sea level to near timberline.

Range: Occurs in all counties in our area.

Similar Species: Henderson sedge *(Carex hendersonii)* and foothill sedge *(Carex tumulicola)*; see key.

Dewey sedge is lacking rhizomes and grows in moist upland forests.

Carex hendersonii
Henderson sedge

Family: Cyperaceae
Status: FAC
Color photo page 358

Henderson sedge is densely tufted with no rhizomes. Stems are round and grow 50-100 cm tall. Leaves are borne all along the stem and are flat, 6-14 mm wide, and shorter than the stems. The lowest leaves are very short with sheaths 1.5-7 cm long. There are several slender flower spikes that are erect, 7-20 mm long, and borne on the upper 3/5 of the stem on stalks. The lowest 2 spikes are subtended by a wide, leafy, sheathing involucral bract. Blooms late May through June.

- male flower spikes terminal, 2-3.5 cm long; female spikes lateral, 2-5 cm long
- female scales white to light brown with pale green midrib, shorter than peri, short awn-tipped, deciduous in mature plants
- peri green, elliptical, tapering at both ends, 4.5-6.5 mm long, smooth, with many obscure veins; body of peri inflated around the achene; beak lacking; style deciduous
- stigmas 3; achene triangular, 3 mm long

Habitat: Lowland forested wetlands, or closed canopy willow-dominated wetlands where soils are saturated but not inundated.

Range: Occurs in all counties in our area.

Similar Species: Dewey sedge *(Carex deweyana)* and foothill sedge *(Carex tumulicola)*; see key.

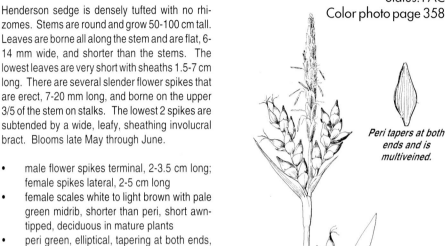

Peri tapers at both ends and is multiveined.

Inflorescence of Henderson sedge has terminal male flower spikes and lateral female spikes.

SEDGES

Henderson sedge has fibrous roots and is lacking rhizomes; the leaves are very wide.

Carex laeviculmus
smooth-stem sedge

Family: Cyperaceae
Status: FACW

Inflorescence of smooth-stemmed sedge is a single head of 4-9 spikes.

The peri has a narrow beak and many veins.

Smooth-stem sedge has densely tufted, slender, weak, arching stems 20-60 cm tall that arise singly from a creeping rhizome. Leaves are pale green, flat, 1-2.5 mm wide, shorter than the stems, and mostly located at the base of the stem. The lowest leaves are very short. Leaves have a ligule. The 4-9 flower spikes, attached directly to the stem, are terminal, erect, and closely aggregated into a single, oval, greenish to brownish green head, 4-6 cm long. The lowest spike is subtended by a short, nonsheathing bract. Blooms June through August.

- female flowers terminal, male flowers below in each spike
- female scales yellowish brown or purple, sometimes with transparent margins, green midribs, equal to or slightly shorter than the peri, occasionally short awn-tipped
- peris a few per spike, lance- to egg-shaped, light green to greenish brown, with many obscure veins, 2-4 mm long; body of peri inflated around the achene, tapering to a narrow beak, to 1 mm long; wings lacking
- 2 stigmas, achene lens-shaped, 1.8-2.6 mm long

Habitat: Forested wetlands from lowlands to midelevations.

Similar Species: Northern clustered sedge *(Carex arcta)* and sawbeak sedge *(Carex stipata)*; see key.

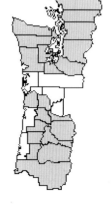

Carex lasiocarpa var. lasiocarpa
slender wetland sedge

Family: Cyperaceae
Status: OBL

Slender wetland sedge has only a few stems per plant, each arising singly or in small clumps from well-developed, creeping rhizomes. Plants are usually 40-120 cm tall. Leaves, which have ligules, are borne above the stem base, are few, longer than the stems, tightly folded or rolled, 1-2 mm wide, and round in cross section. The lowest leaves are short or reduced to sheaths around the base of the plant. Flower spikes, which are few, erect, and located at the top 1/3 of the stem, are attached directly to the stem and 2-20 mm long. Spikes are subtended by sheathless, leafy bracts, the lowest longer than the inflorescence. Blooms May through September.

- male flower spikes 1-3, terminal, 1.5-6 cm long; female spikes 1-3, lateral; or, spikes 1-4.5 cm long, with male flowers, above female flowers
- female scales very narrow, straw-colored to brown with a pale, 3-veined midrib, and brown transparent margins; lower scales longer than the peri, but much narrower
- peri 15-50 per spike, elliptical, densely velvety-hairy, green to greenish brown, obscurely veined; body of peri abruptly tapering to a stout notched beak, 0.8-1.2 mm long
- stigmas 3; achene triangular, 1.5-2 mm long, filling the peri, with persistent and bent style

Peri is densely velvety-hairy.

Habitat: A circumboreal species found in lowland areas in sedge mats in shallow water and pH neutral bogs.

Similar Species: Woolly sedge *(Carex languinosa)* has flat leaves that are 2-5 mm wide.

SEDGES

This mat-forming species has round stems and folded leaves.

Carex lenticularis var. lasiocarpa
(Carex kelloggii)
lenticular sedge; shore sedge

Family: Cyperaceae
Status: FACW+
Color photo page 358

*The obscurely
veined peri has a
peg-like base.*

Lenticular sedge forms dense tufts from fibrous, nonrhizomatous roots. Stems are flat, narrow, and 20-80 cm tall. Leaves are shorter than the stems, narrow, flat, bluish green, 1-3.5 mm wide, and have a ligule. The lowest leaves are brown and very short or just sheaths at base of plant. The 3-6 flower spikes are elongate, cylindrical, narrow, 1.5-5 cm long, and 0.5 cm thick. The lowest spike is subtended by a leafy involucral bract that is nonsheathing and longer than the entire inflorescence. Blooms May through August.

- many dead leaves conspicuous at the bottom of the plant
- male flower spikes terminal and attached directly to stem; female spikes lateral and loosely aggregated on short stalks
- female scales dark red-brown or black, with pale green midrib, white transparent margins, round-tipped, shorter than the peri
- peri lance-shaped with a small stub at the base, light green, membranous, 2-3 mm long, with 3-7 obvious veins; body of peri inflated around the achene, gently tapering to a narrow, black-tipped beak 0.5-1 mm long
- stigmas 2; achene lens-shaped, 1-2 mm long

Habitat: Wet meadows and stream banks. Grows on lakeshores in large single-species communities from sea level to midmontane elevations.

Similar Species: Inflated sedge *(Carex vesicaria)*; see key.

  Plants of lenticular sedge have dense roots but are lacking rhizomes; the involucral bract is longer than the inflorescence.

Carex leporina
harefoot sedge
Family: Cyperaceae
Status: FACW

Harefoot sedge is densely tufted and deeply rooted but nonrhizomatous. Stems are round and grow 40-80 cm tall. Leaves are shorter than the stem, flat, 30-40 cm long, 2-4 mm wide, and borne toward the base. The lowest leaves are greatly reduced. There 4-8 flower spikes are attached directly to the stem, are erect, 7-15 mm long, and closely aggregated into a single, oval head 1.5-4 cm long. The lowest spike is subtended by a short, leafy, nonsheathing involucral bract. Blooms late May through July.

- female flower spikes terminal, or with female flowers above male flowers on same spike
- female scales light to dark brown, occasionally with green midrib and toothed margins, equal in length to the peri
- peri egg-shaped, flat, 3.5-5 mm long, moderately spreading, tan to pale green-brown, with obvious veins along body, and toothed, winged margins to 1 mm wide; beak cleft, base with protruding knob
- stigmas 2; achene lens-shaped, 1-2 mm long

Habitat: Wet meadows from the lowlands to near midmontane elevations.

Similar Species: Slenderbeak sedge *(Carex athrostachya)*, sawbeak sedge *(Carex stipata)*, thick-head sedge *(Carex pachystachya)*, and fox sedge *(Carex vulpinoidea)*; see key.

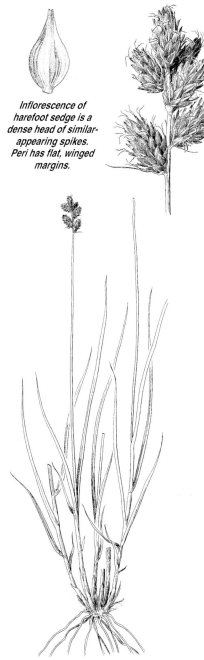

Inflorescence of harefoot sedge is a dense head of similar-appearing spikes. Peri has flat, winged margins.

Harefoot sedge is densely tufted, but has no rhizomes.

SEDGES

277

Carex lyngbyei
Lyngby sedge
Family: Cyperaceae
Status: OBL
Color photo page 359

Lyngby sedge is a common, coastal, wetland, estuarine species. Stems are round, 15-100 cm tall, with a purplish brown base, and arise singly (occasionally clumped) from creeping rhizomes and stolons. Leaves are long, 2-10 mm wide, flat, and shorter than the stem. Leaf margins are rolled under. The lowest leaves are very short or present only as sheaths at base of the plant. There are 3-7 flower spikes that are long-stalked, elongate, cylindrical, drooping, 1.5-5 cm long, and loosely aggregated. The lowest spike is subtended by a long, leafy, nonsheathing involucral bract that is usually longer than the inflorescence. Blooms April through July.

Top, female flower spike on slender, nodding stalk; above, beakless peri with 2 stigmas, scale, and male flower spike.

- male flower spikes 1-3, terminal; female spikes lateral, or with male flowers above female flowers on same spike
- female scales narrow, light to dark brown, with pale green midrib, longer than the peri, with long, white, awned tip
- peri egg-shaped, green to straw-colored, plump, thick-walled, 2-4 mm long; body of peri inflated around the achene; beak lacking
- stigmas 2; achene lens-shaped, fiddle-shaped, or bent over at the middle, 2 mm long

Habitat: Estuaries, coastal marshes, and tidal flats.

Similar species: Lenticular sedge *(Carex lenticularis)* and slough sedge *(Carex obnupta)*; see key.

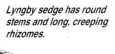

Lyngby sedge has round stems and long, creeping rhizomes.

Carex macrocephala var. *macrocephala*
bighead sedge

Family: Cyperaceae
Status: FAC-
Color photo page 359

Bighead sedge is a common coastal species that is easily identified by its extremely stout, triangular stems that are 10-40 cm tall and by its large inflorescence head. Stems arise singly or a few together from large rhizomes. Leaves are thick, firm and flat, with toothed margins. The upper leaves are usually longer than the stem, 3-8 mm wide, and clustered around the base of the plant. The basal leaves are very short and scale-like. Flower spikes are large, numerous, spiny, and closely aggregated into a single, oval head. The involucral bracts are short and barely distinguishable from the female scales. Blooms June through July.

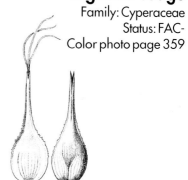

Peri with narrow, cleft beak and 3 stigmas.

- male and female plants separate; male heads 3.5-5 cm long, 1-1.5 cm thick and less common; female heads 3.5-8 cm long, 1.5-5 cm thick
- female scales firm, almost woody, short awn-tipped, multiveined, equal to the peri
- peri large, 10-15 mm long, teardrop-shaped, coarse, shiny, gold, widely spreading at maturity, with many veins; body of peri inflated around the achene, and long tapering to a narrow, cleft, beak 1 mm long
- stigmas 3; achene obtusely triangular, 4 mm long

Habitat: Sandy beaches, on sand dunes along the coast, and in estuaries.

Similar Species: None.

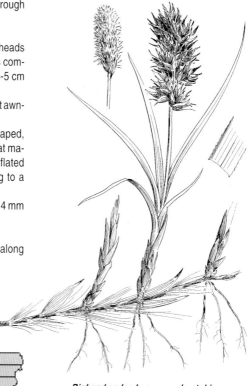

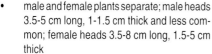

SEDGES

Bighead sedge has very robust rhizomes and triangular stems. The male flower spike, at left, occurs on separate plants.

Carex obnupta
slough sedge

Family: Cyperaceae
Status: OBL
Color photo page 359

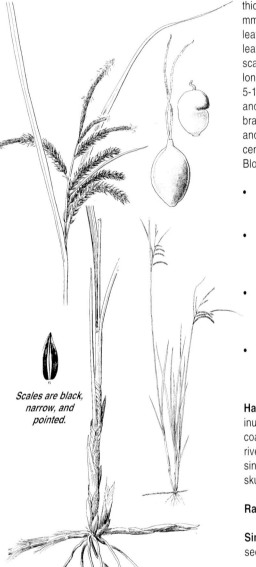

Scales are black, narrow, and pointed.

Slough sedge is the most common sedge in urban areas. Plants are densely tufted on stout, creeping rhizomes and grow 60-150 cm tall. Stems are thick and triangular. Leaves are coarse, firm, 3-7 mm wide, with the margins rolled under; upper leaves are shorter than the stems. The lowest leaves are reduced to sheaths with purplish brown scales around the base that break with age into long fibers. The 4-8, cylindrical flower spikes are 5-12 cm long and loosely aggregated at the tip, and attached directly to each stem. Involucral bracts occur below the lowest two or three spikes and are sheathless and longer than the inflorescence; the lowest is leaf-like and 10-50 cm long. Blooms April through July.

- male flower spikes 1-3, terminal, other spikes female, or with male flowers above female on same spike
- female scales narrow, pointed, dark brown or black with pale brown midrib and transparent margins, multiveined, longer than the peri
- peri elliptic, shiny brown, plump, thick-walled, 2.4-3.1 mm long, with obscure veins; body of peri abruptly tapering to a short beak, 0.1-0.3 mm
- stigmas 2; achene lens-shaped, usually constricted or indented at median area, 2-2.4 mm long, filling the peri

Habitat: In fresh water; prefers wet, shallowly inundated woods, meadows, roadside ditches, coastal swamps, lakeshores, bogs, marshes, and river banks. In muddy areas it can grow as a single-species stand. It is often associated with skunk cabbage *(Lysichiton americanum).*

Range: Occurs in all counties in our area.

Similar Species: Lyngby sedge *(Carex lyngbyei)*; see key.

Slough sedge has achenes that are bent at the middle. Inflorescence has 2 long involucral bracts, terminal male flower spike, and lateral, long-drooping female spikes.

Carex pachystachya
thick-head sedge
Family: Cyperaceae
Status: FAC

Thick-head sedge is densely tufted with short roots and round stems 15-70 cm tall. Leaves are flat, 2-5 mm wide, shorter than the stems, and mostly located on the lower part of the stem. The lowest leaves are reduced to sheaths around the base. There are 3-10 erect flower spikes 7-12 mm long, that are attached directly to each stem and closely aggregated into a single, oval, greenish to brownish green head 1-2.5 cm long. Involucral bracts are barely visible, or appear as a female scale at the very bottom of the inflorescence. Blooms late May through August.

- each flower spike with female flowers occurring above the male flowers on the same spike
- female scales narrow, red-brown with a greenish midrib, shorter and narrower than peri
- peri egg- to lance-shaped, moderately spreading, all copper-brown or with a tan center and green margins, 3.5-5 mm long, gently tapering to a dark-tipped, thin-walled beak 1.2-1.6 mm long, with toothed, wide, winged margins
- stigmas 2; achene lens-shaped, 1.4-2 mm long, much smaller than peri which is compressed around it

Habitat: Open dry to damp slopes, or open forests from lowland to near timberline.

Similar Species: Slenderbeak sedge *(Carex athrostachya)*, sawbeak sedge *(Carex stipata)*, northern clustered sedge *(Carex arcta)*, and harefoot sedge *(Carex leporina)*; see key.

Dense, head-like inflorescence bearing 3-10 tightly aggregated spikes, and peri with flattened wings.

SEDGES

Thick-head sedge forms very dense tufts.

Carex stipata var. *stipata*
sawbeak sedge; prickly sedge

Family: Cyperaceae
Status: OBL
Color photo page 359

Peri has long-tapered beak and obvious veins.

Inflorescence is a loosely packed head of many short spikes.

Sawbeak sedge has thin-wrinkled leaf sheaths.

This plant grows in dense tufts and is lacking rhizomes.

Sawbeak sedge forms densely tufted clumps from nonrhizomatous rootstocks. The stout, triangular stems are spongy inside and 30-100 cm tall. Leaves are yellow-green, usually shorter than the stems, very coarse, flat, and 5-11 mm wide. The flattened face of the leaf sheaths is thin, obviously wrinkled, and tears easily. The lowest leaves are short or reduced to sheaths around the base. The numerous, small, few-flowered spikes are attached directly to the stem and densely aggregated into a single, long, golden head, 3-10 cm long and 1-3 cm thick. Involucral bracts are sheathless and only the lowest is evident. Blooms late May through August.

*   flower spikes each with male flowers above, female flowers below
*   female scales, shorter than the peri, pale brown with a greenish midrib that extends as a short awn
*   peri egg-shaped with an inflated base and a long tapering body, 4-6 mm, greenish to straw-brown, widely spreading with obvious veins
*   beak toothed, extending past the scale and giving plant a prickly appearance; cleft beak elongated (4-8 mm)
*   stigmas 2; achene lens-shaped, 1.3-1.7 mm long

Habitat: Very common, especially in disturbed wet meadows and ditches in lowland to midmontane elevations.

Similar Species: Slenderbeak sedge *(Carex athrostachya)*, northern clustered sedge *(Carex arcta)*, harefoot sedge *(Carex leporina)*, and thick-head sedge *(Carex pachystachya)*; see key.

Carex tumulicola
foothill sedge
Family: Cyperaceae
Status: FACU

Foothill sedge is a small species, 20-80 cm tall, that grows in tufted clusters on short creeping rhizomes. Stems are obscurely triangular. Leaves are shorter than the stem, flat, 1-2.5 mm wide, widely spaced, and borne on the lower stem. The lowest leaves are short or reduced to sheaths around the base of the stem. There are several (less than 10) greenish tan to brown flower spikes attached directly to each stem that are small, erect, and loosely aggregated into a few-flowered cluster 1.5-3.5 cm long. Lower involucral bracts are long, nonsheathing, and awn-tipped. Blooms May through June.

- flower spikes with male flowers above, female flowers below
- female scales broad, red-brown with white margins, short awn-tipped, longer than the peri
- peri lance-shaped, green to straw-colored, 3.8-5 mm long, abruptly tapering to a cleft and toothed beak 1.2-1.9 mm long
- stigmas 2; achene lens-shaped, 1.8 to 2.2 mm long, filling the peri

Habitat: Open, grassy slopes and dry meadows, and open forests, especially adjacent to wet meadows and drainage ditches in pastures.

Similar Species: Henderson sedge *(Carex hendersonii);* see key.

Inflorescence is loosely clustered with involucral bracts of unequal length; peri tapers at both ends.

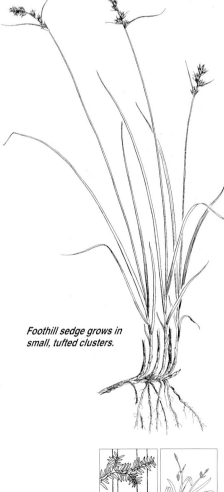

Foothill sedge grows in small, tufted clusters.

SEDGES

Carex unilateralis
one-sided sedge

Family: Cyperaceae
Status: FACW
Color photo page 360

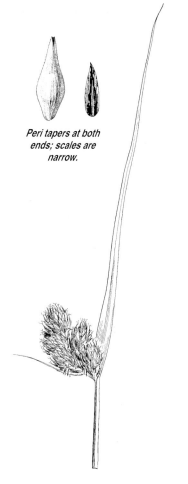

Peri tapers at both ends; scales are narrow.

One-sided sedge is a densely tufted, round-stemmed species, 30-100 cm tall. Leaves are flat, 2-5 mm wide, and borne on the lower half of the stem. The lowest leaves are reduced to sheaths around the base. There are several 6-10 mm long flower spikes attached directly to the stem. They are aggregated into a single, greenish to medium brown, spherical-oval head, 1-2 cm long. The lowest involucral bracts are sheathless and 5-15 cm long. Blooms late May through July.

- female flower spikes above male spikes; or female flowers above male flowers on same spike
- female scales narrow, shorter than the peri, brown to straw-colored, with a green midrib that extends past the tip as a short awn
- peri lance-shaped, widest in the middle, tapering at both ends, moderately spreading, 3-4 mm long, pale green or tan with a brown midrib; margins flattened and winged; body of peri tapering to an obscure, toothed beak
- stigmas 2; achene lens-shaped, 1-2 mm long

Habitat: Moist or wet places at low elevations.

Similar Species: Slenderbeak sedge *(Carex athrostachya)*, northern clustered sedge *(Carex arcta)*, harefoot sedge *(Carex leporina)*, thick-head sedge *(Carex pachystachya)*, and sawbeak sedge *(Carex stipata)*; see key.

The inflorescence of this sedge is borne as a one-sided cluster with a bract that continues and appears stem-like.

Carex utriculata
(Carex rostrata)
beaked sedge
Family: Cyperaceae
Status: OBL
Color photo page 360

Beaked sedge is a robust, tufted species with long rhizomes. Plants are 50-120 cm tall, with thick, coarse, round stems and leaves. The tufts occasionally form continuous mats. Stems emerge singly from stout, deeply rooted and creeping rhizomes. Leaves are V-shaped, leathery, longer than the stems, and 4-12 mm wide. The lower part of the leaf that sheaths the base is brown above and purple at the base. Leaves have a ligule. Flower spikes are cylindrical, erect, and are scattered along the upper portion of the stem. The spikes are yellow to light brown when young, and golden with age. The female spikes are loosely aggregated into a cluster 1.5-3.5 cm long. The lower involucral bracts on the female spikes are longer than the inflorescence and nonsheathing to short-sheathed. Blooms late June through August.

Peri, with 3 stigmas and a short-notched beak, is inflated around achene.

Erect female flower spike shown with long leaf-like involucral bract.

- male flower spikes terminal, 2-7 cm long, 2-4 mm thick; middle spikes with male flowers above female; lower spikes all female, 2-10 cm long, 1 cm thick
- female scales narrow, shorter than the peri, short awn-tipped, straw-colored to golden with transparent to reddish margins
- peri round, smooth, inflated, densely clustered in a cylinder, green to straw-colored, 4-7 mm long, abruptly tapering to a cleft beak, 1-2 mm long; 50-200 peris per spikelet
- stigmas 3; achene triangular, 1.3-2 mm long, smaller than the peri; style persistent and bending inside the peri after the achene is mature

Habitat: Acidic wetlands with permanent standing water, and along the margins of lakes, ponds, and bogs; from lowland to midmontane elevations.

Similar Species: None.

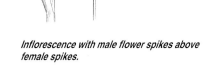

Inflorescence with male flower spikes above female spikes.

SEDGES

285

Carex vesicaria var. major
(Carex exsiccata)
inflated sedge
Family: Cyperaceae
Status: OBL

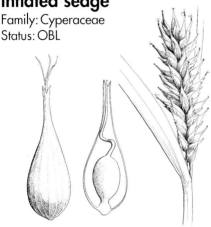

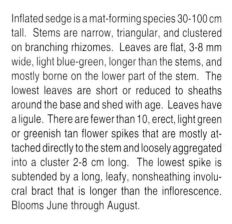

Peri is lute-shaped with with veins, 3 stigmas, and a long, narrow, and notched beak; achene has a bent style; female flower spikes are sharp-tipped and found below the male spikes.

Inflated sedge is a mat-forming species 30-100 cm tall. Stems are narrow, triangular, and clustered on branching rhizomes. Leaves are flat, 3-8 mm wide, light blue-green, longer than the stems, and mostly borne on the lower part of the stem. The lowest leaves are short or reduced to sheaths around the base and shed with age. Leaves have a ligule. There are fewer than 10, erect, light green or greenish tan flower spikes that are mostly attached directly to the stem and loosely aggregated into a cluster 2-8 cm long. The lowest spike is subtended by a long, leafy, nonsheathing involucral bract that is longer than the inflorescence. Blooms June through August.

- male flower spikes 2-3 mm thick, located above female spikes 1-2 cm thick; some spikes with both sexes and female flowers above male
- female scales narrow, straw-colored to reddish brown, sharp-tipped, shorter than the peri
- peri crowded in spike 7-11 mm long, smooth with 10-20 obvious veins; body of peri inflated around the achene but tapering to a long, dented beak, 2-3 mm long; peris number 20-100 per spike
- stigmas 3; achene triangular, 2-2.5 mm long, continuous with a permanent style that is long and bent

Habitat: Wet soil or shallow water in bogs or emergent pristine, freshwater wetlands, and at the margins of ponds or streams, from lowlands to moderate elevations.

Similar Species: Lenticular sedge *(Carex lenticularis)*; see key.

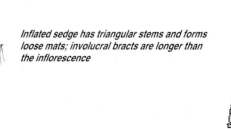

Inflated sedge has triangular stems and forms loose mats; involucral bracts are longer than the inflorescence

Carex vulpinoidea
fox sedge
Family: Cyperaceae
Status: OBL

Fox sedge is a densely tufted species that grows 30-100 cm tall. Leaves are flat, 2-5 mm wide, and scattered on the lower 1/2 to 2/3 of the stem. The leaf sheath facing away from the leaf is red-spotted, the tissue thin and transparent and wrinkled into horizontal bands. The lowest leaves are reduced to sheaths around the base of the stem. There are 10 or more, small, 5-10 cm long, flower spikelets attached directly to the stem that are closely aggregated into a sometimes inter-rupted, greenish to medium brown, spherical-oval head 1-2 cm long. Each spike has a short sheathless involucral bract with the lowest bracts to 5 cm long. Blooms late May through July.

- male flowers above female flowers on the same spike
- female scales narrow, shorter than the peri, gold-brown to straw-colored, with thin but not papery margins, the green midvein often extending as a short (1-5 mm) awn
- peri round, 2-3.5 mm long, straw-colored or light brown, often with greenish margins; veins lacking; body of peri tapering into a cleft beak
- stigmas 2; achene lens-shaped, 1-1.5 mm long

Habitat: Wet meadows and emergent marshes with standing water, and other very moist lowland habitats.

Similar Species: Slenderbeak sedge *(Carex athrostachya)*, northern clustered sedge *(Carex arcta)*, dense sedge *(Carex densa)*, harefoot sedge *(Carex leporina)*, thick-head sedge *(Carex pachystachya)*, and sawbeak sedge *(Carex stipata)*; see key.

Peri with cleft beak

Inflorescence with many similar spikes and short involucral bracts.

Fox sedge is a robust, densely tufted plant. Leaf sheaths are wrinkled across the front.

SEDGES

287

Cyperus strigosus
strawcolor flatsedge; false nutsedge
Family: Cyperaceae
Status: FACW

Spike-like inflorescence occurs in dense, cylindrical clusters.

Strawcolor flatsedge grows in tufts and bears many spikelet clusters.

This species is nonrhizomatous with a bulbous base. Stems are solid, mostly triangular, usually solitary, and to 80 cm tall. Long, grass-like leaves are crowded at the base of the stems and have closed sheaths. Stems have several to many flower spikelets usually arranged in several spike-like clusters. Flowers are inconspicuous, have both male and female organs, and are borne singly at the base of the scales. Stamens number 3, less commonly 1 or 2.

* flower spikelets numerous in dense, short-cylindrical clusters, spreading at right angles from the flower stem, arranged in 2 vertical rows, deciduous at maturity
* involucral bracts sheathless and leafy
* spikelet scales yellow, 3-6 mm long
* style bifid or more often trifid
* achene lens-shaped or 3-angled, not enclosed in a peri

Habitat: Prefers wet habitats along steam banks. Found in lowland areas.

Range: Widespread in Canada and the United States, not common in Washington, but occurs frequently in southern Oregon.

Similar Species: Strawcolor flatsedge could possibly be mistaken for leafy species of bulrushes *(Scirpus)*, but the achenes of those plants have bristles and the flower spikelets are not arranged in 2 vertical rows.

Functional Value: Abundant achenes provide a food source for wildlife.

Dulichium arundinaceum
dulichium; horsetail sedge

Family: Cyperaceae
Status: OBL
Color photo page 360

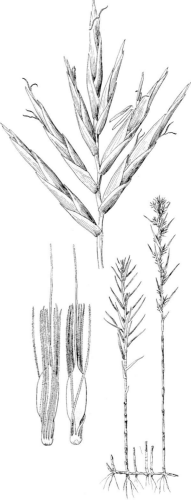

Dulichium is a rhizomatous sedge that grows 30-100 cm tall, and has rounded, or somewhat triangular, hollow stems. Leaves are short, firm, well distributed in 3's along the stem; lower leaves are reduced to bladeless sheaths. Flower spikelets number 7-10 per short, axillary spike. Flowers have both male and female organs and are borne singly at the base of the scales. Stamens number 3; style is forked into 2.

- stems arise singly from the rhizome
- flower spikelets arranged in 2 flattened vertical rows on the flower stem
- bristles barb-like, number 6-9
- achene lens-shaped, not enclosed in a peri

Habitat: Emergent wet meadows and acidic bog wetlands; often along the margins of streams or ponds. Occurs occasionally in the lowlands and more commonly at midelevations in the mountains.

Range: Southwest British Columbia to California. Coastal to Idaho and northwest Montana. Widespread across north America from Minnesota to Newfoundland, south to Texas and Florida.

Similar species: None.

Functional Value: Excellent waterfowl fodder; however, a large flock can decimate a dulichium population quickly.

SEDGES

Above, the 2-sided inflorescence of dulichium; left, achene with many long bristles; and right, the long-running rhizomes of this mat-forming sedge.

Genus: *Eleocharis*
spikerushes
Family: Cyperaceae

The spikerushes are sedges with long needle-like stems. Plants lack actual leaves, but may have sheaths at the base of the stems. Flower spikes are terminal, flame-shaped, and densely compact, consisting of a single, terminal spikelet. The perianth is reduced to bristles around the achene and each flower is located behind a scale. Achenes often have a tubercle.

Habitat: These plants occur in shallow water in wet meadows. Needle spikerush *(Eleocharis acicularis)* grows where the water is mostly persistent across the season while the other two species grow in areas where the water dries by the end of the season. All plants grow in mud along the margins of pools and streams. Found in coastal lowland to midmontane elevations. Often associated with duckweeds *(Lemna* species) and bulrushes *(Scirpus* species).

Range: Spikerushes are circumboreal species found throughout our range.

Functional Value: The stems and fruits are used by birds for nesting material and food. The roots are eaten by mammals. These plants provide effective erosion control on banks when plant populations are dense.

Eleocharis acicularis var. *acicularis*
needle spikerush
Family: Cyperaceae
Status: OBL
photo page 360

Inflorescence is a dense head of overlapping scales and achene with bristles.

Needle spikerush is the smallest of the common spikerushes with stems only 3-12 cm tall. It can be annual or perennial. Spikelets are 3-7 mm long and 3- to 15-flowered. Stigmas number 3; style is bifid or trifid, thickened toward the base, the thickened part persistent as a tubercle.

- forms dense tufts (mats) of thread-like, branching rhizomes
- stems angular to rounded or flattened, needle-like
- basal sheaths purple
- scales with green midrib and red transparent margins
- bristles lacking to 3, equal to or longer than achene, giving the mature flowering plant a white-tipped appearance, few-flowered
- achene lens-shaped, round to slightly 3-angled, yellow-brown, ribbed both vertically and horizontally, with conic flat tubercle

Needle spikerush grows in spreading, needle-like clumps in shallow water.

Eleocharis obtusa var. *ovata*
(Eleocharis ovata)
ovoid spikerush

Status: OBL
Color photo page 360

Ovoid spikerush is a medium-sized, loosely tufted annual. The stems are only 5-50 cm tall. Leaves are all basal and appear as dark sheaths. Flower spikes have 40-80 flowers. Stigmas number 2.

- underground rhizomes absent
- scales 1.7-2.5 mm long, purple or brown with a green midrib and pale transparent margins
- bristles 6-7, equal to the achene
- achene broad-based, lens-shaped, dark brown, 1-1.5 mm long, smooth with a flat triangular-shaped tubercle that is constricted at the base

Above left, flat tubercle; below, lens-shaped achene; and right, compact inflorescence of 40-80 flowers.

Plants are lacking rhizomes and grow in clumps of short stems. Leaves appear only as sheaths at the base of the stems.

SEDGES

Spikerushes continued on next page...

291

Eleocharis palustris
creeping spikerush

status: OBL
Color photo page 360

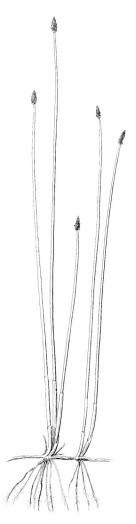

Creeping spikerush grows to 1 m tall. Leaves appear only as sheaths around the base of the stem.

Creeping spikerush, the largest of the common spikerushes, is perennial and grows to 1 m tall. Flower spikes are 5-20 mm long, lance-shaped to oval, with many flowers and empty scales at the base. Stigmas number 2.

- grows scattered in small clusters along a dark brown rhizome
- basal sheaths reddish
- scales light to dark brown or chestnut
- bristles 4-6, slightly longer than the achene
- achene lens-shaped, yellow to medium brown, smooth, with a long (0.4-0.7 mm) spear-shaped tubercle

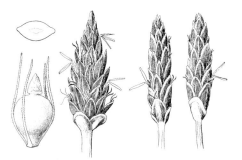

Achene with 4 long bristles and arrow-shaped tubercle. Flower spikes can appear open and inflated (left) or narrow (right), and bear fewer than 30 flowers.

Eriophorum chamissonis
russet cottongrass; Chamisson's cotton-grass

Family: Cyperaceae
Status: OBL
Color photo page 361

This is the only cottongrass species found in the lowlands of Washington and Oregon. Leaves are few, mostly borne near the base, with a well-developed dark brown sheath that is broad and flattened.

- stems, 30-40 cm tall, emerge singly from creeping rhizomes, often in large colonies
- stems flattened, channelled, and twisted along their length
- flower spikes subtended by 4-6 large, sterile, dark brown scales
- scales small, blackish green, nestled down within the cottony bristles
- perianth bristles red-tinged to white, far exceeding length of achene
- achenes dark, 3-angled, small, ridged along the back, sharp-pointed

Habitat: Mostly bogs, but sometimes emergent wet meadows. Grows in lowland to moderate elevations in the mountains.

Range: Canada and Alaska south to Minnesota, Wyoming, and coastal Oregon. Present in many counties in Washington and Oregon.

Similar Species: None when in flower. The stems of Baltic rush *(Juncus balticus)* appear similar to the sterile stems of russet cottongrass; however, the rush grows in coastal habitats and lacks basal leaves. Beakrush *(Rhynchospora alba)* is also similar in the vegetative state, but has sharply 3-angled stems, and lacks basal leaves.

Functional Value: Bristles are used as nesting material by some birds.

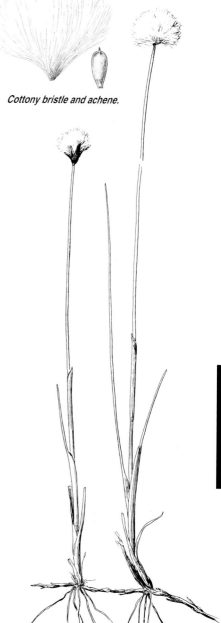

Cottony bristle and achene.

SEDGES

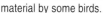

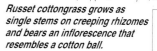

Russet cottongrass grows as single stems on creeping rhizomes and bears an inflorescence that resembles a cotton ball.

Rhynchospora alba
beakrush

Family: Cyperaceae
status: OBL
Color photo page 361

Achene with many long bristles and scale-covered achenes with bristles showing.

Beakrush has sharply 3-angled stems and grows in spagnum bogs.

This slender, few-flowered, acid bog sedge grows in small clumps from spreading rhizomes. Stems are 15-50 cm tall and superficially resemble those of rushes *(Juncus* species). Leaves are gray-green, very narrow (1 mm wide), and grow along the flowering stem; the lowermost are reduced to sheaths. Flower spikelet clusters number 1-3 per stem and are compact. Each spikelet has 2-5 flowers. Achenes are 1.5-2 mm long.

- stems sharply 3-angled
- flower spikelets light brown to off-white
- scales whitish to pale greenish brown
- bristles 10-12, equal to, or slightly longer than, achene and tubercle
- achenes brownish green, lens-shaped, with a lance-shaped tubercle

Habitat: Sphagnum bogs and other acidic wetlands at low elevations. Often found associated with beaked sedge *(Carex utriculata)*, bog Labrador-tea *(Rhododendron groenlandicum)*, and russet cottongrass *(Eriophorum chamissonis)*.

Range: Circumboreal, but not continuously so, from Newfoundland to North Carolina, across southern Canada to the Pacific. From the Alaska panhandle to central California. Mainly west of the Cascades.

Similar Species: Russet cottongrass *(Eriophorum chamissonis)* appears similar in the vegetative state; however, it has mostly basal leaves and twisted stems. Baltic rush *(Juncus balticus)* and slender rush *(Juncus tenuis)* both vaguely resemble beakrush, but lack leaves along the stem and have a different flower structure. Baltic rush is coastal and neither rush tolerates the acid conditions required by beakrush.

Functional Value: Beakrush adds to the species diversity of sphagum bogs.

Key to Identifying the Bulrushes (Genus: *Scirpus*)

1a. Plant tolerates shallow inundation but does not grow under water...2
1b. Aquatic; rhizomes and leaves grow under water; inflorescence plus stem end flaccid, float horizontally on the water surface...subterminate bulrush *(Scirpus subterminalis)*

   2a. Flowering stems with no leaves – basal leaf sheaths only..3
   2b. Flowering stems with leaf blades...4

      3a. Stems tough, not easily crushed, spikelets dull gray-brown, 0.8-1.5 cm long, scales gray-white with red-brown stripes, 3.5-4 mm long...
....hardstem bulrush *(Scirpus lacustris* spp. *acutus)*
      3b. Stems easily crushed, spikelets reddish brown, less than 1 cm long, scales brown, 2.5-3 mm long..softstem bulrush *(Scirpus tabernaemontanii)*

      4a. Spikelets solitary to a few, attached directly to stem...5
      4b. Spikelets numerous, on branched inflorescence; 2 or more involucral bracts..............6

         5a. A single large involucral bract extending past the inflorescence as a continuation of the stem; bristles shorter or equal to achene ....
....three-square bulrush *(Scirpus americanus)*
         5b. Involucral bracts occurring as 2 or 3 empty very short scales of a solitary spikelet, bristles well exceed achene ....tufted bulrush *(Scirpus caespitosus)*

         6a. Flowering stems triangular and soft; bristles shorter than scales...........................7
         6b. Flowering stems stiff, almost woody, round; inflorescence branching; bristles longer than scales...woolly sedge *(Scirpus atrocinctus)*

            7a. Spikelets 12-20 mm long, barely branching, not very numerous (fewer than 50), stems sharply triangular........................seacoast bulrush *(Scirpus maritimus)*
            7b. Spikelets 3-8 mm long, numerous (greater than 50), inflorescence highly branching; stems large, pithy, round-triangular..
....small-fruited bulrush *(Scirpus microcarpus)*

SEDGES

Scirpus acutus
(Scirpus lacustris ssp. acutus)
hardstem bulrush; tule

Family: Cyperaceae
Status: OBL
Color photo page 361

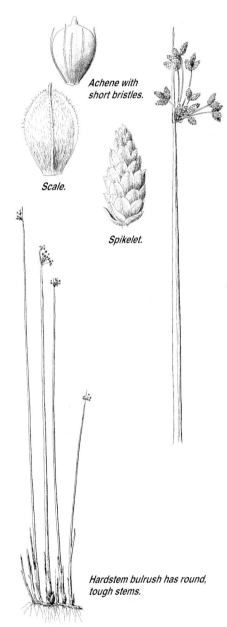

Achene with
short bristles.

Scale.

Spikelet.

Hardstem bulrush has round,
tough stems.

Hardstem bulrush is a stout 1-3 m tall bulrush. Gray-green stems arise from a thick rhizome and can form extensive stands. Flower spikelets are tightly compact, dull gray-brown, 8-15 mm long, and borne in terminal clusters that attach directly to the stem. Blooms June to August.

- stems round, can be over 1 cm thick toward the base, firm (not easily crushed)
- basal sheaths (leaves) well developed
- involucral bracts single, green, erect, 2-10 cm long, appearing as a continuation of stem, longer than inflorescence
- flower spikelets many
- scales 3.5-4 mm long, with reddish brown marks on a gray-white background, jagged-edged, with an awn, inserted in a notched tip
- bristles 3-6, equal to or shorter than the achene; achene not visible at maturity

Habitat: Lakeshores, emergent marshes, and mostly freshwater marshes, although tolerates salt and alkali. Favors mud substrates and tolerates water up to 1 m deep. Often associated with cattails *(Typha* species) and yellow pond-lily *(Nuphar luteum).*

Range: Common throughout our area and in other temperate climates in North America. Occurs in all counties in our area.

Similar Species: Softstem bulrush *(Scirpus tabernaemontanii)* is very similar; there are reports that the two species hybridize. However, softstem bulrush prefers coastal areas, is smaller, and seldom forms extensive colonies. In addition, stems of softstem bulrush are not as tough, and easily crushed between the fingers, flower spikelets are borne singly, scales are grayish brown, and achenes are visible at maturity.

Functional Value: Stems are used by birds for nesting material and as nest attachment sites. Achenes are a favored food of waterfowl.

Ethnobotanical Uses: Stems are used in basketry and for making mats.

Scirpus americanus
three-square bulrush; Olney's bulrush; American threesquare

Family: Cyperaceae
Status: OBL
Color photo page 361

Three-square bulrush is 15-100 cm tall with stout rhizomes. Stems are thin, firm, and sharply triangular. Leaves are 2-4 mm broad. Spikelets are 7-20 mm long and borne in a compact cluster. Blooms May to August.

- leaves sheathing, borne near nonbulbous base, often folded or channeled
- flower spikelets solitary to few, attached directly to stem
- involucral bracts single, 2-15 cm long, appearing as a continuation of the stem
- scales yellowish brown or reddish brown to blackish purple, thin, the midrib extends past as an awn
- bristles 2-6, unequal, shorter or equal to achene
- achenes lens-shaped with an obvious sharp tip

Habitat: Marshes with either fresh or brackish water, in shallow water or soil saturated to the surface.

Range: Europe, New Zealand, and Australia; widespread in North America and in coastal areas throughout our range.

Similar Species: Seacoast bulrush *(Scirpus maritimus)* has a bulbous base, leaves arranged along the stem, up to 20 flower spikelets, and usually 2-3, long, leaf-like involucral bracts.

Functional Value: Adds to community diversity in shallow brackish areas.

Ethnobotanical Uses: Native Americans use this species extensively in basketry.

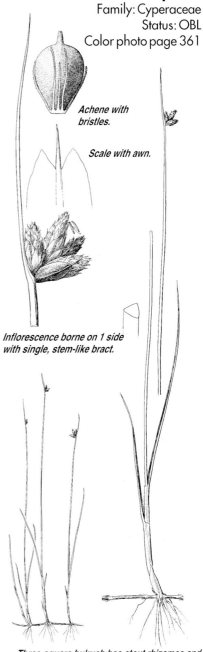

Achene with bristles.

Scale with awn.

Inflorescence borne on 1 side with single, stem-like bract.

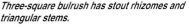

Three-square bulrush has stout rhizomes and triangular stems.

SEDGES

Scirpus atrocinctus
(Scirpus cyperinus var. brachypodus)
woolly sedge; wool-grass
Family: Cyperaceae
Status: OBL
Color photo page 361

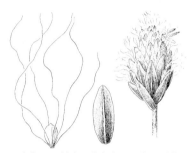

Achene with long bristles, scale, and flower spikelet.

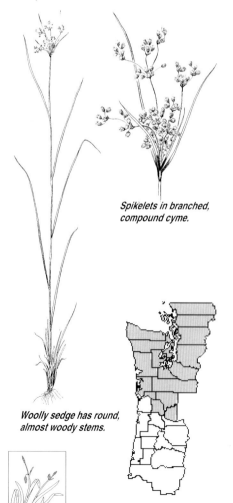

Spikelets in branched, compound cyme.

Woolly sedge has round, almost woody stems.

Woolly sedge is a leafy, tall, nonrhizomatous sedge that grows in dense, raised tufts, 80-150 cm tall. Stems are firm, almost woody, round, and leafy. Leaves are grass-like, elongate, flat, 2-6 mm wide, and orange to reddish green. Blooms from July to August.

*   flower spikelets numerous in a compound, branched, terminal cyme
*   involucral bracts many, leaf-like, unequal, a few exceeding the length of the inflorescence
*   scales numerous, blunt, red-brown, striate on a pale to often blackish or blackish green background
*   bristles 6, up to 5 x longer than achene, giving plant woolly appearance
*   achenes pale, small (less than 1 mm)

Habitat: Shallow acidic marshes, especially in less disturbed sites. Often found with American brooklime *(Veronica americana)*, various rushes *(Juncus* species), and other sedge species such as *Carex* and *Eleocharis*. Originally reported as rare, it is currently very common in less disturbed urban and suburban areas.

Range: Throughout our range, particularly in central to northern Washington; much more common than reported in Hitchcock's *Flora of the Pacific Northwest.*

Similar Species: Small-fruited bulrush *(Scirpus microcarpus)* also has long stems but they are triangular and not woody-appearing, leaves are wider and yellow-green, bristles number 4 and are equal in length to the achene; it grows in more disturbed sites.

Functional Value: An excellent food source, woolly sedge is grazed by waterfowl. Leaves are used by waterfowl for nesting material.

Scirpus caespitosus
tufted sedge; tufted clubrush

Family: Cyperaceae
Status: OBL

This low-growing, 10-40 cm tall sedge is densely tufted and rhizomatous. Stems are round in profile. Leaves are present only as short, 4-6 mm long scales at the base of the plant. Flower spikelets are terminal, medium to light brown, and 4-6 mm long. Blooms July to August.

- flower spikelets solitary
- involucral bracts 2-3, deciduous with age, appearing as empty or very short scales; lowermost scale has long, broad awn that is continuous with the midstripe
- bristles white, longer (2 x) than the achene, but subequal to the scale
- achenes with short, rounded tip

Habitat: Prefers sphagnum bogs, but also grows in acidic fens.

Range: Circumboreal. In the West, south to southwest Montana, northeast and central Utah, and western Washington to central Oregon.

Similar Species: Tufted sedge is the only small, common *Scirpus* species found in sphagnum bogs that has involucral bracts which look identical to scales.

No illustration available.

SEDGES

Scirpus maritimus
seacoast bulrush

Family: Cyperaceae
Status: OBL
Color photo page 362

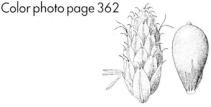

Spikelet, and achene with bulbous tip and short bristles.

Seacoast bulrush is stout, rhizomatous, 20-150 cm tall, and grows from a bulbous base. Leaves are many, erect, flat, 1 cm wide, often 1 m long, and borne evenly along the stem. Reddish brown flower spikelets numbering from 3-20 are each 1-2 cm long, and mostly attached in a cluster to the stem, but a few may be attached in groups of 2 or 3. Blooms June to September.

- rhizomes often bearing thick tubers with few rootlets
- stems sharply triangular with concave edges, 5-10 mm in diameter
- flower spikelets 12-20 mm long, fewer than 50
- involucral bracts, 2-3 (several), unequal, leaf-like, long, often surpassing the inflorescence
- scales tan or darker brown, thin, with a short awn from a notched tip
- bristles very short, half as long as achene
- achenes bulbous at tip

Habitat: High brackish or salt marshes that are inundated 1-2 times a day. Occasionally found in low salt marshes. Often associated with Pacific silverweed *(Potentilla anserina)* and Lyngby sedge *(Carex lyngbyei)*.

Range: Along the coast throughout our range.

Similar Species: Three-square bulrush *(Scirpus americanus)* does not have a bulbous base, leaves are mostly near the base, flower spikelets are few and all attach directly to the stem, and instead of leaf-like involucral bracts, it has only a single, slightly longer scale at the base of the flower spikelet cluster.

Functional Value: It is an important food source for migrating and wintering waterfowl, especially snow geese.

Ethnobotanical Uses: Stems can be used for basketry.

Seacoast bulrush has thick tubers, a bulbous base, and triangular stems.

Scirpus microcarpus
small-fruited bulrush

Family: Cyperaceae
Status: OBL
Color photo page 362

This common perennial bulrush is very robust and tufted. Plants emerge from well-developed, stout, creeping rhizomes. Stems are coarse, 60-150 cm tall, and arise singly or in a dense basal clump. Leaves are 10-15 mm wide with a deep, central vein. Leaf sheaths are purple-tinged with white cross-walls. Flower spikelets are borne in small clusters, some on stalks and others directly on the stem. Blooms from June to August.

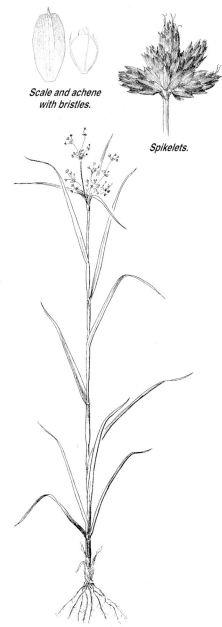

Scale and achene
with bristles.

Spikelets.

- stems triangular with rounded edges, made of spongy tissue
- leaves yellow-green, rough-margined, sharp, cutting easily
- inflorescence diffuse, with many erect branches emerging from a single point on the end of the stem
- spikelets 3-8 mm long, more than 50
- involucral bracts many, unequal, leaf-like
- scales green with black midstripe that extends past the tip as a short awn
- bristles 4, subequal to achene
- achenes tiny, oval

Habitat: Shade-intolerant, found on wet to inundated, nitrogen-rich soils. Grows particularly well in disturbed sites. Commonly associated with skunk-cabbage *(Lysichiton americanum)*, soft rush *(Juncus effusus)*, Scouler willow *(Salix scouleriana)*, and Sitka willow *(Salix sitchensis)*.

Range: Asia and western North America. Occurs in all counties in our area.

Similar Species: Woolly sedge *(Scirpus atrocinctus)* is less robust, has round, firm, almost woody stems, narrower, orange-green leaves, and 6 bristles that are 5 times the length of the achene. Slough sedge *(Carex obnupta)* when not in flower resembles small-fruited bulrush; however, slough sedge has leaves that are green and attached at the base, and stems are not spongy.

Functional Value: Valuable food and nesting material for wildlife.

Ethnobotanical Uses: Traditionally used by Native Americans for trim on hide clothing and for weaving light-duty baskets.

SEDGES

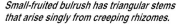

Small-fruited bulrush has triangular stems
that arise singly from creeping rhizomes.

tolerant of low water quality

Scirpus subterminalis
subterminate bulrush

Family: Cyperaceae
status: OBL

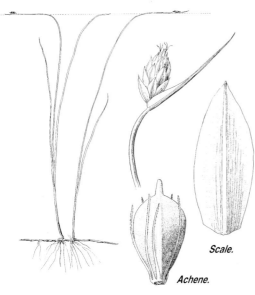

Scale.

Achene.

Subterminate bulrush plants are aquatic; leaves and stems are submerged or float on the surface of the water.

Subterminate bulrush is the only common aquatic bulrush in our area. It is rhizomatous. Leaves are few, long and linear, and located mostly near the base of the plant. Flower spikelets are light brown and short (7-12 mm long). Blooms July to August.

- stems round, slender, with tips that grow floating on the surface of the water, occasionally emergent with erect stems
- involucral bracts single, appearing to be a continuation of the stem
- flower spikes solitary
- scales thin, almost translucent, with a firm midstripe
- bristles 6, shorter than the achene
- achenes triangular with prominent tip

Habitat: Quiet shallow water, 20-80 cm deep.

Range: Occurs in all counties in our area; however, subterminate bulrush is less common east of the Cascades. Also found in Idaho (isolated occurences) and northwest Montana.

Similar Species: None.

Scirpus tabernaemontanii
(Scirpus lacustris ssp. validus)
softstem bulrush; tule

Family: Cyperaceae
Status: OBL
Color photo page 362

Softstem bulrush is a nonleafy, round-stemmed, perennial bulrush that usually grows in large colonies. Olive-gray-green stems arise from a medium rhizome. Flower spikelets are compact, shiny reddish brown, and less than 1 cm long. They are all borne in open, terminal clusters, some are borne singly on stalks and others are attached directly to the stem. Blooms June to August.

- stems to 2 m, soft and easily crushed
- involucral bracts single, green, erect, 2-10 cm long, appears as a continuation of stem, shorter than inflorescence
- bristles more than 5, equal to the achene
- spikelet scales brown, 2.5-3 mm long, with slightly visible reddish stripes
- achenes partially visible above the scales, egg-shaped with largest end at top

Spikelet, scale, and achene with bristles.

Habitat: Emergent marshes and muddy shores of lakes and streams at lower elevations, especially coastal areas; tolerant of alkali and salt. Same habitat as hardstem bulrush *(Scirpus acutus)*.

Range: Throughout our range and other temperate climates in North America.

Similar Species: Hardstem bulrush is very similar and there are reports that they hybridize. However, hardstem bulrush has stems that are hard, do not crush, and are taller and wider, scales are more notched at the tip, are gray-white with reddish midrib, and achenes are concealed by scales. In addition, hardstem bulrush is more common than softstem bulrush and forms more extensive colonies.

Softstem bulrush has tall, round, wide stems that are soft and easily crushed.

Threesquare tule *(Scirpus triqueter)* is known from freshwater tidal areas of the Columbia River, where it is quite common. It occurs on intermittently exposed sandy shoals, especially Eureka Bar, a dredged material island, and Puget Island. This species is not described from any other location in our region and was appar-

ently undiscovered until 1981. It is a common Eurasian species particularly well known from the river Thames. It is very similar to softstem bulrush, but the stems grow to 1 m tall and are sharply triangular. It often grows intermixed with softstem bulrush. Apparently the two species form hybrids that are morphologically intermediate, i.e., the stems are somewhat triangular.

Functional Value: Stems are used for nesting material by wildlife. Achenes are a favored food of waterfowl. Transplants easily and is useful for wetland creation and restoration.

Ethnobotanical Uses: The stems are used in basket weaving because, when dried, they bend easily without breaking.

SEDGES

303

Guide to Identifying the Grasses

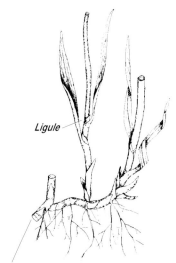

Ligule

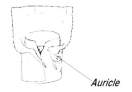

Rhizome or stolon; rhizomes are creeping underground stems, and stolons are creeping aboveground stems.

Auricle

Grasses are an important, if not the primary, component of emergent wetlands. There are many anatomical features found only in the grasses that are necessary to describe in order to differentiate the many species.

Wetland grasses are most often perennial and can grow in clumps or from *rhizomes* (creeping underground stems) and/or *stolons* (creeping aboveground stems). Annual grasses usually have only a few, very fine, fibrous roots and no evidence of old dead shoots or seed heads, and no rhizomes or stolons. Perennial grasses have shoots that grow into stems. These can arise along rhizomes or stolons in a *continuous mat* or in clumps or *tufts*. Shoots and stems can grow *erect* or *prostrate* (flat along the ground), or the stems can be prostrate but with an erect flower stalk, a condition refered to as *decumbent*. Leaves attach to the stems at *nodes*, which are swollen joints from where each leaf emerges. The lower portion of a leaf can wrap around the stem to form a *sheath*. Sheaths are described as *open or closed* depending on whether the sheath is fused into a tube down to the node, or (a swollen joint), or is unfused and open for all or most of its length. Occasionally, there are two *auricles*, tags of tissue at the top of the sheath, at the point where the leaf blade breaks away. Often, there is another tag of tissue called a *ligule* on the inside of the sheath opposite the auricles. The ligule can be thin and *membranous* (transparent), or consist of a fringe of hairs.

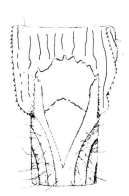

Closed sheath with a flat, membranous ligule.

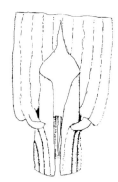

Open sheath with pointed, membranous ligule.

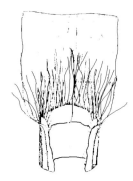

Open sheath with hairy ligule.

The inflorescences of grasses are composed of one to many *spikelets.* A spikelet is either a single *flower (floret)* or cluster of flowers, the whole of which is subtended by a pair of cup- or boat-shaped bracts *(glumes)* that is attached at the base. Glumes are difficult to see, but determining their size and shape is often critical to identifying the species. A hand lens and a steady hand are a necessity. Other paired bracts occur for each floret, the inside bract or *palea*, (which is often absent), and the outside bract or *lemma*. Glumes and lemma can be rounded or folded on the back or ridged *(keeled)*. They can also have obvious *veins*. Glumes and lemmas may have attached at the base, midback or tip, a needle-like appendage, called an *awn*. The ovary with a stigma and style, and the stamens are found inside between the lemma and palea. The base of the lemma can have a patch of fine cottony hairs *(cobwebby base)*. Each spikelet is either attached directly to the flowering stem *(rachis)*, or attached to the rachis by a shorter stem. If the attachment of the spikelets to the rachis is without a stem, the inflorescence is a *spike*. If there are short unbranched stems the inflorescence is a *raceme*, or if there are branched stems, (not all of which are directly attached to the stem) the inflorescence is referred to as a *panicle*. (See glossary for inflorescence types.)

Multiflowered spikelet with veined lemmas.

Lemma with awn attached midback.

Multiflowered spikelet with awns attached at lemmas tips.

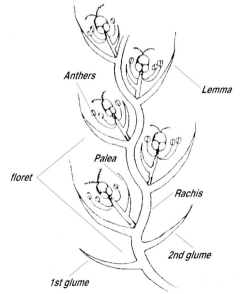

Anthers

Lemma

Palea

floret

Rachis

2nd glume

1st glume

Spikelet structure.

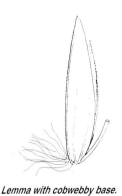

Lemma with cobwebby base.

GRASSES

Key to the Genera of Grasses

1a. Inflorescence a spike or spike-like
    2a. Spikelets single at each node
        3a. Spikelet with flat side facing stem..*Agropyron*
        3b. Spikelet with edge facing stem..*Lolium*
    2b. Spikelets 2, 3 at each node, or spikelets whorled on stem
        4a. Spikelets 2, 3 at each node; and flowering stem twisted....................................*Elymus*
        4b. Spikelets whorled on stem
            5a. Spikelets 1-flowered
                6a. Spikes dense and cylindrical, lemmas not cobwebby at base
                    7a. Glumes awned bearing a distinct keel with bristles on the keel.....*Phleum*
                    7b. Glumes awnless; lemma awned from midback....................*Alopecurus*
                6b. Spikes loose and tapered at the ends, lemmas with cobwebby base...*Ammophila*
            5b. Spikelet 3-flowered; 1 perfect terminal flower above a pair of staminate flowers....
              ....*Anthoxanthum*
1b. Inflorescence a panicle or raceme
    8a. Spikelets 1-flowered
        9a. Ligules ciliate; glumes unequal, narrow..*Spartina*
        9b. Ligules membranous
            10a. Glumes lacking...*Leersia*
            10b. Glumes present
                11a. Glumes boat-shaped to strongly inflated to a globe and equal....*Beckmannia*
                11b. Glumes long and lance-shaped
                      12a. Lemma with prominent cobwebby base.........................*Calamagrostis*
                      12b. Lemma without cobwebby base or hairs indistinct...................*Agrostis*
    8b. Spikelets 2 or more flowered
        13a. Spikelets dense and arranged to one side of flowering stem, or dense and plume-like,
              glumes shorter than first floret
            14a. Lemmas awned
                15a. Spikelets with long silky hairs, inflorescence appears feathery....*Phragmites*
                15b. Spikelets with no hairs, lemmas (at least 1) awned and short bristles on back
                    16a. First lemma very long awned..*Echinochloa*
                    16b. All lemmas short awned...*Dactylis*
            14b. Lemmas unawned, thick and hard, elliptical..*Panicum*
        13b. Spikelets uniformly arranged on the flowering stem
            17a. Lemmas awned
                18a. Lemmas awned from the tip. Stamens 3 per floret; perennial............*Festuca*
                18b. Lemmas awned from below the tip
                    19a. Glumes longer than lemma
                      20a. Lemma awned from below middle; small annuals...................*Aira*
                      20b. Second floret lemma with short awn attached above the middle,
                          hooked at tip; lower lemma awnless; perennial...................*Holcus*
                  19b. Glumes shorter than lemma
                    21a. Lemmas rounded, awned from below the middle....*Deschampsia*
                    21b. Lemmas keeled, awned from above the middle..............*Trisetum*

17b. Lemmas without awns
    22a. Plants from coastal (saline) habitats
        23a. Stems solid, leaves in 2's arranged alternately on stem; plant rhizomatous, male and female on separate plants...*Distichlis*
        23b. Stems hollow; plants tufted; flowers perfect...........................*Puccinellia*
    22b. Plants not of coastal (saline) habitats
        24a. Spikelets compressed on the back and borne in 2 rows on one side of the rachis...*Paspalum*
        24b. Spikelets not compressed on the back and evenly arranged
            25a. Lemmas mostly obviously cobwebby at base; spikelets small, oblong; lemma nerves not obvious...*Poa*
            25b. Lemmas appear cobwebby at base, but hairs are actually 2 sterile lemmas separable as flaps from the upper fertile lemma...*Phalaris*
            25c. Lemmas not cobwebby at base; spikelets long and narrow; lemma strongly parallel-nerved..*Glyceria*

Genus: *Agrostis*
bentgrasses
Family: Poaceae (Gramineae)

Common perennial grasses in the Pacific Northwest, the bentgrasses all have narrow leaves and knee-high stems. With the exception of some varieties of creeping bentgrass *(Agrostis stolonifera)*, all of the species listed below have large, diffuse, panicle inflorescences. Their many one-flowered spikelets are known for being among the smallest in our area. The basic differences and distinguishing characteristics are treated individually and in the comparison table below.

Similar Species: In the vegetative state and when growing in standing water, redtop, creeping bentgrass, and slender bentgrass all appear similar to water foxtail *(Alopecurus geniculatus)* and short-awn foxtail *(Alopecurus aequalis)*; however, the foxtails have ligules that are pointed, not flat-topped.

Functional Value: The bentgrasses are all palatable and nutritious forage grasses. Several species are commonly used as turf grasses.

Chart for Comparison of the Bentgrass Species				
species	colonial bentgrass *(A. capillaris)*	redtop *(A. gigantea)*	Oregon bentgrass *(A. oregonensis)*	rough bentgrass *(A. scabra)*	creeping bentgrass *(A. stolonifera)*
habit	erect to creeping with erect tips; tufted; slender; with short stolons, creeping rhizomes sometimes present	strongly rhizoma-tous, forming turf; erect; creeping base; erect leafy sterile shoots, sometimes with prostrate and stolonous to decumbent or erect stems	rhizomes absent, stolons sometimes present	erect; in small, dense tufts (occ. with short rhizomes or stolonous stems)	densely turf-matted, with creeping stolons; creeping with erect tips and rooting at the nodes
stem length	10-70 cm	flat; 20-100 cm	50-80 cm	stems erect; 20-75 cm	8-60 cm
leaf width	lower leaves 2-5 mm	upper leaves 3-8 mm	2-4 mm	flat, 1-3 mm; scabrous, the basal ones thin, linear	>4 mm, flat or occ. involute; roughened above
ligule	0.5-2 mm; flat topped; margin whole	2-6 mm; blunt to higher at edges; margin jagged	2-4 mm; flat to pointed; margin jagged	2-5 mm; blunt to pointed; slightly jagged	2-5 mm; blunt to higher at edges
panicle character	5-20 cm long, open, delicate, slender forked branches not spikelet-bearing to base, spikelets not crowded; often remaining open with age; purple-tinged	pyramidal-oblong; reddish; 5-30 cm long; branches spreading with age; erect in fruit; sometimes condensing later	oblong; 10-30 cm long, open, the branches whorled, rather stiff and ascending, numerous in the lower whorls, the longer 5-10 cm long, branching above the middle, spikelets to past midlength of panicle branch	8-25 cm long, the brittle hairy branches ascending and spreading, sometimes drooping, above the middle; spikelets arranged at the ends of branchlets; open; strongly purple-tinged	straw-colored or lavender, cylindric; 2-15 cm long, with ascending branches, stiff, condensed, narrow
spikelet length	2-3 mm; awnless	2-3.5 mm	2.5-3 mm	2-2.7 mm, loosely arranged on the branchlets	2-3 mm

Agrostis capillaris (Agrostis tenuis) colonial bentgrass

Status: FAC
Color photo page 362

- tufted perennial, creeping with erect tips or fully erect; stems 10-70 cm tall
- mostly with slender stolons or rhizomes to 5 cm long
- leaves 2-5 mm wide, 3-10 cm long, folded when young, flat when mature
- ligules 0.5-2 mm long, flat-topped, mostly without jaggedness, wider than long
- lower panicle branches naked (not spikelet-bearing) at base, 1.5-4 cm long, slender, delicate, diffuse, usually purple tinged
- glumes slightly unequal, pointed-tipped; lemma 3/4 length of first glume

Habitat: Commonly grows along roadsides, near stream banks, and in wet pastures. Slender bentgrass is a component of many seed mixes.

Range: Native to Eurasia; extremely common in the Pacific Northwest and east to the Atlantic Coast. Occurs in all counties in our area.

Inflorescence diffuse with spikelets borne at the ends of long branches.

Spikelet with lemma shorter than glumes.

Colonial bentgrass plants arise from stolons and rhizomes.

GRASSES

309

Agrostis gigantea
(Agrostis alba var. *alba)*
redtop
Status: FAC
Color photo page 362

- mat-forming; stems 20-100 cm tall
- stolons and rhizomes may or may not be present; when present to 25 cm long
- leaves 3-8 mm wide, 4-10 cm long, flat to folded
- ligules 2-6 mm long, flat-topped, jagged
- lower panicle branches reddish, straw-colored or bronze, flowers occurring to base, 4-7 cm long, stiff, diffuse
- glumes subequal; lemma as long as glume

Habitat: Stream banks, wet pastures, and areas in or near ditches with slow-moving water. This variety of bentgrass occurs frequently in open, disturbed areas; shade-intolerant.

Range: Native to Eurasia; common in the Pacific Northwest and east to the Atlantic Coast.

Mature inflorescence diffuse with spikelets attached to bases of short branches.

Red top is a mat-forming species with long rhizomes.

Immature inflorescence and spikelet with bristly equal glumes that are longer than lemma.

Agrostis oregonensis
Oregon bentgrass
Status: FAC

- bunchgrass; stems 50-80 cm tall
- nonrhizomatous; stolons sometimes present
- leaves 2-4 mm wide, 10-30 cm long, flat, minutely roughened
- ligules 2-4 mm long, usually with jagged margins
- inflorescence large, diffuse, 10-30 cm long, bearing spikelets to below the midlength of the panicle branch
- lower panicle branches erect, 5-10 cm long, slender

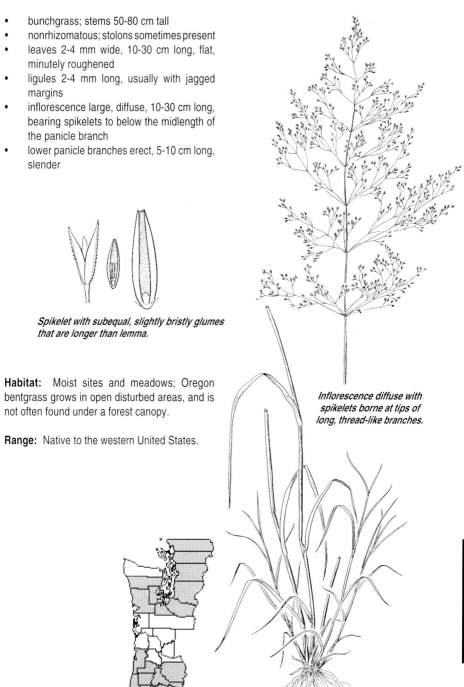

Spikelet with subequal, slightly bristly glumes that are longer than lemma.

Habitat: Moist sites and meadows; Oregon bentgrass grows in open disturbed areas, and is not often found under a forest canopy.

Range: Native to the western United States.

Inflorescence diffuse with spikelets borne at tips of long, thread-like branches.

Plants are nonrhizomatous.

GRASSES

Agrostis scabra
rough bentgrass
Status: FAC

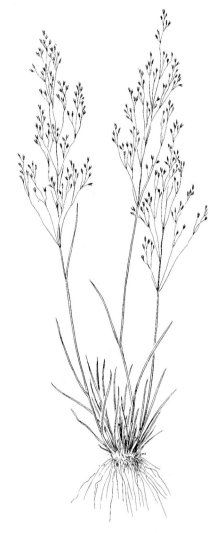

Inflorescence of rough bentgrass is clustered
at the ends of wiry branches; leaves occur at
the base of the plant; roots are usually
fibrous.

- erect bunchgrass, with small, compact tufts, bearing basal leaves; stems 20-75 cm tall
- fibrous roots usual; occasionally stolons or rhizomes
- stems, leaves, glumes, and panicle branches roughened by short bristly hairs
- leaves 1-3 mm wide, 4-14 cm long, margins curled inward
- ligules 2-5 mm long, transparent, smooth-surfaced, sharp-tipped
- lower panicle branches very long, brittle, naked to base, 4-11 cm long, slender
- upper panicle branches drooping or erect, open, branching above the middle; spikelets clustered at ends of panicle branches, strongly purple-tinged
- glumes unequal, first 2-3 mm, second shorter; lemma 2/3 length of first glume

*Spikelet with unequal glumes that are longer
than lemmas.*

Habitat: Dry to wet disturbed areas. Open road-sides, meadows, and forests, especially in gravelly soils.

Range: Native to the United States; somewhat common in the Pacific Northwest and east to the Atlantic Coast.

Agrostis stolonifera
(Agrostis alba vars. *major* and *palustris)*
creeping bentgrass; browntop bentgrass

Status: FAC

- mat-forming, spreading at base; stems 8-60 cm tall, creeping with erect tips
- stolons mostly 5-100 cm long
- leaves greater than 4 mm wide, 2-10 cm long, flat
- ligules 2-5 mm long, blunt to higher at edges
- lower panicle branches 2-15 cm long, pale or purple, relatively stiff, with florets to base

Habitat: Stream banks, wet pastures, and areas in or near ditches with slow-moving water.

Range: Native to Eurasia; common in the Pacific Northwest and east to the Atlantic Coast. Occurs in all counties in our area.

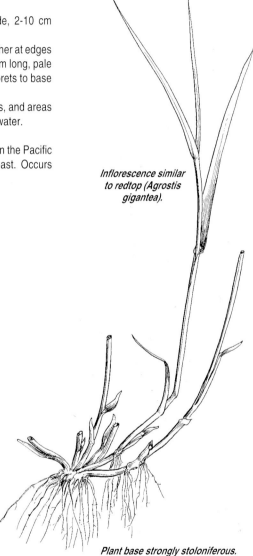

Inflorescence similar to redtop (Agrostis gigantea).

Plant base strongly stoloniferous.

GRASSES

313

Aira caryophyllea
silver European hairgrass

Family: Poaceae (Gramineae)
Status: Not listed (fac-)

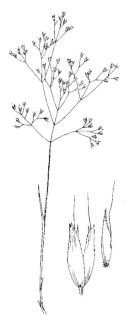

The inflorescence of silver European hairgrass is a tiny, open panicle with 2-flowered spikelets.

Silver European hairgrass is a delicate, 5-30 cm tall, annual grass that grows in small tufts in waste areas. Roots are few and wire-thin. The inflorescence is an open, diffuse panicle, 2-6 cm long. Spikelets are 2-flowered with awns from near base of lemma and relatively large (2.5-3.5 cm long). Blooms from May through July.

• leaves very narrow (0.3-0.7 mm wide) and short, often no more than a 2 cm tag of leaf tissue, inrolled, mostly basal, roughened on both surfaces
• ligules 1.5-3.5 mm long with a torn margin, longest at center
• glumes 3 mm long, equal to or longer than lemmas
• lemmas 2 mm long with long awns (2-4 mm) attached from below midback

Habitat: Waste sites in poorly drained gravels and sands. Tolerates moist to dry conditions.

Range: Introduced European species, common in the low elevations from southwest British Columbia to northern California; most common west of the Cascades, especially along the coast. Also found along the Gulf and Atlantic coasts of the United States, and occasionally in the Midwest. Occurs in all counties in our area.

Similar Species: None.

genus: *Alopecurus*
foxtails

Family: Poaceae (Gramineae)

The three foxtails described here are all mat-forming perennial grasses. Inflorescences are cylindrical, narrow, silvery, spike-like panicles which are densely flowered and, as a result, appear hairy like a fox's tail. Spikelets are always 1-flowered, separate below the glumes, and are long-awned from the base to the middle of the back. Glumes are pointed, partially joined at the base, have a densely hairy back, and are as long as the lemmas.

Similar Species: The foxtails have a distinctive compact, cylindrical inflorescence which is uncommon in other wetland grasses. Common timothy *(Phleum pratense.)* is the only other grass that has tall stems and cylindrical, densely flowered inflorescences. Common timothy, however, has glumes with short stubby bristles along the keel, an awn that comes from the tip of the glume, awnless lemmas, a plant base that is thickened into a bulb, and purple-tinged leaf nodes. Vegetatively, the foxtails are similar to the bentgrasses (*Agrostis* species), but the ligules of the bentgrasses are flat-topped and without hairs.

Functional Value: Foxtails are all palatable and nutritious forage grasses. Some populations may provide forage for waterfowl.

Alopecurus aequalis var. *aequalis*
short-awn foxtail

Status: OBL
Color photo page 363

Short-awn foxtail is a tufted perennial grass with narrow, flat leaves. Stems often root at the nodes. It is often found growing in shallow standing water where it grows below the waters' surface. The stems grow to 50 cm tall when erect. Glumes are longer than the lemmas, 2 mm long, and long-hairy. This common species grows in shallow water, where leaves can either be found spreading and lying flat on the surface of the water or submerged. Blooms May to July.

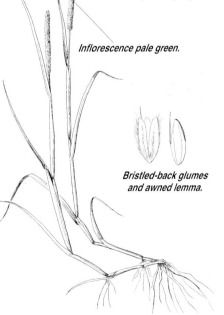

Inflorescence pale green.

Bristled-back glumes and awned lemma.

- leaves 1-5 mm wide, rough on the inside surface
- ligules 4-8 mm long, membranous, sharply pointed with jagged margins and tips folded back
- inflorescence a pale green spike-like panicle, 2-8 cm long
- lemmas awned, the awn inserted near the middle of lemma and barely extending above the glumes

Habitat: Short-awn foxtail favors areas in or near slow-moving water, such as ditches, stream banks, and wet pastures. It grows mostly in open areas, and are infrequently found in the shade.

Stems grow to 50 cm tall, but leaves are often found spreading on the water.

Range: Relatively abundant in wet sites in the Pacific Northwest and east to the Atlantic Coast.

Foxtails continued on next page...

GRASSES

✻ blue-green stems

315

Alopecurus geniculatus var. *geniculatus*
water foxtail

Status: OBL

Color photo page 363

Inflorescence often purple-tinged.

Water foxtail stems grow to 55 cm tall, but often are found spreading on the water.

Water foxtail is a small, tufted foxtail with stems that grow to 55 cm tall when erect. Leaves also grow horizontally, spreading on the surface of the water. Spikelets are about 2-3 mm long. Glumes are as long as the lemma and hairy, with keels that are fringed with hairs. The glumes are partially united at the base, and are slightly purplish toward the tips. Blooms June to July.

- leaves flat, 2-6 mm wide
- ligules 3-5 mm long, membranous, pointed
- inflorescence pale green to light purple-tinged, pointed, 2-4 cm long (occasionally up to 7 cm)
- lemmas awned, the awn bent, arising from near the base of the lemma and extending 4-5 mm, up to 3.5 mm above the glumes

Habitiat: Same as short-awn foxtail.

Range: Same as short-awn foxtail.

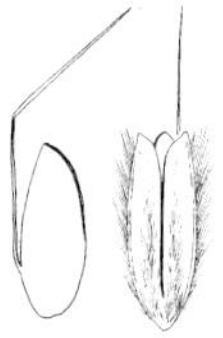

Awned lemma and glumes.

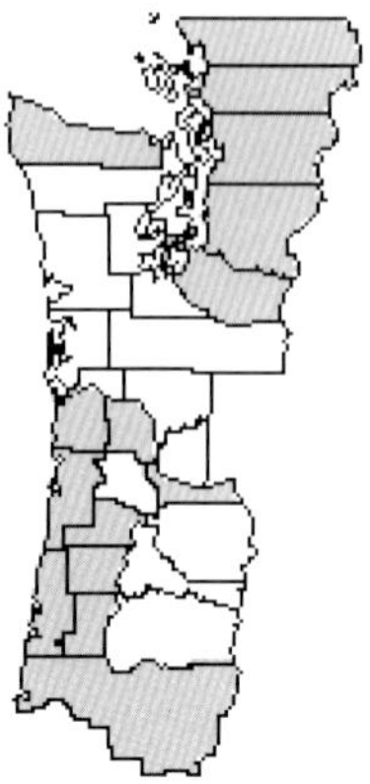

* green-green stems

Alopecurus pratensis
meadow foxtail

Status: FACW
Color photo page 363

Meadow foxtail is the largest of the common wet-land foxtails. It has waist- to chest-high stems and wide, flat leaves. Spikelets are about 5 mm long. Glumes awned, to 5 mm long and usually deep purplish toward the tips, especially when young. Blooms June to July.

- erect and tufted; stoloniferous, with stems to 90 cm tall
- leaves to 6 mm wide
- ligules of upper leaves to 6 mm long, mem-branous, with a minutely hairy flat top
- inflorescence deep purple, to about 7.5 cm long
- lemmas awned, the awn bent, extending 2-5.5 mm above the glumes

Habitat: Meadow foxtail is an introduced pasture grass that often grows in seeded pastures and abandoned agricultural fields. It also invades and becomes established in emergent wetlands. It grows most frequently in open sites.

Range: Meadow foxtails are present in all counties in our area.

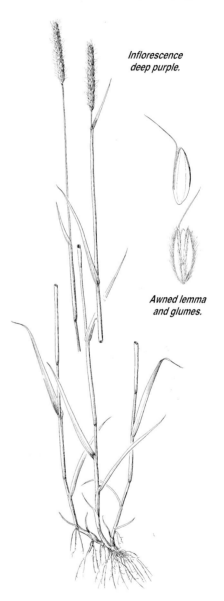

Inflorescence deep purple.

Awned lemma and glumes.

Stems are to 90 cm tall and erect; meadow foxtail plants do not grow in water.

GRASSES

Ammophila arenaria
European beachgrass
Family: Poaceae (Gramineae)
Status: FACU

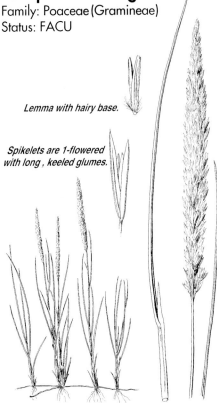

Lemma with hairy base.

Spikelets are 1-flowered with long, keeled glumes.

Plants grow from stiff rhizomes, and the inflorescence is 30 cm long and robust.

European beachgrass is an erect, perennial, tufted dune grass with stiff, narrow stems that grow almost 1.5 m tall. The leaves are 2-4 mm wide, with smooth sheaths and long ligules. There are no auricles. Inflorescence is a cylindrical compact panicle, to 30 cm long, with some spikelets attached directly and others on short stalks. Spikelets are about 15 mm long. Glumes are keeled and slightly longer than the single flower in each spikelet.

- tufts connected by robust creeping rhizomes
- leaves dark green to yellowish, thickened, or sometimes with margins curled inward
- ligules 10-25 mm long, membranous, and sharp-pointed
- lemma notched at the tip, with 2-3 mm long hairs at the base

Habitat: Common as a dominant species on foredunes of coastal areas. It may extend into the lee side of foredunes and hinddunes in certain areas, but rarely extends any great distance inland in our area.

Range: Native to Europe. European beachgrass has been extensively planted as a sand stabilizer and is extremely common in coastal sand dune habitats along the Pacific and Atlantic coasts. Present in all coastal counties in our area.

Similar Species: European beachgrass is often mistaken for American dunegrass *(Elymus mollis)*, a native dunegrass, which has broader leaves (to 16 mm wide) that are dark blue-green, not curled inward, and usually with prominent auricles and short (1 mm long) ligules. The inflorescence of American dunegrass is similar in appearance but is actually a compact spike with spikelets paired at each node and attached directly and alternately along one side of the rachis. American dunegrass favors the lee side of foredunes and more stabilized dunes inland. American beachgrass *(Ammophila breviligulata)* occurs along the immediate foredunes and coexists with European beachgrass. American beachgrass is native to the Atlantic Coast and infrequently grows along the Washington and Oregon coasts. It differs in having very short (about 3 mm long), stiff ligules.

Functional Value: European beachgrass provides cover and habitat to small mammals. Because of its invasive nature, it can dominate native foredune species. All beachgrass species are excellent sand-binders.

Anthoxanthum odoratum
sweet vernalgrass

Family: Poaceae (Gramineae)
Status: FACU
Color photo page 363

Sweet vernalgrass is a short (30-60 cm tall), intro-duced perennial tufted grass. The stems are hollow with open sheaths. Leaves are flat, 3-7 mm wide, and slightly hairy toward the base. The inflorescence is a congested panicle, 2-9 cm long, that is brownish yellow (bronze) when young and golden with age. The lower two lemmas of each spikelet are 3 mm long, hairy, sterile and empty with an awn attached below the midpoint; the fertile flower is hairless, awnless, and 2 mm long. Stamens have 2 anthers which are long (4-5 mm). Blooms in early spring and rarely reappears after mowing.

- sweet vanilla-like odor when fresh, espe-cially during flowering
- auricles 1 mm long with long hairs
- ligules 2-3 mm long, membranous
- spikelet 3-flowered (appearing as 1-flow-ered)
- glumes pointed-tipped, unequal in length; first glume 1-veined, second 3-veined
- awn on sterile lemmas 7-10 mm long, twisted, slightly bent

Habitat: Sweet vernalgrass prefers drier sites in unimproved or native moist pastures, often asso-ciated with higher mounds in wet pastures, or along dry fringes of wet pastures.

Range: Occurs throughout our area, mostly west of the Cascades.

Similar Species: No other pasture species is this short and has a bronze-to-golden compact inflo-rescence. The vanilla odor of the foliage, as well as sweet taste of the lower stems, is diagnostic.

Functional Value: Grazing animals use it as forage, although it produces relatively little herb-age and does not seem to be preferred.

Spikelets of sweet vernalgrass are 3-flowered but appear to be 1-flowered; inflorescence golden when mature; roots are thin and fibrous.

GRASSES

319

Beckmannia syzigachne
American sloughgrass

Family: Poaceae (Gramineae)
Status: OBL
Color photo page 363

Inflorescence very robust
with each spikelet visible.

Spikelets have
inflated glumes.

Lemmas are
awnless.

*Base of American sloughgrass is slightly
bulbous and roots are spongy.*

American sloughgrass is a robust annual grass
that grows to 1 m tall, with a base that can be
slightly bulbous. Stems are hollow and sheaths
are open. Leaves are flat and 5-10 mm broad.
Blooms June through July.

- ligules membranous, pointed, 6-11 mm long,
  often jagged-margined and folded back
- inflorescence a densely clustered panicle, to
  30 cm long, with 2 parallel rows of numerous
  erect branches that are flattened to one side
  of rachis
- spikelet 1-flowered, distinctively disk-like,
  sharp-pointed, 3 mm long
- glumes rounded-inflated from front view, but
  flattened from side view
- lemmas lance-shaped, in length equal to
  glume, awnless

Habitat: Grows in freshwater, seasonal wetlands,
vernal ponds, pond shores, marshes, shallow water, and occasionally in ditches where there are
remnants of native plant communities. Not found
at moderate or high elevations. Prefers sunny or
lightly shaded sites.

Range: Along the Pacific Coast (in fresh water)
from Alaska to California (although not in Washington) and east scattered across the United States
to western New York. In our area, it is most
common in the Willamette Valley. Also found in
Asia.

Similar Species: Other genera with rounded
glumes (e.g., *Digitaria*, *Setaria*, *Panicum*,
Paspalum) have relatively globular spikelets, unlike the compressed spikelets of sloughgrass.
Large barnyard grass *(Echinochloa crusgalli)* is an
annual weed with a similar dense inflorescence,
but the inflorescence is much shorter, spikelets
are not in parallel rows, and glumes and lemmas
are bristly-haired.

Functional Value: Sloughgrass produces copious fruits. Although it
surely provides some food
to waterbirds, mammals,
and invertebrates, it rarely
occurs in large stands, and
thus is not a critical food
species.

Ethnobotanical Uses:
Rarely included in orna-
mental dried plant ar-
rangements. It is occa-
sionally cultivated for ornamental use.

Calamagrostis canadensis
bluejoint reedgrass

Family: Poaceae (Gramineae)
Status: FACW+
Color photo page 364

Bluejoint reedgrass is a strongly rhizomatous, coarsely tufted, widespread perennial grass that grows to 1 m tall. It is quite variable and is represented by many varieties. Leaf buds are rolled like those of the bluegrasses *(Poa* species). Leaves are to 8 mm wide and bend over with age. Glumes are 2.5-6 mm long and often purple. Glume awns are slender and inserted from midlength to tip of the glume. Paleas are well developed. Blooms from June to August.

- stems and leaves generally smooth
- joints distinctly blue on stout, vigorous stems
- ligules membranous, 3-8 mm long, with a jagged edge; lowest leaves with ligules that are only 3 mm long.
- panicle inflorescence variable; compact and 1.5 cm long, to diffuse, open, to 30 cm long; bent over and with a purple cast when mature
- spikelets usually 1-flowered, 2 flowers possible
- lemmas membranous, papery, bearded at the base with hairs equal to length of lemma

Glumes are longer than the lemmas, which are bearded.

Habitat: Bluejoint reedgrass grows in upland as well as distinctly wet habitats such as meadows, bogs, wet thickets, open woods (alder or crabapple swamps), ditches, streams, and lake margins. Lowlands to midmontane.

Range: Aleutian Islands and northern Alaska across northern Canada to South Baffin Island, Newfoundland, and Labrador; Alaska south to California and northern New Mexico, and across United States through Kansas, Missouri, Tennessee, and North Carolina.

Similar Species: Bluejoint reedgrass is one of the few grasses that is 1-flowered. Reed canarygrass *(Phalaris arundinacea)* appears 1-flowered, is taller and has distinctly reddish rhizomes close to the surface, leaves that are covered with fine hairs, and a smaller, tighter panicle.

Plants grows from long, spreading rhizomes in tufts of erect stems to 1 m tall.

Functional Value: The seeds are eaten by waterfowl when it grows along waterways. It is used in hydroseed mixes for drainage ditches that are designed to filter stormwater.

Ethnobotanical Uses: Bluejoint reedgrass has been used for hay in the northern midwestern states.

GRASSES

Calamagrostis nutkaensis
Pacific reedgrass

Family: Poaceae (Gramineae)
Status: FACW

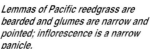

Lemmas of Pacific reedgrass are bearded and glumes are narrow and pointed; inflorescence is a narrow panicle.

- strongly rhizomatous, often spreading to form continuous hummocks
- inflorescence an erect panicle, narrow but loosely flowered, 1.5 cm wide, 12-30 cm long, greenish yellow to purplish with stiff erect branches
- spikelets usually 1-flowered, 2 flowers possible
- lemmas with very short awn inserted at the midpoint of the back of the lemma, base with numerous short, unequal hairs that are half the length of the lemma

Habitat: Pacific reedgrass is a coastal species that often grows in sand dunes and along coastal headlands; it is most common in areas exposed to sea winds, especially under Sitka spruce *(Picea sitchensis)* forests. It is usually found within 40 km of the coast. Also may occur in subalpine mountain hemlock forests.

Range: Alaska to northern California.

Similar Species: Pacific reedgrass is found only in coastal areas on sand dunes; no other sand dune species is similar. Seashore saltgrass *(Distichlis spicata)* is another mat-forming saltmarsh grass, but it has two-ranked leaves and a tightly compact panicle inflorescence. American dunegrass *(Elymus mollis)* is a very robust, almost woody, tufted grass with blue-green foliage. The other common species of reedgrass is bluejoint reedgrass *(Calamagrostis canadensis)*, which is not coastal, has very long (to 10 mm) long, jagged-edged ligules, and leaves that are covered by fine hairs.

Functional Value: When Pacific reedgrass grows along waterways, the seeds are useful food for waterfowl. Pacific reedgrass seed is used in hydroseed mixes for drainage ditches designed to filter stormwater.

Ligule rounded with fine hairs along tip edge.

Pacific reedgrass is a tall, mostly smooth, tufted perennial grass 0.5-1.5 m tall. Leaves are thick, leathery, 6-12 mm broad, and slightly rough on the inside surface. Ligules are thick, 2-6 mm long with very fine hairs, and nearly concealed by the leaf base. Glumes are slightly longer than the lemma. Blooms from June to September.

Dactylis glomerata
orchardgrass

Family: Poaceae (Gramineae)
Status: FACU
Color photo page 364

Orchardgrass is a tall, hollow, flat-stemmed, perennial bunchgrass that grows to 1.5 m tall. Early growth is light bluish green; older leaves and stems are tan and lack auricles. Leaf sheaths are partially open. The inflorescence is a mostly erect, compressed panicle 3-15 cm long. Spikelets are 3- to 5-flowered. Glumes are 4-6 mm long and differ from one another; the first has 2 veins and is lopsided; the second has one vein, a hairy back, and a short awn. Paleas are present and slightly shorter than the lemmas. Occasionally the flowers become bulblets on the plant. Blooms from June through August.

- stems somewhat flattened at base
- leaves smooth to slightly roughened, 3-10 mm wide, folded when young, flat when mature
- ligules membranous, 3-9 mm, with ragged and pointed top
- spikelets grouped closely together in 1-sided clusters at the end of panicle branches
- lemmas awn-tipped, 5-8 mm long, hairy on back along the keel
- anthers very long (4 mm)

Habitat: Grows in natural or planted pastures, along roadsides, and in forested understory on moist and dry sites. It is frequently found in montane situations, where it is often seeded for erosion control after timber harvest or road-building.

Range: Native to Eurasia; found throughout our area.

Similar Species: Canada bluegrass *(Poa compressa)* also has folded leaves and flattened stems, but the bluegrass ligules are shorter than those of orchardgrass, and leaf color and inflorescence are much different. Reed canarygrass *(Phalaris arundinacea)* has a more pointed inflorescence, open sheaths, small auricles, wider blue-green to straw-colored leaves (7-17 mm), and is more common in wetter habitats.

Functional Value: Orchardgrass is a good forage species for grazing animals. This tall grass provides cover for birds and small animals. It is moderately useful as an erosion-control species.

Inflorescence with spikelets in 1-sided clusters.

Lemmas hairy along back.

Orchardgrass grows in bunches to 1.5 m tall.

GRASSES

Deschampsia cespitosa
tufted hairgrass

Family: Poaceae (Gramineae)
Status: FACW

Tufted hairgrass has 2- to 3-flowered
spikelets (top) and glumes that are equal in
length to the 2 lemmas (right); plants grow in
dense hummocks.

Tufted hairgrass is a common, erect, perennial
grass that grows in dense hummocks. The height
is variable, 0.5-2 m tall. Leaves are dark green
when young, greenish yellow with age, 2-4 mm
wide, flat or folded, and have rough edges. Panicles
are large, loose, triangular, highly-branched, and
8-35 cm long. Panicle branches are often drooping and terminate the stems. Flowers are borne at
the ends of the branches. Glumes are as long as
the spikelets. The flowering stalk is prolonged
above the upper flower, occasionally bearing a
sterile flower at its tip. Flowering time varies with
each variety, of which there are many, but occurs
between June and August.

* stems dark when young, pale by midsummer
* ligules prominent, sharp-tipped, 3-8 mm long
* spikelets reddish purple, to about 5 mm long,
  2- to 3-flowered, with a flattened tip
* lemmas 4 mm long, hairy at the base, awned
  from below the middle; awn extends slightly

Habitat: Grows in coastal mountain meadows,
coastal brackish marshes, occasional in wet freshwater meadows, gravelly river bars, rocky ridges,
and lakeshores. In the lowlands it occurs most
frequently in coastal areas in brackish marshes. In
the Willamette Valley tufted hairgrass is the most
important grass in wet prairie remnants. It prefers
full sun, and does not tolerate year-round flooding.
Its growth is vigorous in nutrient-rich sites or following dry season burns.

Range: Circumboreal distribution; may be native
worldwide. Occurs in all counties in our area.

Similar Species: Meadow fescue *(Festuca
pratensis)* is also tufted but with prolific bright
green leaves, and short ligules (0.2 mm). Meadow
fescue usually has a narrow diffuse panicle, with
stiffer panicle branches and is 2- to 12-flowered.
Slender hairgrass *(Deschampsia elongata)* is similar vegetatively, but is smaller than tufted hairgrass
(less than 50 cm tall) and has a shorter (20 cm
long), narrower inflorescence. Cordgrasses
(Spartina species) are also found in coastal salt
marshes but are more robust (almost woody) and
have a short compact inflorescence.

Functional Value: In wet prairie remnants, tufted
hairgrass forms mounded clumps, which define
the structure of the plant community. The dense
foliage provides food and shelter to a number of
small animals. It tolerates light grazing.

Distichlis spicata var. spicata
seashore saltgrass

Family: Poaceae (Gramineae)
Status: FAC+
Color photo page 364

Seashore saltgrass is the most common perennial coastal grass in our area. The stems are solid, coarse, woody, and mostly decumbent, with open sheaths. Leaf buds are rolled like those of blue-grasses *(Poa* species); leaves are present on the stolons as short scales. Salt crystals are often found on the leaf surface. Ligules are membranous, 0.5 mm long, and fringed with hairs. Blooms from May to September.

* rhizomes and stolons scaly, forming continuous mats below the mean high water zone
* leaves 5 cm long, opposite, 2-ranked, angling sharply from stem in one plane
* inflorescence a terminal panicle with 5-15 flattened, purplish, compressed spikelets
* spikelets 5- to 9-flowered; male and female flowers on separate plants
* lemmas larger than glumes, hardened-woody, unawned, slightly larger than paleas, 3-5 mm long

Habitat: Grows in salt marshes and other moist saline sites.

Range: Coastal sites throughout our area.

Similar Species: Bermuda grass *(Cynodon dactylon)* has leaves that grow in a similar pattern, but this species never occurs in moist, saline areas. The leaves of tall mannagrass *(Glyceria elata)* also grow in a similar pattern, but this species is found only in freshwater habitats, and has erect stems with mostly closed sheaths. Pacific reedgrass *(Calamagrostis nutkaensis)* is also a salt marsh species, but the leaves are greenish yellow to purplish and not 2-ranked, and the inflorescence is an open dif-

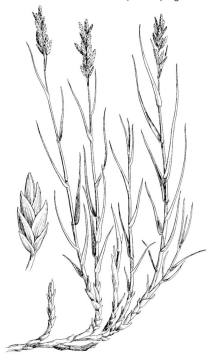

The spikelets of seashore saltgrass are 5- to 9-flowered (left) with lemmas larger than glumes; plants have scale-covered rhizomes and stolons.

fuse panicle. Cordgrasses *(Spartina* species) can be superficially similar, but grow in clumps on mud flats, not in the tidally influenced banks of estuarine habitats. The stems of spartina are hollow and glumes woody with spines along a prominently keeled back.

Functional value: Seashore saltgrass is an excellent erosion control species in coastal areas. It also has high productivity for a saline habitat.

GRASSES

Echinochloa crusgalli
large barnyard grass
Family: Poaceae (Gramineae)
Status: FACW

Spikelets are large
and inflated.

Large barnyard grass is a common, weedy, loosely tufted annual grass. It grows 50-150 cm tall. Leaves are flat, bright green, 5-15 mm wide, and with open sheaths. The purple-tinged inflorescence is a 10-20 cm long, lobed panicle composed of many branches with densely packed, large, inflated spikelets. Blooms from June through October.

- stems stout, hollow, purple at the base
- ligules lacking
- spikelets 2-flowered, 3-4 mm long, arranged on one side of stem
- glumes unequal, bristly, unawned, the first barely visible
- first lemma sterile and awned, second lemma smooth, shiny, hardened, unawned but long-bristly

Glumes are subequal, very small, and borne at the base of the spikelet; first lemma has a long awn.

Habitat: Moist, open, disturbed areas such as cultivated fields. Tolerates the shallow inundation of poorly drained gravel pits and drainage ditches.

Range: An introduced European weedy species, large barnyard grass is found in southern Canada and throughout United States; tropics and subtropics in both northern and southern hemispheres. Present in all counties in our area.

Similar Species: American sloughgrass *(Beckmannia syzigachne)* has similar, large, single-flowered spikelets borne in compact panicles, but the leaves are bright green, the base slightly bulbous, ligules long (6-10 mm), and lemmas awnless.

Large barnyard grass grows in scattered bunches from spongy rhizomes.

Functional Value: This grass is an invasive weed in agricultural areas. The spikelets are easily shed and can be difficult to remove from the eyes of domestic animals. Large barnyard grass is too succulent for fodder.

Elymus mollis
(Leymus mollis)
American dunegrass

Family: Poaceae (Gramineae)
Status: Not listed (facu)
Color photo page 364

American dunegrass is one of the most common, robust perennial grasses found on coastal dunes of Washington and Oregon. It grows in large clumps of ascending, scale-covered rhizomes. Stems are erect, 50-150 cm tall, and have hairs that are rough to the touch. Salt crystals are often found on the leaf surface. Auricles are usually present. Glumes are soft-hairy. Blooms from June to August.

- leaves very tough, almost woody, dark blue-green, 6-16 mm wide, with prominent veins
- ligules hairy, less than 1 mm long, flat and collar-like
- inflorescence very large, a compact spike, 15-30 cm long, 1-2 cm wide
- spikelets attached directly to stalk, paired at each node, 4- to 6-flowered, 20-30 mm long, arranged alternately along the flowering stalk
- lemmas 15-25 mm long, soft-hairy, with 3-6 prominent veins and membranous margins, pointed-tipped

Habitat: Grows in coastal dunes and on the edges of gravel beaches.

Range: Greenland, eastern arctic, and western North America to Asia.

Similar Species: European beachgrass *(Ammophila arenaria)* is another dune grass that has an inflorescence that appears similar but is actually a cylindrical panicle: some spikelets are attached by short stalks to the flowering stalk, while others are attached directly as with American dunegrass. In addition, European beachgrass has dark-green to yellowish, nonwoody leaves, lacks auricles, and has ligules to 25 mm long. Pacific reedgrass *(Calamagrostis nutkaensis)* is another tall dune grass, but it has a delicate open panicle inflorescence, the ligule is 1-2 mm long, thick, and tipped by fine hairs, and the spikelets have only 1-2 flowers.

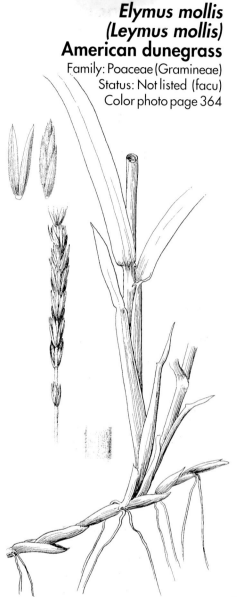

The inflorescence of American dunegrass is robust, compact, and composed to 4- to 6-flowered spikelets; stems are hairy; plants grow from scale-covered rhizomes.

Functional Value: American dunegrass is an effective dune stabilizer.

Ethnobotanical Use: American dunegrass has been used for weaving fishing gear and baskets. It is used in Japan for making ropes and mats and is also used in decorative paper.

GRASSES

Elytrigia repens
(Agropyron repens)
quackgrass

Family: Poaceae (Gramineae)
Status: FAC-

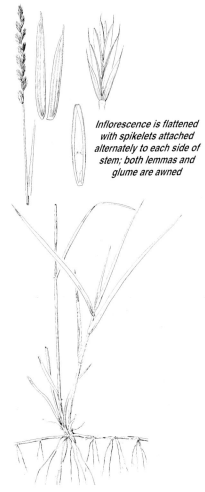

Inflorescence is flattened with spikelets attached alternately to each side of stem; both lemmas and glume are awned

Leaves and stems of quackgrass are short-hairy and rhizomes are thin and wiry.

Quackgrass is a sod-forming grass with long, tough, and wiry rhizomes. Leaves have open sheaths. There is almost no ligule (0.5 mm of membrane). Inflorescence is a terminal, stiff, erect spike, which is 7-15 cm long. Glumes are 6-7 mm long, usually awn-tipped. Lemma is slightly longer than glumes, to 10 mm, and sometimes with a straight awn. Blooms from June through August.

- young stems often soft hairy, to 1 m tall, arising singly from rhizomes, forming dense patches
- auricles clawed and well developed.
- leaves slightly bluish in color (depending on soil fertility), flat, 5-10 mm broad for their length, more or less hairy, and often twisted
- spikelets 5- to 9-flowered, attached directly, 1 per node, overlapping, borne alternately and pressed flatwise against the axis of the flowering stem

Habitat: Quackgrass is a common, non-native, persistent, weedy grass that occurs in lawns, waste areas, meadows, and pastures, especially in heavily used areas. Quackgrass is most often associated with other pasture grass species. Although typically found in upland environments, it is tolerant of some wetland conditions and grows on irrigated lands, creek bottoms, or in heavy muck soils in drier environments.

Range: Widespread over much of temperate and subarctic North America, including the lower elevations of western Washington and Oregon.

Similar Species: Perennial ryegrass *(Lolium perenne)* has smooth-margined ligules 0.5-1.5 mm long and spikelets that are 6- to 10-flowered, which align on edge against the axis of the flowering stem. Other *Elytrigia* species are present but very uncommon in wetlands in the Puget Sound region and northwestern Oregon.

Functional Value: The sod-forming habit of quackgrass make it an effective species for erosion control. The belowground root and rhizome mass far exceeds the aboveground mass. The growth rate compares favorably with orchard grass and exceeds that of meadow foxtail *(Alopecurus pratensis)* and Kentucky bluegrass *(Poa pratensis)*. It is considered a noxious weed, among the most troublesome, because it is so invasive, and is a prohibited noxious weed under the Oregon Seed Law.

Ethnobotanical Uses: Quackgrass is included in seed mixes for lawns. It has also been used as a pasture grass, and is fairly palatable and nutritious forage for livestock. Although not a common practice, the large seeds can be ground into flour.

Genus: *Festuca*
fescues
Family: Poaceae (Gramineae)

The wetland-associated fescues are perennial bunchgrasses with hollow stems. Leaves are flat to folded, stiff, coarse on the edges, prominently veined, bright green when fresh, and glossy on undersides. Sheaths are smooth and often open. Ligules are short, 1 mm or less, membranous, and higher on the sides than in the middle. The inflorescences are panicles with 2- to 12-flowered spikelets. The glumes are generally unequal, unawned, and smaller than the lemmas. The first glume has 1 vein, the second 3 veins. Lemmas are mostly short-awned, or the awns are lacking. Paleas are prominent and almost equal to the lemmas.

Range: Natives of Eurasia, these fescues were introduced throughout the cooler parts of North America. They are well established where the average annual precipitation is above 15 inches, especially in Idaho, western Washington, and Oregon.

Functional Value: The leaves and stems provide forage for grazing wildlife, but are not highly valuable as fodder. Tall fescue *(Festuca arundinacea)* has been implicated as the cause of certain hoof-related diseases. Much of the commercial seed sources are fungi-infested. All are good cover for wildlife.

Similar Species: Wild bromes *(Bromus* species; not treated in this guide) have hairy, closed sheaths and a longer ligule. See individual fescues for more detailed information regarding similar plants for each species.

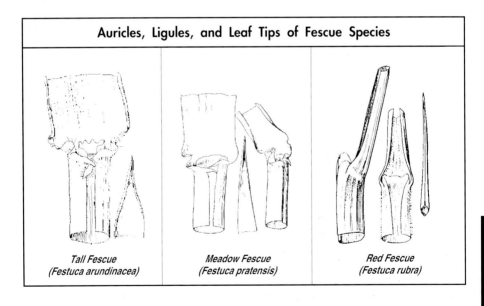

Auricles, Ligules, and Leaf Tips of Fescue Species

Tall Fescue *(Festuca arundinacea)*	*Meadow Fescue* *(Festuca pratensis)*	*Red Fescue* *(Festuca rubra)*

GRASSES

Festuca arundinacea
tall fescue; reed fescue
Status: FAC-

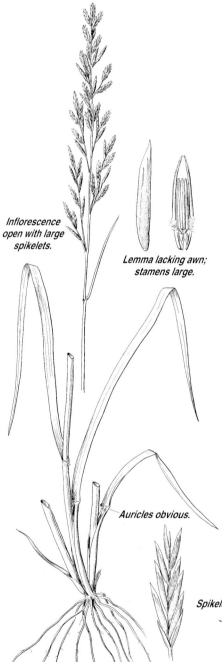

Inflorescence open with large spikelets.

Lemma lacking awn; stamens large.

Auricles obvious.

Spikelets are 6- to 8-flowered.
- redish color

This robust perennial fescue has stems 1-2 m tall. It forms the most robust tussocks of all the wetland fescues. Leaves stay lush and green even though other grasses around it have been affected by frost or drought. Ligules are 0.2 mm long. Spikelets are large (12-15 mm long), 6- to 8-flowered, with glumes 5-7 mm long, and lemmas 7- 9 mm long. Blooms May through July.

- leaves 4-10 mm wide, to 70 cm long, rough-surfaced on top, smooth below -shiny yellow
- auricles large, prominent, fringed with short hairs
- panicles 15-32 cm long, open
- lemma sometimes extending as a tiny awn past the midvein

Habitat: Tall and meadow fescues (facing page) grow in pastures, ditchbanks, and roadsides. They are tolerant of poorly drained acidic soils, saline and alkali soils, as well as being drought-tolerant. Roots will penetrate clay. These species are most often found growing with other grass species in areas that are not inundated throughout the growing season.

Similar Species: Tall fescue is occasionally confused with perennial ryegrass *(Lolium perenne)* which has soft leaves, short nonfringed auricles, and a compact spike inflorescence.

Tall fescue plants grow in clumps from large roots, but lack rhizomes; leaves are large and wide.

Festuca pratensis
meadow fescue; English fescue

Status: FACU+

Meadow fescue has stems 70-130 cm tall. Ligules are 0.2 mm long. Spikelets are 4- to 10-flowered, with glumes 3- 4 mm long, and lemmas 5-7 mm long. Blooms June to July.

- leaves 3-5 mm wide, to 30 cm long, flat, roughened on both surfaces
- auricles smooth, prominent, not fringed with hairs
- panicles 10-20 cm long, erect or nodding, with short branches
- awns lacking on lemmas

Ethnobotanical Uses: Meadow fescue is frequently planted in agricultural areas, both wet and dry, as a pasture or hay crop. It is also used in lawns and for erosion control.

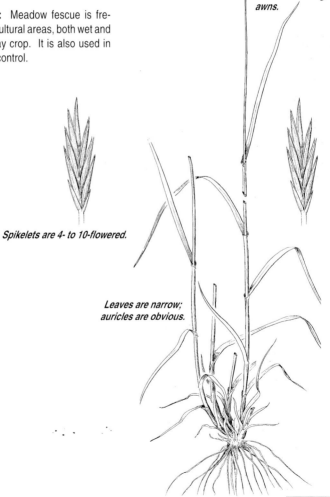

Lemmas with obvious veins and lacking awns.

Spikelets are 4- to 10-flowered.

Leaves are narrow; auricles are obvious.

Plants grow in clumps from thin-fibrous roots and are lacking rhizomes.

Fescues continued on next page...

GRASSES

Festuca rubra
red fescue, English fescue
Status: FAC+

Spikelets 4-
to 7-flowered;
lemmas awned.

Leaves very narrow.

This perennial fescue forms large loose clumps from creeping rhizomes. It grows 20-100 cm tall. The basal leaf sheaths are reddish purple when young and become brown and shredded with age. Ligules are less than 0.5 mm long and fringed with short hairs. Glumes are unequal, the first 2-4 mm long, the second 4-8 mm long. Lemmas are 5-8.5 mm long and either smooth or hairy. Blooms from June through August.

- leaves yellow-green, folded-inrolled, 1.5 mm broad, long, with purplish red veins, smooth on both sides
- auricles lacking
- panicles 4-20 cm long, congested, narrow
- spikelets 4- to 7-flowered, reddish purple or green
- awns 1-3 mm long, at tips of lemmas

Habitat: Red fescue grows in sandy or gravelly soils, such as in coastal marshes and sand dunes, but also occurs in montane forests and meadows. It grows in shade or sun, and like the other fescues, tolerates acidic soils. Red fescue will withstand inundation if the substrate is well drained.

Similar Species: Red fescue can be confused with tufted hairgrass *(Deschampsia cespitosa)*, which also has narrow, folded leaves and grows in dense tufts in a variety of habitats. However, tufted hairgrass has ligules that are 4-8 mm long, 2-flowered spikelets, and awns emerging from the middle of the lemma. Escape of introduced cultivars with many forms can make identification difficult.

Red fescue grows from many, thin, fibrous roots and rhizomes.

genus:*Glyceria*
Mannagrasses
Family: Poaceae (Gramineae)

The mannagrasses are rhizomatous or stoloniferous perennials. They have hollow stems, closed sheaths, and prominent ligules that are membranous. Auricles are lacking. The inflorescence is a diffuse panicle. Glumes are shorter than the lowest lemma, papery, 1-veined, and pointed-tipped. Lemmas are awnless and broadly rounded, with 5-9 obvious parallel veins (7 for *Glyceria borealis* and *Glyceria elata*), and membranous, torn-looking margins. Paleas are either slightly shorter or longer than the lemmas. Each floret has 3 stamens.

Similar Species: Weak alkaligrass *(Torreyochloa pauciflora)* has open leaf sheaths, glumes that have a prominent vein, and lemmas with a purple band below the tip. Seashore saltgrass *(Distichlis spicata)* has leaves that are 2-ranked similar to reed mannagrass, but the leaf sheaths are open and the inflorescence is a very compact panicle. Reed canarygrass *(Phalaris arundinacea)* is also tall and robust, but has almost woody stems, open sheaths, flat-topped ligules, small auricles, and a compressed, less open inflorescence.

Functional Value: All species are edible, but are usually not present in large enough populations to be of much value for wildlife.

Glyceria borealis
northern mannagrass
Status: OBL
Color photo page 364

The stems of northern mannagrass are erect but some may grow horizontally similar to a floating aquatic plant. Plants are freely rooting and to 1 m tall. Leaves are 2-6 mm broad, flat or folded. The inflorescence is narrow and to 40 cm long, with a few erect branches. Blooms from May through October.

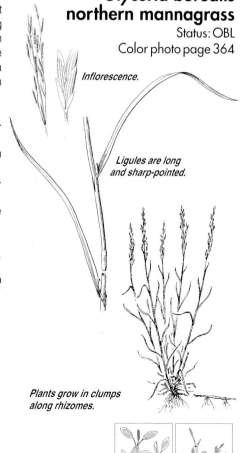

Inflorescence.

Ligules are long and sharp-pointed.

- sheaths often flattened, smooth, open for 1-4 cm
- ligules 5-10 mm long, sharply pointed, often split
- spikelets 10-15 mm long, cylindrical in outline, 6- to 10-flowered
- lemmas 3-4 mm long, 7-veined, hairy on the veins

Habitat: Northern mannagrass is usually aquatic, growing in wet meadows, and along stream and lake margins; it normally occurs in 30-100 cm of water.

Range: Northern mannagrass occurs from Alaska to Newfoundland, Maine to Pennsylvania; British Columbia to central California, and eastward to Arizona and New Mexico.

Plants grow in clumps along rhizomes.

Mannagrasses continued on next page...

GRASSES

Glyceria elata
tall mannagrass; fowl mannagrass
Status: FACW+

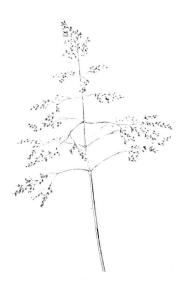

Tall mannagrass has erect stems to 1.5 m tall. Plants are soft and almost succulent when young. Leaves are flat, 6-12 mm broad, and tend to bend over. The inflorescence is 15-25 cm long, with loose, open, spreading branches. Blooms from May through July.

- older sheaths roughened, closed nearly to the top
- ligules hairy, 3-6 mm long
- spikelets long, flattened, egg-shaped, 4- to 8-flowered
- glumes hairy, first 1 mm long, second 0.5 mm long
- lemmas bright green, 2 mm long, distinctly 7-veined

Habitat: Tall mannagrass grows along stream and lake margins, and in moist woods and ditches; it prefers more open habitats.

Range: Tall mannagrass occurs from British Columbia to Montana and south to California, Arizona, and New Mexico; in Washington it grows on both sides of the Cascades.

The inflorescence of tall mannagrass is large, open and delicate, and composed of 4- to 8-flowered spikelets.

Spikelets are compact, with glumes shorter than the lemmas; lemmas have 7 distinct veins.

Plants arise as single stems along a creeping rhizome.

Glyceria grandis
reed mannagrass

Status: OBL
Color photo page 364

Reed mannagrass is a strongly rhizomatous, yet also tufted, perennial that grows to 2 m tall. Leaves are 6-18 mm broad, flat, and bright green when young. The inflorescence is 20-40 cm long, loose, open, and with numerous spreading branches. Stamens occasionally number 2 but usually 3. Blooms from late June through early August.

- sheaths smooth, closed completely or open only 1 cm, soft at the base ~ smooth
- leaves 2-ranked, with a brown patch at the leaf node
- ligules smooth, smooth-margined, 4-9 mm long, with pointed tip
- spikelets long, flattened, oblong, 4- to 7-flowered
- first glume 1.5-2 mm long; second glume 0.7-1 mm long, torn-looking
- lemmas purplish, 2-3 mm long, torn-looking, with blunt tip

Habitat: Reed mannagrass also occurs in sloughs, wet meadows, and along stream and lake margins; tolerates drier and more shady habitats than tall mannagrass.

Range: Reed mannagrass occurs from Alaska to northern Oregon and northern Nevada.

The inflorescence of reed mannagrass is long and open; lemmas have obvious veins (left); and, spikelets are 4- to 7-flowered (right).

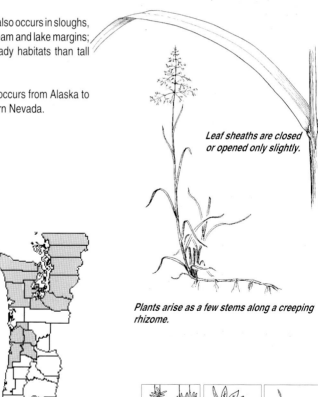

Leaf sheaths are closed or opened only slightly.

Plants arise as a few stems along a creeping rhizome.

GRASSES

335

Genus: *Holcus*
velvetgrass
Family: Poaceae (Gramineae)

The velvetgrasses are tufted perennial grasses known for their soft, hairy stems that are weak, hollow, and almost succulent. Stems have open sheaths and membranous ligules that are flat and topped with short hairs. Two-flowered spikelets are crowded onto narrow panicles; the upper flowers are male and the lower ones both male and female. Glumes are equal in size, longer than the lemmas. The awn of the uppermost lemma of each spikelet extends above both flowers and is bent or curved.

Similar Species: Few other grass species have such distinctly soft-velvety herbage. Many of the bromes *(Bromus* species; not treated in this guide) have hairy stems and/or leaves, but have many-flowered spikelets with awned lemmas and closed sheaths.

Functional Value: These are not a preferred forage by most grazing animals and hold little fodder value. They are a moderately effective erosion control species.

Holcus lanatus
common velvetgrass
Status: FAC
Color photo page 365

Common velvetgrass is a perennial plant that grows to 1 m tall. The velvety leaves have ligules 1-2 mm long that are finely hairy. Glumes are hairy and equal in size. Lemmas are fringed with short hairs. Blooms from May through September.

- tufted or stoloniferous
- stems and leaves covered with velvety, grayish hairs
- leaves flat, 3-10 mm wide
- inflorescence purplish when new, fading to tan, 5-15 cm long
- lemmas smooth, shiny; upper lemma with hooked awn

Habitat: Invades planted meadows and other agricultural lands. Common velvetgrass is found in unimproved pastures, along roadsides, and in other disturbed areas. It prefers moist sites. It is, as its name implies, common and frequently abundant.

Range: Native to Eurasia, the occurs in western Washington and Oregon to California; scattered in eastern United States.

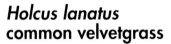

Florets with hooked awn.

spikelet

Plants grow in clumps and are lacking rhizomes.

Holcus mollis
creeping velvetgrass; creeping softgrass
Status: FACU

Creeping velvetgrass is also a perennial, but is not as common as common velvetgrass, nor as hairy. The ligules are 2-3 mm long and appear more ragged and hairy than those of common velvetgrass. Lemmas are 2.2 mm long; upper lemma is strongly bearded at the base. Blooms from June though September.

- rhizomes creeping
- nodes of stems and leaves with velvety greenish gray hairs
- leaves flat, 4-10 mm wide
- inflorescence greenish, more compact than common velvetgrass when mature
- lemma smooth, not shiny; upper lemma with bent, not hooked, awn

Habitat: Same as common velvetgrass, although creeping velvetgrass prefers acid sites. Creeping velvetgrass is less common than common velvetgrass.

Range: Same as common velvetgrass.

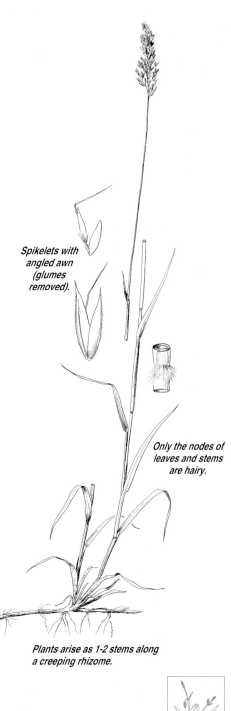

Spikelets with angled awn (glumes removed).

Only the nodes of leaves and stems are hairy.

Plants arise as 1-2 stems along a creeping rhizome.

GRASSES

Leersia oryzoides
rice cutgrass
Family: Poaceae (Gramineae)
Status: OBL
Color photo page 365

Inflorescence is an open panicle.

Leaves are minutely toothed and sharp to the touch.

Rice cutgrass spikelets are flattened, 1-flowered, and lack glumes; ligules are inconspicuous; plants arise singly from extensive rhizomes.

Rice cutgrass is a rhizomatous perennial that forms dense colonies. It has minutely toothed leaf margins, sharp enough to easily cut flesh if carelessly handled, and leaf sheaths with a surface that is unidirectionally roughened. The leaves and flattened spikelets are pale yellow-green when young. Ligules are inconspicuous. The inflorescence is an open panicle. Lemmas are leathery, 4 mm long, and bordered with prominent bristles on the keel and veins; the bristles aid in dispersal of the fruits.

- stems to 1.5 m tall, velvety at the joints
- leaves 10-28 cm long, 6-12 mm wide; leaf margins sharply toothed
- spikelets 1-flowered, 4-6 mm long, strongly flattened sideways
- glumes lacking; lemmas with bristled keel

Habitat: Rice cutgrass can grow on a wide variety of sunny and shady sites, from low to midelevations. It is most commonly found beside pools, ponds, mudflats, beaver areas, rivers, and in ditches and gravel pits; usually in shallow water (to 0.3 m).

Range: Widespread across southern Canada and most of the United States, as well as the warmer parts of Europe. In freshwater systems, occurs most commonly in northwestern Oregon, but found occasionally in Washington.

Similar Species: The sharp, skin-cutting foliage of this species is distinctive. Other grasses of the same general size and with a similar open panicle (e.g., *Poa*, *Agrostis*, *Festuca*, *Bromus*, *Deschampsia*, *Aira*, etc.) have soft leaves, glumes, and lack the long bristles on the keel and nerves of the lemmas.

Functional Value: Provides cover for many small aquatic and amphibious organisms and forage for some species of waterfowl.

Genus: *Lolium*
Ryegrasses

Family: Poaceae (Gramineae)

Ryegrasses have hollow stems and open sheaths. Auricles are present and to 2 mm long. Ligules are membranous and 0.5-1.5 mm long. Inflorescence is a compact spike with numerous flattened spikelets attached on edge in an alternating pattern, with one multiflowered spikelet per node. There is one glume opposite the flowering stalk; the terminal spikelet has 2 glumes. Glumes have 5-9 veins; lemmas 5 veins. Paleas are obvious and slightly shorter than the lemmas.

Similar Species: Quackgrass *(Elytrigia repens)* also has auricles, hollow stems with open sheaths, and a compact spike with one multiflowered spikelet per node, but the spikelets of quackgrass are attached flat-wise to the axis of the flowering stalk and the ligules are only 0.5 mm long, membranous, and rough-margined. Tall fescue *(Festuca arundinacea)* has stiffer leaves with edges that are rough to the touch, auricles that are fringed with short hairs, a yellowish collar area at the node, and a panicle inflorescence.

Functional Value: Palatable forage for grazing animals. Both species are excellent erosion-control species and frequently included in hydroseed mixes for wetland buffer zones and sidewalls of drainage swales.

Lolium multiflorum
Italian ryegrass; annual ryegrass

Status: FACU

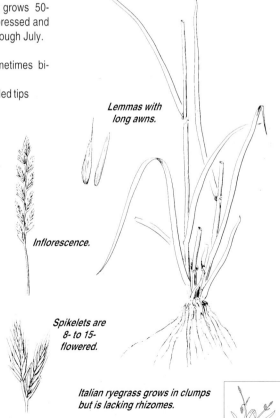

Italian ryegrass is a robust grass that grows 50-120 cm tall. Inflorescences are compressed and 10-35 cm long. Blooms from May through July.

- bunchgrass, usually annual, sometimes bi-ennial
- leaves 4-8 mm wide, flat, with rolled tips when young
- spikelets 8- to 15-flowered
- lemmas awned

Habitat: Italian ryegrass occurs in improved pastures, lawns, and disturbed areas especially where seeding for erosion control has occurred. It prefers moist to moderately dry sites.

Range: Natives of Europe; occur throughout our area.

Lemmas with long awns.

Inflorescence.

Spikelets are 8- to 15-flowered.

Italian ryegrass grows in clumps but is lacking rhizomes.

Ryegrasses continued on next page...

GRASSES

Lolium perenne
perennial ryegrass

Status: FACU

Color photo page 365

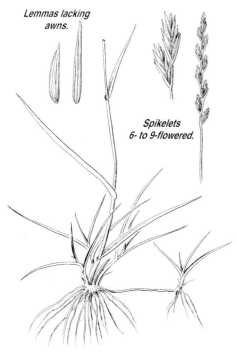

Lemmas lacking
awns.

Spikelets
6- to 9-flowered.

Plants arise in small clumps along a short-creeping rhizome.

Perennial ryegrass is less robust than Italian ryegrass. It is finely rhizomatous and grows 30-80 cm tall. Many new shoots are always present at the base of each plant. Blooms from May through July.

- bunchgrass, short-lived perennial
- leaves 3-4 mm wide, strongly folded when young, soft to the touch
- spikelets 6- to 10-flowered
- lemmas sharp-pointed; awns lacking

Habitat: Same as Italian ryegrass.

Range: Same as Italian ryegrass.

Western panic grass is a branched, spreading, low-growing perennial grass with erect tips. When erect it grows only to 40 cm tall. Leaves are flat, 5-12 mm broad, and often covered with fine hairs. The inflorescence is an open panicle, 3-11 cm long and wide. Blooms from June to August.

- leaf sheaths open, hollow, covered with bristle-like hairs
- stems and nodes yellow-green, with long spreading hairs
- ligules composed of hairs 2.5-4 mm long
- spikelets 2-flowered (1 sterile), less than 2 mm long, round
- glumes are unequal; first barely visible, second 0.5 mm long

Spikelets (top right) are 2-flowered with small glumes at the base of rounded lemmas.

Leaves are broad and covered with fine hairs.

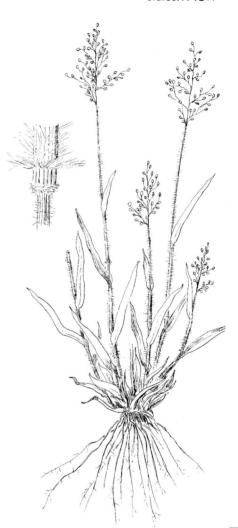

Habitat: Grows along rocky or sandy banks, lake margins, and in open woods; also found in marshy woods to dry prairies, from sea level to 2,600 m.

Range: Occurs from British Columbia south along the coast and in the mountains to the central valley of California, and east of the Cascades along water courses or near springs; occasionally in central Washington and eastern Oregon; rarely in the Willamette Valley. Found in all counties in our area.

Similar Species: There are no other species as short as western panic grass that have hairy stems and nodes, and long hairy ligules.

Functional Value: Valuable forage for wildlife because of the large achenes.

The leaf sheaths (left) of western panic grass are hollow and covered with bristle-like hairs; plants grow in clumps from fine, fibrous roots.

GRASSES

Paspalum distichum
knotgrass, joint paspalum
Family: Poaceae (Gramineae)
Status: FACW

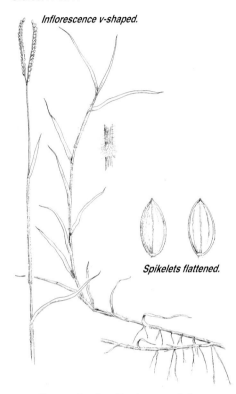

Inflorescence v-shaped.

Spikelets flattened.

*Stems and nodes of knotgrass are hairy;
stems arise singly along long stolons.*

Knotgrass is a 40-100 cm tall colonial grass with vigorous stolons; it often grows to the exclusion of other species. The inflorescence is most commonly a V-shaped pair of branches at the top of the stem, with paired spikelets 3.0-3.5 mm long in two rows on one side of each of the flattened branches. Rarely there are up to 5 alternate branches. Blooms August to October.

- stems hairy and nodes densely hairy
- leaves coarse, 3-8 mm wide, bluish
- ligules 1-1.5 mm long, membranous, usually with slightly torn edge
- spikelet flattened, 3-3.5 mm long, with one fertile flower
- first glume often lacking, or up to 1.5 mm long; second glume hairy
- stigma and anthers purple

Habitat: Found in periodically inundated habitats, such as low elevation sloughs, ditches, lakeshore marshes, coastal pond outlets, shallow water (to 1 m deep), exposed streamsides, and in mud, silt, or sand along rivers.

Range: Knotgrass ranges east to the southeastern United States, and south to Mexico and South America. Occurs in and around freshwater ponds on the coast at the southern end of our area; otherwise, largely confined to the valleys and floodplains of the Columbia and Willamette rivers. Washington State distribution unknown.

Similar Species: The coarse terminal pair of inflorescence branches is unique among our wetland grasses. Occasionally crabgrass species (genus *Digitaria*), upland plants which are similar in form, stray into damp margins of wetlands. They are fibrous-rooted annuals and lack the stolons of knotgrass. Weedy Bermuda grass *(Cynodon dactylon)*, a recent upland invader at the southern limit of our area, is similar but is a much shorter plant, with short, narrow, and strongly two-ranked leaves. Dallis grass *(Paspalum dilatatum)* is a coarse, rhizomatous plant, with many long hairs on the margins of the relatively large spikelets, and up to 10 panicle branches.

Functional Value: Winter browse for ducks, much preferred over adjacent clones of reed canarygrass in sloughs of the Columbia River. Knotgrass is a native wetland grass with clonal growth that stabilizes shorelines.

Phalaris arundinacea
reed canarygrass
Family: Poaceae (Gramineae)
Status: FACW
Color photo page 365

Reed canarygrass is the most invasive grass species that occurs in wetlands in the Pacific Northwest. It is a stout, mat-forming, rhizomatous perennial with stems to 1 cm wide and 2 m tall. The sheaths are open, stems hollow and often with small auricles. Leaves are 5-17 mm wide and 30 cm long. Ligules are membranous, 4-10 mm long, obtuse, frequently with jagged margins, and a pointed-folded tip. Only one lemma per 3-flowered spikelet is obvious, the others appear as basal bristles 1-1.5 mm long at the bottom of the central lemma. Blooms June through August.

- rhizomes distinctly reddish
- stems robust, bamboo-like, smooth, occasionally branching at the nodes
- leaves blue-green when fresh, straw-colored when dry
- inflorescence a compressed, loosely branched, 1-sided, narrow panicle 3-15 cm long, sometimes exceeding 20 cm, reddish when young

Habitat: Reed canarygrass dominates areas that are irregularly inundated. It will not persist under water for an entire growing season. It commonly grows in disturbed locations both wet and dry, and is a dominant species in emergent wetland meadows. It is shade-intolerant.

Range: Reed canarygrass is a Eurasian native. It is one of the most broadly ranging and commonly occurring species in the Pacific Northwest.

Similar Species: Reed mannagrass *(Glyceria grandis)* has closed sheaths, no auricles, and an open, diffuse panicle composed of 4- to 7-flowered spikelets with glumes that are much smaller than the prominently veined lemmas. Tall fescue *(Festuca arundinacea)* has open leaf sheaths. It grows in thick tufts, has large auricles, and very small ligules. Leaves are only 4-10 mm wide. The open panicle has large spikelets (12-15 mm long) giving a more compressed appearance; glumes are much smaller than the entire spikelet. Orchardgrass *(Dactylis glomerata)* has a compressed but loosely branched panicle and hollow stems, but the sheaths are closed. It grows in drier habitats, has 3-10 mm wide (and thus narrower) leaves, and spikelets all attached to one side of the rachis.

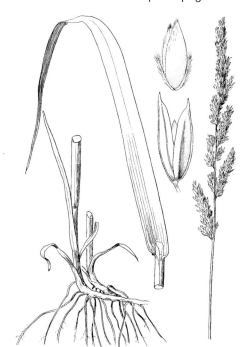

Plants grow as a thick mat; ligules are long; leaves are wide with prominant nodes; spikelets have 2 bristle-like lemmas; inflorescence is a compressed narrow panicle.

Functional Value: Reed canarygrass is not considered to have significant wildlife value once it has dried, although many wildlife species find it attractive for cover. It produces high biomass, providing organic matter for detrital-based food chains. It was recommended for use in erosion control, sediment retention, and water quality protection from the 1930's until the late 1980's. Its use is now discouraged because of its highly invasive nature.

Ethnobotanical Uses: Canarygrass is planted in wet agricultural areas for pasture. The variegated varieties are used as a garden ornamentals. It has been used in basketry.

GRASSES

Phleum pratense var. *pratense*
common timothy

Family: Poaceae (Gramineae)
Status: FAC-
Color photo
page 366

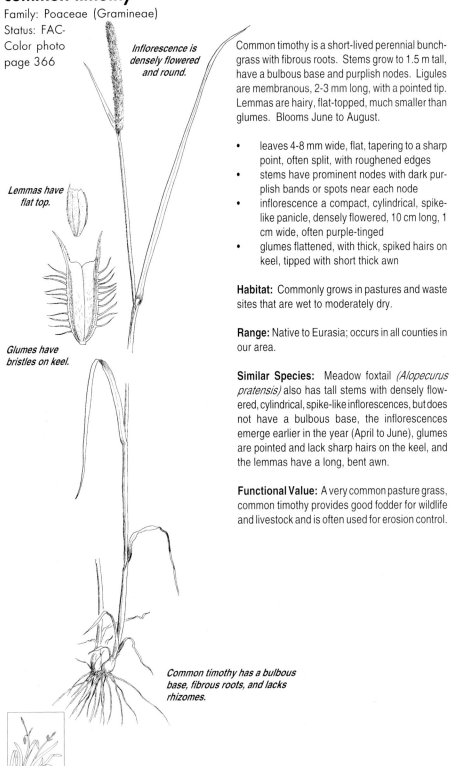

Inflorescence is densely flowered and round.

Lemmas have flat top.

Glumes have bristles on keel.

Common timothy has a bulbous base, fibrous roots, and lacks rhizomes.

Common timothy is a short-lived perennial bunch-grass with fibrous roots. Stems grow to 1.5 m tall, have a bulbous base and purplish nodes. Ligules are membranous, 2-3 mm long, with a pointed tip. Lemmas are hairy, flat-topped, much smaller than glumes. Blooms June to August.

- leaves 4-8 mm wide, flat, tapering to a sharp point, often split, with roughened edges
- stems have prominent nodes with dark purplish bands or spots near each node
- inflorescence a compact, cylindrical, spike-like panicle, densely flowered, 10 cm long, 1 cm wide, often purple-tinged
- glumes flattened, with thick, spiked hairs on keel, tipped with short thick awn

Habitat: Commonly grows in pastures and waste sites that are wet to moderately dry.

Range: Native to Eurasia; occurs in all counties in our area.

Similar Species: Meadow foxtail *(Alopecurus pratensis)* also has tall stems with densely flowered, cylindrical, spike-like inflorescences, but does not have a bulbous base, the inflorescences emerge earlier in the year (April to June), glumes are pointed and lack sharp hairs on the keel, and the lemmas have a long, bent awn.

Functional Value: A very common pasture grass, common timothy provides good fodder for wildlife and livestock and is often used for erosion control.

Phragmites australis
(Phragmites communis)
common reed

Family: Poaceae (Gramineae)
Status: FACW+
Color photo page 366

Common reed is a vigorously rhizomatous grass of freshwater and brackish marshes. Leaves are flat, 1-4 cm wide and 20-45 cm long. Spikelets are 10-15 mm long and 3- to 6-flowered. Glumes are unequal; the first is 6-9 mm long, the second 9-12 mm long. The first lemma is 9-12 mm, unawned; remaining lemmas are smaller, with awns as long as the lemma. Blooms from August to September.

- stems woody, hollow, to 3 m tall
- leaf sheaths smooth-surfaced, loose, woody, twisting in the wind so leaves align to one side
- ligules 1.5-3 mm, membranous, with a fringe of hairs in older plants
- spikelet axis (rachilla) with many silky bristles
- inflorescence a large, feathery panicle, reddish or purplish when young, 15-35 cm long
- lemmas longer than glumes, with many long, silky hairs at the base

Habitat: Common reed is a dominant grass of springs, ponds, lakes, rivers, and freshwater marshes where it grows in dense patches. Occurs in saturated soils and can be found in association with many other obligate freshwater plants, such as cattails (*Typha* species), sedges, and rushes. Common reed is occasionally invasive in salt marshes and intertidal areas, where it can compete aggressively with other plants.

Range: Native to North America, but is considered an invasive weed of salt marshes and is listed as a noxious weed for much of the Atlantic Coast. Common reed is found in both saltwater and freshwater habitats in Washington and Oregon, but is uncommon on the west side of the Cascades.

Similar Species: No other species has such tall, woody stems with a feather-like inflorescence.

Functional Value: Common reed provides significant cover and nesting habitat for several birds. It has considerable value in cleansing water of suspended sediments, dissolved nutrients, and

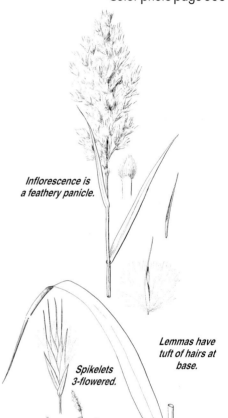

Inflorescence is a feathery panicle.

Lemmas have tuft of hairs at base.

Spikelets 3-flowered.

Plants are tall and woody with long, flat leaves.

chemicals. The woody, dead shoots can be a serious fire hazard.

Ethnobotanical Uses: Common reed is occasionally used for thatching and matting. The foliage is too coarse for livestock forage.

GRASSES

Genus: *Poa*
bluegrasses
Family: Poaceae (Gramineae)

The bluegrasses are important forage grasses. They can be either annuals or perennials, but the wetland-associated species are all perennials except annual bluegrass *(Poa annua)*. The plants are usually rhizomatous and/or stoloniferous, tufted, and have hollow stems and partially closed sheaths without auricles. Ligules are membranous. Leaves fuse to a point much like the prow of a boat. The inflorescence is a panicle and can be either open or compact. Spikelets are 2- to 7-flowered. Glumes are unequal, keeled, and remain on the stem after the seeds have been shed. Both the glumes and lemmas are spear-shaped and sharp-pointed. Lemmas are also keeled and awnless, and in many species, the bases of the lemmas are webbed, having small tufts of long hairs.

Range: All common bluegrasses associated with wetlands in the Pacific Northwest are native to Europe and extremely common across North America. Many of these species may invade and aggressively compete with native wetland species. These species, except rough bluegrass *(Poa trivialis)* occur in all counties in our area.

Similar Species: The bluegrasses are extremely variable in morphology and consist of more than 200 species in the United States. They all appear similar and differentiating between species is difficult. It is easiest to remember the characteristics listed for the genera to identify a bluegrass.

Functional Value: The bluegrasses are all palatable and nutritious forage grasses, and the perennial species are excellent for erosion control.

Chart for Comparison of the Commom Species of Bluegrass						
Species	*Overall size*	*Stems*	*Ligule*	*Spikelet*	*Flowers per spikelet*	*Lemma*
annual bluegrass *(Poa annua)*	to 20 cm annual	smooth	1-2 mm	3-8 mm	3-6	hairy along back, not webbed at base
Canadian bluegrass *(Poa compressa)*	to 40 cm perennial	smooth, flattened	< 2mm	4-6 mm	4-6	slightly hairy along back, not webbed at base
fowl bluegrass *(Poa palustris)*	to 120 cm perennial	smooth or slightly rough	3-5 mm	3-4.5 mm	2-4	hairy along back, mod. webbed at base
Kentucky bluegrass *(Poa pratensis)*	to 100 cm perennial	smooth	1.5-3 mm	4-6 mm	3-5	slightly hairy along back, heavily webbed at base
rough bluegrass *(Poa trivialis)*	to 120 cm perennial	rough	3-7 mm	4 mm	2-3	sparse hair along back, webbed at base

Poa annua
annual bluegrass
Status: FAC

This is the only annual wetland-associated blue-grass. Stems are smooth and reach 5 -20 cm when erect, but usually grow decumbent and in clumps. Leaves are smooth. The compact panicle is 3-8 cm long and is composed of a few spikelets. Blooms from May through August.

- leaves blue-green, 10 cm long, 1-4 mm wide, often folded in the middle
- ligules less than 2 mm long
- spikelets 3-8 mm long, pale green, 3- to 6-flowered
- lemmas 3.5 mm long, with long hairs along the lower third, 5-veined, not webbed at base

Habitat: Annual bluegrass is common in lawns, gardens, meadows, and disturbed places such as roadsides and abandoned lots. Occurs in poor soils and seeds itself abundantly. Annual blue-grass grows quickly early in growing season and during mild winters. It often associates with many other weedy grasses and herbs.

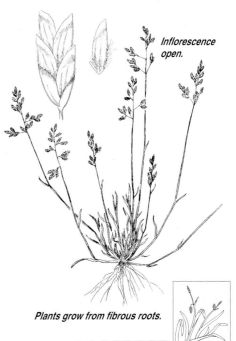

Inflorescence open.

Plants grow from fibrous roots.

Poa compressa
Canada bluegrass
Status: FACU+

Canada bluegrass is a tufted perennial grass with stout rhizomes. The narrow compact panicle grows up to 12 cm long and has spikelets along the entire branches. Blooms from early May through August.

- stems smooth, strongly flattened at base, to 40 cm tall
- leaves narrow, grayish blue-green, smooth, to 10 cm long, 4 mm wide, folded at midrib, tips sharply pointed-prow-like
- ligules less than 2 mm long, rounded, hairy, and very finely ciliate
- spikelets 4-6 mm long, 4- to 6-flowered
- lemmas 2.5 mm long, with a few long hairs along midveins, not webbed at base

Habitat: Canada bluegrass is common in mead-ows, lawns, older disturbed places, and moist to dryish low ground. Occurs in poor soils and seeds itself abundantly. It is often associated with other weedy grasses and herbs.

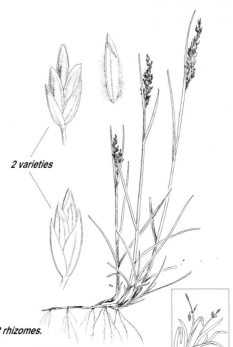

2 varieties

Plants grow in clumps from stout rhizomes.

GRASSES

Poa palustris
fowl bluegrass
Status: FAC

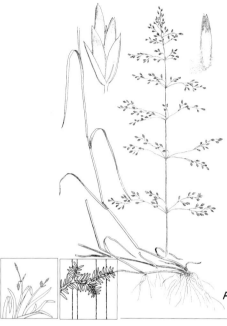

Fowl bluegrass is a loosely tufted, perennial grass that can form a dense sod. Stems are smooth (maybe rough), usually erect, and grow 40-120 cm tall from purplish base. The panicle is loose, open, and 10-30 cm long. Blooms from June to July.

- plants stoloniferous but not rhizomatous
- leaves smooth to rough, 20 cm long, 1-3 mm wide, either flat or folded at the middle
- ligules to 5 mm long, pointed-tipped
- spikelets to 4.5 mm long, 2- to 4-flowered, in open, sometimes nodding panicles
- lemmas bronze-green at the tip, 2-3 mm long, with few long hairs along midveins, moderately webbed at base

Habitat: Fowl bluegrass is occasional in many plant communities including meadows, woods, ditches, and stream banks. It is frequently associated with pasture grasses and herbs.

Plants grow in a mat from creeping stolons.

Poa pratensis
Kentucky bluegrass
Status: FAC
Color photo page 366

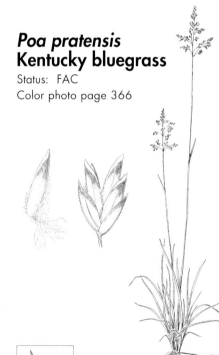

This is a dense, mat-forming, perennial grass with long rhizomes. Short, erect stems grow to 1 m tall. The panicles are loose, open, 15 cm long, with many evenly spaced spikelets. Blooms April through June.

- plants truly rhizomatous
- leaves bright green, 2-3 mm wide, flat or folded at the vein, with smooth leaf sheaths
- ligules 1.5 mm long (occasionally to 3 mm long), with a flat top
- panicle usually curved to one side with 3-5 branches per joint
- spikelets large, 4-6 mm long, 3- to 5-flowered
- lemmas 2-4 mm long, with keel and marginal veins long and hairy; webbed base — red streaking

Habitat: Kentucky bluegrass is found mostly in open areas such as dry or wet meadows, pastures, or lawns. It is common in drier meadows adjacent to wet meadows. It may be found in open woods, along stream banks, and in disturbed areas.

Plants grow in clumps from long-creeping rhizomes.

Poa trivialis
rough bluegrass
Status: FACW

Rough bluegrass is a loosely tufted perennial grass with rough stems to 120 cm long that are often prostrate and root at the nodes. The panicle is open, to 15 cm long, loose, with 5 branches per node. Blooms May through July.

- stoloniferous but not rhizomatous
- leaves pale green, rough to touch, to 20 cm long, 4 mm wide, flat, tips only slightly prow-like
- ligules pointed, 3-7 mm long, usually hairy
- spikelets to 4 mm long, 2- to 3-flowered
- lemmas 2-3 mm long, 5-veined, with a few long hairs along the midveins, webbed at base,

Spikelets 2- to 3-flowered.

Habitat: Rough bluegrass is occasional in disturbed moist sites in many plant communities including meadows, woods, and stream banks. It is found in association with pasture grasses and weedy herbs.

Plants grow in clumps from fibrous roots.

GRASSES

349

Genus: *Spartina*
Cordgrasses
Family: Poaceae (Gramineae)

The cordgrasses are deciduous and strongly rhizomatous perennial coastal grasses that form dense circular patches. Stems are hollow and sheaths are open for most of their length. Leaves are rolled inward when emerging from the bud. Ligules are short and composed of a fringe of hairs. Inflorescence is a spike with two to many spikes per plant. Spikelets are 1-flowered and arranged in two tightly compressed rows on one side of the flower stalk. Glumes are woody, and strongly flattened with a prominent keel along the back from which spiny bristles protrude. Lemmas are also keeled, but lack robust bristles and are not woody as are the glumes.

Similar Species: Tufted hairgrass *(Deschampsia cespitosa)* is a taller, more delicate bunchgrass with much longer stems and open, delicate panicles. Other saltmarsh grasses are annual, smaller (if a bunchgrass), or form diffuse patches, such as seashore saltgrass *(Distichlis spicata)*.

Functional Value: Voles and rails use cordgrasses for cover, marsh wrens nest in them, and bitterns and great blue herons hunt along the edges of patches. Smooth and common cordgrasses are listed as noxious weeds in Washington.

Ethnobotanical Uses: Along the Atlantic Coast both smooth and common cordgrasses are used as a mulch ("salt hay") and livestock hay. They can be used as a fiber source for paper.

Chart for the Comparison of the Cordgrass Species			
species	smooth cordgrass *(Spartina alterniflora)*	common cordgrass *(Spartina anglica)*	saltmeadow cordgrass *(Spartina patens)*
plant height	60-120 cm	130 cm	15-80 cm
ligule length	1.5 mm	2-3 mm	-
leaf width	5-12 mm	8-15 mm	0.5-3 mm
leaves flat or folded	flat, with rolled margins	flat	folded
number of spikes	6-15	3-6	1-4
spike length	4-15 cm	12-40 cm	2-5 cm
spikelet length	1 cm	1.5-2 cm	9-13 mm
1st glume length	6-9 mm	13-16 mm	4 mm
2nd glume length	9-11 mm	14-21 mm	5 mm

Spartina alterniflora
smooth cordgrass; spartina
Status: OBL
Color photo page 366

Smooth cordgrass is an intertidal salt marsh grass. The first glume is 6-9 mm long and narrow; the second glume is wider, blunt-tipped, 9-11 mm long, and barely longer than the flower. Lemmas are softer than the glumes. The palea is as long as, or longer than, the lemma. Anthers are 3.5-4 mm long. Blooms from August through September.

- stems 60-120 cm tall, 1-2 cm in diameter, spongy at base
- leaves bright green when young, 5-12 mm wide, 40 cm long with rolled margins
- sheaths with scattered hairs all over except on nodes
- ligules 1.5 mm long
- spikes number at least 6 (up to 15), 4-15 cm long, all terminal on upright branches, compressed and barely discernable as separate, with terminal bristle 2.5 cm long
- spikelets 1 cm long
- glumes sparsely hairy

Habitat: Smooth cordgrass invades established salt marshes and the lower intertidal areas in the Pacific Northwest. It grows as tall as tufted hairgrass *(Deschampsia cespitosa)* and rapidly colonizes unvegetated mudflats. It can also establish in open habitats in fresh water. Smooth cordgrass requires saturated soils, cobble, gravel, sand or silt, saline, fresh or brackish water; is not tolerant of severe water pollution. Established plants trap large amounts of silt and raise the level of the ground within smooth cordgrass meadows.

Range: Smooth cordgrass is native to the Atlantic and Gulf coasts of North America. It has been accidentally introduced around the world from seed used in shipping ballast. It is naturalized in England, France, South Africa, and New Zealand, and in Washington, Oregon, and California.

Functional Value: Drift mats of smooth cordgrass have been seen fifty miles

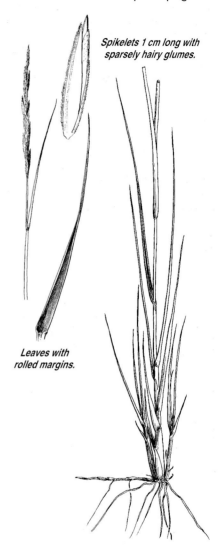

Spikelets 1 cm long with sparsely hairy glumes.

Leaves with rolled margins.

Smooth cordgrass plants spread by short rhizomes and form dense, circular mats.

up the Pacific Coast from Willapa Bay, and are known to drag crab pots, anchored boats, and gill nets, and to smother native marsh plants. Major changes in hydrology can be expected where this plant colonizes large intertidal areas. In its native range, it is used as an erosion-control species.

Cordgrasses continued on next page...

GRASSES

Spartina anglica
common cordgrass; rice grass
Status: OBL

Common cordgrass is a robust intertidal salt marsh grass. The circular clumps of common cordgrass frequently grow together into extensive meadows; it has often been planted for erosion control. The lower glume is 2/3-4/5 the length of the upper; the upper glume is the same length as the spikelet and lance-shaped to oblong. The palea is 8-13 mm long. Blooms from July through November.

- stems very robust, to 1.3 m tall, 1.5 cm wide
- leaves yellow-green to gray-green, 8-15 mm wide
- sheaths smooth
- ligules 2-3 mm long
- spikes dense, erect, 3-6 per plant, 12-40 cm long, with terminal bristle 5 cm long
- spikelets 14-21 mm long, 2.5-3 mm wide, distinctly hairy

No illustration available.

Habitat: Common cordgrass is dominant in the lower intertidal communites. It grows in native marshes and up rivers in estuarine areas, and can tolerate the full range of salinities from marine to fresh water. As with smooth cordgrass, regardless of the original substrate, it forms a dense-rooted, silt-dominated mud base.

Range: Common cordgrass is a fertile, natural hybrid that was first seen in England. It has been widely introduced around the world as a "land reclamation" plant, to New Zealand, the Netherlands, France, Germany, Denmark, Australia, and China; and in Washington, Oregon, and California.

Functional Value: Within the ecosystem, common cordgrass provides a huge pulse of organic material late in the growing season, composed of flowering shoots which drift around and break down over the subsequent two years. (Seeds are spread in this fashion). Common cordgrass has been planted for its sediment-trapping abilities and as food for livestock.

Saltmeadow cordgrass is a vigorous salt marsh grass. Glumes are unequal in length; the first glume is linear and 4 mm long; the second glume is lance-shaped, 1 mm long, pointed, roughened on the keel and nerves, and smooth on the sides. The lemma is 5-6 mm long, obtuse, and scarcely as long as the palea. Blooms in late summer.

- stems 15-80 cm tall, slender
- leaves dull gray-green when young, 0.5-3 mm wide, folded
- spikes 2-5 cm long, barely seen above leaves, alternate on stem, loosely overlapping, slightly drooping, 1-4 per plant
- spikelets 9-13 mm long

Habitat: Saltmeadow cordgrass prefers sites high in the intertidal in established marshes. It dominates the upper salt marsh zone and can colonize sand dunes, swale grasslands, sand flats, and coastal scrublands.

Range: Saltmeadow cordgrass is native to the Atlantic and Gulf coasts of North and Central America. At present, it is found in a few places in the Pacific Northwest; a population on the Siuslaw River in southern Oregon is slowly dominating the native salt marsh species. It has been introduced to China, the Mediterranean, British Columbia, Oregon, California, and (tentatively) Washington.

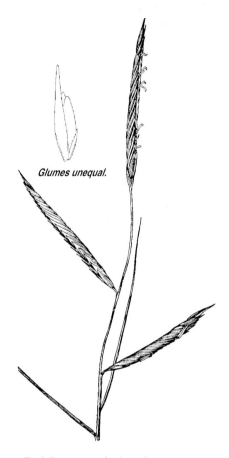

Glumes unequal.

The inflorescence of saltmeadow cordgrass has spikelets attached to one side.

GRASSES

Torreyochloa pauciflora
(Puccinellia pauciflora)
weak alkaligrass; weak mannagrass
Family: Poaceae (Gramineae)
Status: OBL

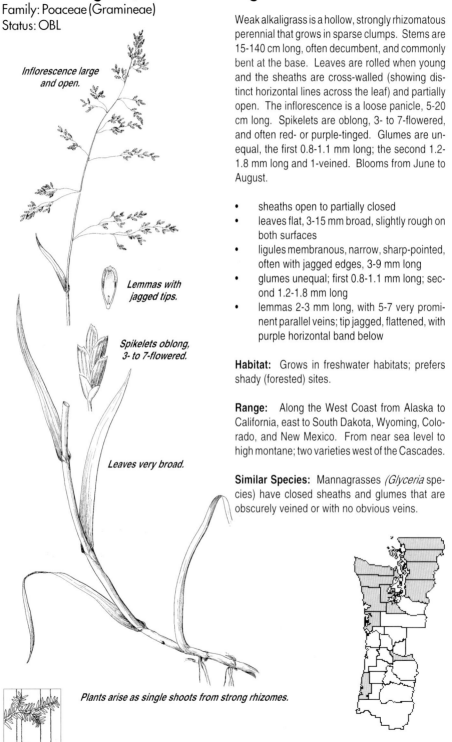

Inflorescence large
and open.

Lemmas with
jagged tips.

Spikelets oblong,
3- to 7-flowered.

Leaves very broad.

Plants arise as single shoots from strong rhizomes.

Weak alkaligrass is a hollow, strongly rhizomatous perennial that grows in sparse clumps. Stems are 15-140 cm long, often decumbent, and commonly bent at the base. Leaves are rolled when young and the sheaths are cross-walled (showing distinct horizontal lines across the leaf) and partially open. The inflorescence is a loose panicle, 5-20 cm long. Spikelets are oblong, 3- to 7-flowered, and often red- or purple-tinged. Glumes are unequal, the first 0.8-1.1 mm long; the second 1.2-1.8 mm long and 1-veined. Blooms from June to August.

- sheaths open to partially closed
- leaves flat, 3-15 mm broad, slightly rough on both surfaces
- ligules membranous, narrow, sharp-pointed, often with jagged edges, 3-9 mm long
- glumes unequal; first 0.8-1.1 mm long; second 1.2-1.8 mm long
- lemmas 2-3 mm long, with 5-7 very prominent parallel veins; tip jagged, flattened, with purple horizontal band below

Habitat: Grows in freshwater habitats; prefers shady (forested) sites.

Range: Along the West Coast from Alaska to California, east to South Dakota, Wyoming, Colorado, and New Mexico. From near sea level to high montane; two varieties west of the Cascades.

Similar Species: Mannagrasses *(Glyceria* species) have closed sheaths and glumes that are obscurely veined or with no obvious veins.

Trisetum cernuum
nodding trisetum

Family: Poaceae (Gramineae)
Status: FACU

Nodding trisetum is an erect, medium-sized perennial bunchgrass. Leaves are thin, flat, to 12 mm wide. Stems are tall, terminally drooping, and can grow to 110 cm tall. Ligules are about 2 mm long, smooth to hairy, and sometimes fringed with hairs. Spikelets are 6-12 mm long. Glumes are as long as the first lemma. Lemmas have a slender awn, inserted near the tip, that extends 5-10 mm. Blooms from May to July.

- panicles open, drooping, to 30 cm long
- spikelets 2- to 3-flowered, borne at ends of nodding open diffuse panicle branches
- lemmas to 6 mm long, prolonged above the upper flower, borne on short, hairy flowering stalk

Habitat: Nodding trisetum grows scattered in moist evergreen and mixed evergreen-deciduous woods at low to moderate elevations. It rarely occurs in large stands; more often it is found singly or in small populations in small clearings or openings under taller shrubs.

Range: Native to western North America; occurs from Alaska to Alberta, and south to northern California.

Similar Species: Because many of the common wetland grasses are often found in meadows, or along stream banks, they are not easily mistaken for nodding tristeum. However, at certain times of the year some mannagrasses *(Glyceria* species) have a vegetative growth form similar to trisetum, appearing tufted with thin, flat, lax leaves. However, the leaf arrangement of mannagrasses often appears two-ranked – the leaves arranged on either side of the stem in a single plane. Nodding trisetum is more tufted, with the leaves arising from a crown at ground level.

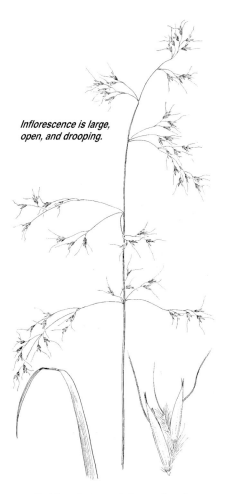

Inflorescence is large, open, and drooping.

Nodding trisetum spikelets are 2- to 3-flowered; lemmas are borne on hairy flowering stalks and have a long slender awn.

GRASSES

355

Juncus acuminatus (tapertip rush)
Photo by Sarah Spear Cooke

Juncus articulatus (jointed rush)
Photo by Binda Colebrook

Juncus effusus (soft rush)
Photo by Sarah Spear Cooke

Juncus bufonius (toad rush)
Photo by Clayton Antieau

Juncus ensifolius (daggerleaf rush)
Photo by Binda Colebrook

Juncus falcatus (sickleleaf rush)
Photo by Sarah Spear Cooke

Juncus oxymeris (pointed rush)
Photo by Fred Weinmann

Juncus supiniformis (spreading rush)
Photo by Sarah Spear Cooke

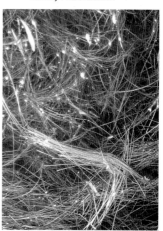

Juncus supiniformis (spreading rush)
Photo by Sarah Spear Cooke

Juncus tenuis (slender rush)
Photo by Binda Colebrook

Carex amplifolia (bigleaf sedge)
Photo by Clayton Antieau

357

Carex aurea (golden sedge)
Photo by Clayton Antieau

Carex comosa (bearded sedge)
Photo by Binda Colebrook

Carex hendersonii (Henderson sedge)
Photo by Clayton Antieau

Carex lenticularis (lenticular sedge)
Photo by Binda Colebrook

Carex lyngbyei (Lyngby sedge)
Photo by Marty Chaney

Carex macrocephala (bighead sedge)
Photo by Sarah Spear Cooke

Carex obnupta (slough sedge)
Photo by Marty Chaney

Carex sitchensis = C. aquatilis (water sedge)
Photo by Clayton Antieau

Carex stipata (sawbeak sedge)
Photo by Sarah Spear Cooke

Carex utriculata (beaked sedge)
Photo by Sarah Spear Cooke

Carex unilateralis (one-sided sedge)
Photo by Clayton Antieau

Eleocharis acicularis (needle spikerush)
Photo by Sarah Spear Cooke

Dulichium arundinaceum (dulichium)
Photo by Sarah Spear Cooke

Eleocharis ovata (ovoid spikerush)
Photo by Dyanne Sheldon

Eleocharis palustris (creeping spikerush)
Photo by Dyanne Sheldon

Eriophorum chamissonis (russet cottongrass)
Photo by Clayton Antieau

Rhynchospora alba (beakrush)
Photo by Sarah Spear Cooke

Scirpus americanus (three-square bulrush)
Photo by Fred Weinmann

Scirpus acutus (hardstem bulrush)
Photo by Dyanne Sheldon

Scirpus atrocinctus (woolly sedge)
Photo by Sarah Spear Cooke

Scirpus microcarpus (small-fruited bulrush)
Photo by Vic Yoshino

Scirpus maritimus (seacoast bulrush)
Photo by Dyanne Sheldon

Scirpus tabernaemontanii (softstem bulrush)
Photo by Marc Boule

**Agrostis capillaris & Agrostis gigantea
(colonial bentgrass & redtop)**
Photo by Fred Weinmann

Agrostis gigantea (redtop)
Photo by Marty Chaney

Alopecurus aequalis (short-awn foxtail)
Photo by Binda Colebrook

Alopecurus pratensis (meadow foxtail)
Photo by Sarah Spear Cooke

Alopecurus geniculatus (water foxtail)
Photo by Sarah Spear Cooke

Anthoxanthum odoratum (sweet vernalgrass)
Photo by Al Hanners

Beckmannia syzigachne (American sloughgrass)
Photo by Clayton Antieau

Calamagrostis canadensis (bluejoint reedgrass)
Photo by Clayton Antieau

Dactylis glomerata (orchardgrass)
Photo by J. Chris Hoag

Distichlis spicata (seashore saltgrass)
Photo by Clayton Antieau

Elymus mollis (American dunegrass)
Photo by Sarah Spear Cooke

Glyceria borealis (northern mannagrass)
Photo by Binda Colebrook

Glyceria grandis (reed mannagrass)
Photo by Binda Colebrook

364

Holcus lanatus (common velvetgrass)
Photo by Sarah Spear Cooke

Leersia oryzoides (rice cutgrass)
Photo by Heather Erickson

Lolium perenne (perennial ryegrass)
Photo by Marty Chaney

Phalaris arundinacea (reed canarygrass)
Photo by Dyanne Sheldon

Phleum pratense (common timothy)
Photo by Marty Chaney

Phragmites australis (common reed)
Photo by Sarah Spear Cooke

Poa palustris (fowl bluegrass)
Photo by Sarah Spear Cooke

Spartina alterniflora (smooth cordgrass)
Photo by Kathleen Sayce

Ferns are a group of vascular plants, like our familiar trees and flowering plants, that have "tubes" for transporting food and water throughout the plant. We have relatively few species of fern in the lowlands of the Northwest, but these species are often quite common. They are distinguished by the fact that they do not reproduce by seed. Instead, they have two very different life forms, the first associated with the sexual phase of their life cycle, where they exist as a barely visible lettuce-leaf-like plant that lives on moist soil; and the second more prominent nonsexual phase, which we recognize as ferns. The fern plant is usually seen as a large, erect cluster of compound leaves or *fronds* that arise either in clumps from an erect stem-like rhizome or singly from creeping rhizomes. A *pinna* is the primary segment of a frond which is equivalent to a leaflet, or in some cases represents a branch of many leaflets. *Spores* (nonsexual reproductive seed-like structures) are usually found on the undersides of the frond pinnae in round or oblong *spore sacs*. Spore sacs are occasionally held in round or oblong clumps or *sori*, which are normally covered by a membrane or hood-like flap called an *indusium*. One of our species, deer fern *(Blechnum spicant)*, has *dimorphic* fronds, which means there are separate fertile fronds which produce spores and other infertile fronds which lack spores. Young fronds emerge from the rhizome as a tightly curled *fiddlehead* which slowly unfolds into a mature frond. Fiddleheads should not be eaten as many species found in the Northwest potentially cause cancer. There is one species of aquatic fern, Pacific water-fern *(Azolla filicilloides)*, which is found floating on water as a small cluster of highly dissected leaves.

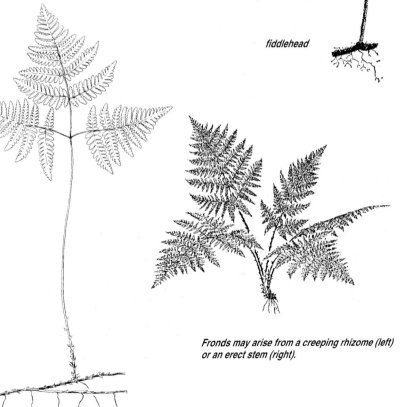

fiddlehead

Fronds may arise from a creeping rhizome (left) or an erect stem (right).

FERNS

367

Frond Arrangements:

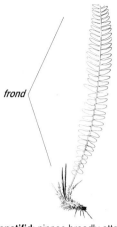

frond

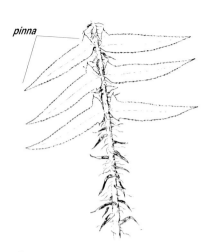

pinna

- **Pinnatifid**: pinnae broadly attached to frond stalk, (deer fern and licorice fern).

- **Once-Pinnately Compound**: pinnae attached to frond stalk by slender stems (sword fern).

- **Twice-Pinnately Compound**: frond once-pinnately compound with the primary segments again once-pinnately compound (lady fern).

- **Thrice-Pinnately Compound**: frond twice-pinnately compound with the secondary segments again once-pinnately compound (spreading wood fern).

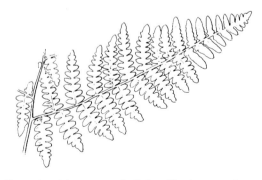

- **Once-pinnately compound with the ultimate segments pinnatifid** (bracken fern and oak fern).

Key to Identifying the Ferns

1a. Fronds pinnatifid to once-pinnately compound...2
1b. Fronds more divided, twice- to thrice-pinnately compound..4

2a. Fronds pinnatifid, the pinnae broadly attached to the frond stem..3
2b. Fronds truly once-pinnately compound, each pinna attached to frond by a slender stalk, or at one point..sword fern *(Polystichum munitum)*

3a. Fronds arising singly from a creeping rhizome, mostly with hairy (scaly and "furry") rhizomes; fronds deciduous, often growing on tree limbs, spore sacs naked (indusium lacking) ....licorice fern *(Polypodium glycyrrhiza)*
3b. Fronds erect, arising from a clump, dimorphic, the evergreen vegetative ones with broad pinnae, the deciduous fertile ones with narrower, more widely spaced pinnae...........................
....deer fern *(Blechnum spicant)*

4a. Fronds with the pinnae pinnatifid; margins rolled over as an indusium; frond stems wiry, brown to black...maidenhair fern *(Adiantum aleuticum)*
4b. Fronds not as above, mostly truly twice- to thrice-pinnately compound; if pinna margin rolled as an indusium, the plants strongly rhizomatous and the thrice-pinnately compound fronds 0.5 m- 3 m tall...5

5a. Fronds arising singly from rhizomes; plants often forming large mats as complete groundcover, or tall fronds dominating herbaceous layer...6
5b. Fronds from an erect stem; plants appearing tufted, or individually clumped..................7

6a. Fronds dark green, rarely over 0.5 m tall, stems thin, wiry, brown to black; plant often blanketing moist forest floors at higher elevations...
....oak fern *(Gymnocarpium dryopteris)*
6b. Fronds often yellow-green, mostly over 1 m tall, often to 3 m tall; stems thick green and grooved; plants common in disturbed and logged lands at various elevations..........
....bracken fern *(Pteridium aquilinum)*

7a. Fronds oval-lance-shaped in outline, the pinnae becoming gradually shorter towards the base, lowermost pinnae smaller than pinnae in the middle of frond; pinnae almost to base; many brown scales along stem..................lady fern *(Athyrium filix-femina)*
7b. Fronds triangular in outline, the lowermost pinnae longer than pinnae in the middle of the frond; stem bare for lower half of its length; sparse brown scales along stem.....
....spreading wood fern *(Dryopteris expansa)*

FERNS

Adiantum aleuticum
(Adiantum pedatum)
maidenhair fern

Family: Adiantaceae
Status: FAC
Color photo page 384

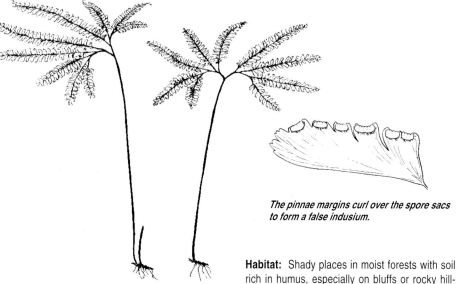

The pinnae margins curl over the spore sacs to form a false indusium.

The lacey fronds of maidenhair fern are palmately branching.

Maidenhair fern is a smooth-surfaced, small to medium-sized fern with delicate, deciduous, palmately branched fronds 20-60 cm tall. A row or clump of few to several fronds may arise from a slender, short-creeping rhizome in a season.

- fronds lacy, twice-pinnately compound, large, fan-shaped, 10-40 cm broad, with dark green pinnae
- frond stalks lustrous, wiry, black or deep reddish brown, erect
- edges of the fronds curling over marginal oblong spore sacs to form a false indusium

Habitat: Shady places in moist forests with soil rich in humus, especially on bluffs or rocky hillsides, or along stream banks and seeps.

Range: Throughout western Washington and Oregon, extending from lowlands to midmontane, occurrence decreasing with elevation. Also from Alaska to Newfoundland, south to California, Utah; also found in eastern North America. Occurs in all counties in our area.

Similar Species: No other similar fern found in western Washington.

Ethnobotanical Uses: The frond stalks have been used for basketry by Native Americans. In Europe, an extract from this fern is used as an ingredient in cough medicine, and is mixed with sugar to make an emetic.

Athyrium filix-femina var. *cyclosorum*
lady fern

Family: Dryopteridaceae
Status: FAC

This common fern is large and deciduous with tightly bunched fronds that are typically 0.5 m long (sometimes to 2 m) and 20-30 cm wide. Fronds arise in tufts from a stout, ascending, and scaly rhizome.

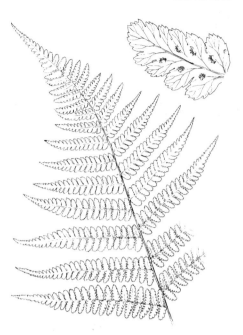

- fronds pale green and delicate, lance-shaped, appearing thrice-pinnately compound because of teething on pinnae, tapering toward tip and base, widest at midsection, with 20-50 pairs of pinnae along entire length of stem
- brown scales common along stem at bottom half
- lowermost pairs of pinnae symmetrical and pointing forward from frond stalk
- indusium crescent-shaped, covering round spore sacs

Habitat: Most typically an understory component of coniferous and deciduous forests and densely shrubbed wetlands where it is often dominant; also grows in saturated soils along stream banks.

Range: Circumboreal; lowland to montane, widespread in suitable habitats throughout western Washington, Oregon, and California. Occurs in all counties in our area.

Lady fern fronds have pinnae with crescent-shaped indusia covering round spore sacs.

Similar Species: Spreading wood fern *(Dryopteris expansa)* has truly twice- to thrice-pinnately compound fronds that are broadly triangular and taper only towards the tip, and the stem is bare at the bottom half of its length with only a few brown scales. The more delicate fronds of lady fern often dry and curl by fall, while those of spreading wood fern feel tough and firm. Oak fern *(Gymnocarpium dryopteris)* is typically much smaller, with fronds that are twice-pinnately compound and broadly triangular.

Ethnobotanical Uses: Lady fern fronds were used by Native Americans for laying out or covering food, and in the spring the fiddleheads were eaten boiled, baked, or raw. (As cautioned in the introduction, some species of ferns are carcinogenic, so fiddleheads of this fern should not be eaten unless identification is certain.) These can be invasive in Northwest gardens.

Fronds are tightly bunched and arise from a stout rhizome.

FERNS

Genus: *Azolla*
water-ferns; mosquito-ferns

Family: Salviniaceae

Status: OBL

Pacific water-fern *(Azolla filiculoides)* and Mexican mosquito-fern *(Azolla mexicana)* are both moss-like aquatic ferns that are found floating on the surface of slow-moving and stagnant water. The roots are inconspicuous, thread-like, and hang down into the water. They have alternate leaves that are minute, unequally bilobed, scale-like, and attached directly to base. Leaves are pinnately branched from a central axis and branched in 2's at the branch tips. The bilobes of the leaves include one larger lobe that floats, and one smaller lobe that is submerged. The upper lobe contains a symbiotic blue-green bacteria. Spore sacs, when present, are shaped like an egg wearing a conical hat, and are borne on the first leaf of a branch.

Azolla filiculoides
Pacific water-fern; fern-like mosquito fern

Color photo page 384

Pacific water-fern is the larger and coarser of the two ferns. Each plant is 2-6 cm across.

- upper leaf lobes 1 mm long, usually blue to bright green
- spore sacs 0.4 mm long, with no line of attachment visible between the conical tip and the bottom of the sac

Pacific water-fern has bilobed, scale-like leaves.

Azolla mexicana
Mexican mosquito-fern

Mexican mosquito-fern is the more common of the two water ferns. It tends to form continuous mats on the water's surface, with each plant less than 2 cm across. The leaves are very small.

- upper leaf lobes less than 1 mm long, reddish purple with green edges
- spore sacs 0.2-0.3 mm long, with flap-like line of attachment visible between the conical tip and the bottom of the pitted surface of the sac

Habitat: Aquatic; occurs in slow-moving and stagnant water.

Range: Throughout most of the coastal states in the United States and in central and southern South America. These species occur in all counties in our area.

Similar Species: Small duckweed *(Lemna minor)* often grows in the same habitats, but consists only of a pair of flat, bright green, floating leaves to 1.5 mm long. Different-leaved water-starwort *(Callitriche heterophylla)* also grows in the same habitat, but has single, irregularly shaped, 2-4 cm long leaves arranged along a long stem, and conspicuous roots hanging down into the water. It is often found rooted in saturated soil.

Functional Value: Good forage for aquatic insects; also useful for filtering and uptake of toxicants in drainage swales.

Blechnum spicant
deer fern

Family: Blechnaceae
Status: FAC+
Color photos page 384

Deer fern is a common evergreen fern that is medium-sized and tufted. The woody and erect rhizomes are short, creeping, and have abundant chestnut-colored scales. As mentioned in the fern introduction, it is our only species with dimorphic fronds. The sterile evergreen fronds arise in a spreading rosette and are linear, sword-like in outline, to 100 cm long and 9 cm wide, with 35-80 pairs of leaflets. The less numerous deciduous fertile fronds appear in summer and are erect, to 125 cm long, pinnae not more than 2 mm wide.

* fronds pinnatifid with rounded pinnae tips, tapering both towards the tip and the base, dark green
* spore sacs continuous, extending entire length of pinnae parallel to midveins; indusium a flap along the margin of the frond segment; whole fertile leaflet often rolled into a cylinder around spore sac clusters

Habitat: Mossy hummocks in moist to wet places in conifer or alder forests, typically in heavy shade.

Range: Interruptedly circumboreal; Alaska to California, west of the Cascades in our area. From near sea level to midmontane. Widespread in suitable habitats throughout western Washington and Oregon.

Similar Species: Deer fern is most easily confused with the extremely common sword fern *(Polystichum munitum)*, but the fronds of the sword fern are much larger, once-pinnately compound, wider at the base, have sharply toothed pinnae margins, and are not dimorphic. Licorice fern *(Polypodium glycyrrhiza)* is the only other fern in the Pacific Northwest with pinnatifid fronds; however, the fronds of the almost exclusively epiphytic licorice fern arise from long-creeping, long-scaly (hairy) rhizomes, have round, noncontinuous spore sacs, and are not dimorphic.

Functional Value: Important winter food for deer and elk.

Ethnobotanical Use: The young tender leaves of deer fern were used as a hunger suppressant by hunting parties of some Northwest Native American tribes. The leaves have also been used as a medicine for skin sores.

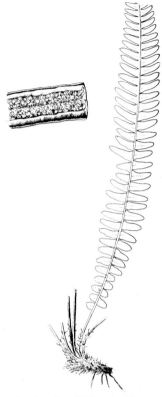

Deer fern has pinnatifid fronds with continuous spore sacs.

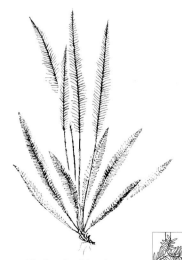

The fronds of deer fern are dimorphic.

FERNS

373

Dryopteris expansa
(Dryopteris austriaca)
spreading wood fern

Family: Dryopteridaceae

Status: FACU

Color photo page 384

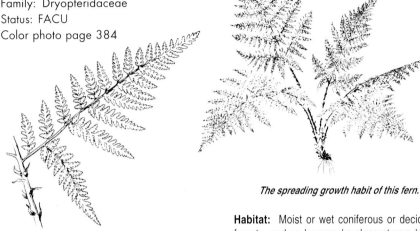

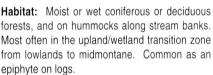

The spreading growth habit of this fern.

Spreading wood fern fronds are thrice-pinnately compound and have pinnae with horseshoe-shaped indusia.

Spreading wood fern is a common, medium to large, tufted fern. The spreading fronds may be deciduous, but remain tough and firm in fall. Fronds are usually 20-50 cm long (sometimes to 1 m tall), and generally 1/2-2/3 as wide. They arise from a stout rhizome that is erect or ascending, and covered in brown scales.

- fronds broadly triangular and erect, essentially thrice-pinnately compound, tapering only toward tip, bottom half of stem bare with a few scattered brown scales
- pinnae 5-25 pairs; lowest pinnae broadly oval to triangular, noticeably asymmetrical, with prominent teeth
- indusium horseshoe-shaped, covering round spore sacs

Habitat: Moist or wet coniferous or deciduous forests, and on hummocks along stream banks. Most often in the upland/wetland transition zone from lowlands to midmontane. Common as an epiphyte on logs.

Range: Circumboreal; southern Alaska to Newfoundland, south to California, northern Idaho, northwestern Montana, New England, and the mountains of North Carolina and Tennessee. Widespread in suitable lowland to midmontane habitats throughout western Washington and Oregon. Occurs in all counties in our area.

Similar Species: Lady fern *(Athyrium filix-femina)*, also has fronds that are typically twice-pinnately compound (or appear thrice-pinnately compound), but are lance-shaped, tapering towards the tip and the base, with the lowest pinnae symmetrical and pointed forward from the stalk, and has prominent brown scales at the base of the stem. In addition, the fronds of lady fern are much more delicate and fragile. Oak fern *(Gymnocarpium dryopteris)* also has fronds that are twice- to thrice-pinnately compound and triangular with asymmetrical lower pinnae, but they are typically smaller and lack the horseshoe-shaped indusium. Oak fern is also rhizomatous, but tends to form a continuous herbaceous carpet of even-sized, delicate fronds in deep, midelevation coniferous forests. Bracken fern *(Pteridium aquilinum)* also has deciduous fronds that are broadly triangular and woody, but they are typically much larger and have pinnae edges that tend to curl in; the spore sacs, when present, are continuous along the edge of the pinnae.

Gymnocarpium dryopteris var. *disjunctum*
oak fern

Family: Dryopteridaceae
Status: FAC
Color photo page 384

Oak fern is a common, medium-sized fern with delicate, deciduous fronds to 40 cm tall. It often forms a mat of herbaceous cover in forests. Frond stalks are thin, dark, and wiry. Slender rhizomes bear thin, pale brown scales.

- fronds dark green, twice- to thrice-pinnately compound (appear as three terminal compound fronds), broadly triangular, with the two lateral pinnae shorter than the central one, and the lowest pinnae noticeably asymmetrical
- fronds with up to 20 pairs of leaflets, the ultimate segments round-toothed
- spore sacs small, circular, arranged in two rows on lower leaflets; indusia lacking

Habitat: On hummocks and over stumps or logs in moist or wet forests, along stream banks, and on shady rocky slopes and wet cliffs. It forms carpets under dense, shady conifers. Most common in midelevations.

Range: Circumboreal; southern Alaska to Newfoundland, south to Oregon, the mountains of eastern Arizona and New Mexico, northern Kansas, Iowa, Pennsylvania, West Virginia, and Virginia. Widespread in suitable habitats throughout Washington and northern Oregon. Occurs in all counties in our area.

Similar Species: Most easily confused with spreading wood fern *(Dryopteris expansa)*, also a deciduous fern that has broadly triangular fronds with the lowest pinnae noticeably asymmetrical; however, the fronds of the spreading wood fern are tufted, do not appear as three terminal compound fronds, and have spore sacs woth horseshoe-shaped indusia. Lady fern *(Athyrium filix-femina)* has fronds that are widest in the middle and taper to both the tip and base. Bracken fern *(Pteridium aquilinum)* also has triangular fronds, but frond stalks are very tall (to 2 m), woody, and thick.

Functional Value: Forms dense herbaceous stands useful as a cover for forest wildlife.

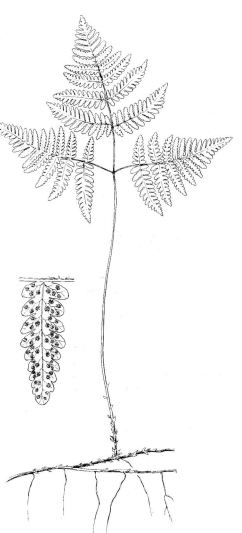

Oak fern fronds are twice- to thrice-pinnately compound with the ultimate segments pinnatifid; spore sacs are small and circular.

FERNS

375

Polypodium glycyrrhiza
licorice fern

Family: Polypodiaceae
Status: Not listed (facu)
Color photo page 385

The pinnatifid fronds of licorice fern have pinnae with round sori. These ferns are evergreen and epiphytic.

Habitat: Epiphytic in moss on trees, and on logs and rock faces; most often found in the branch notches of big-leaf maple *(Acer macrophyllum)*. Light- intolerant, this species grows best in shade.

Range: Coastal, but not maritime, inland to the base of the western Cascade Mountains, and in the Columbia Gorge; from Kamtchatka and the Aleutian islands to southern Alaska, and south to California. Occurs in all counties in our area.

Similar Species: The fronds of sword fern *(Polystichum munitum)* are once pinnately-compound, larger (to 1.5 m long), have pinnae with sharply toothed margins, and spore sacs that are smaller and aligned in two rows parallel to the pinna midvein. Sword fern grows in soil in dry forest understories, or on mounds or stumps in wetlands. Deer fern *(Blechnum spicant)* also has pinnatifid evergreen fronds, but the segment tips are more rounded than those of licorice fern, it is dimorphic, tufted, and is not epiphytic.

Licorice fern is a small to medium-sized, usually epiphytic evergreen fern. Fronds are persistent, to 70 cm long, and have smooth-margined pinnae that cut deeply to the stem; the largest pinnae is 15-50 cm long and 5-20 cm wide. Spore sacs are held in round sori and borne at the ends of each pinnae vein. Indusia are lacking.

- fronds thin, bright green, pinnatifid; bases of pinnae broadly attached to stem
- leaflets to 3 cm with rounded tips
- rhizomes/stolons licorice-flavored, long, thick, succulent, with red-brown scales
- imprints of the sori visible as bumps on the upper surface of the frond

Ethnobotanical Uses: Licorice-flavored rhizomes were used for flavoring, as a candy, and as an important medicine for colds and sore throats by Native Northwest Americans. Settlers used the dried rhizomes in smoking mixtures.

Polystichum munitum
sword fern

Family: Dryopteridaceae
Status: FACU
Color photo page 385

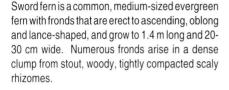

Sword fern is a common, medium-sized evergreen fern with fronds that are erect to ascending, oblong and lance-shaped, and grow to 1.4 m long and 20-30 cm wide. Numerous fronds arise in a dense clump from stout, woody, tightly compacted scaly rhizomes.

- fronds leathery, wider at the base, once-pinnately compound, with pinnae attached to frond stalk by slender stalk, and having a thumb-like appendage on lower edge near stem
- pinnae alternate, pointed, terminating in a slender spine, with strongly sharp-toothed margins; pinnae arranged along the entire length of frond stalk
- spore sacs continuous, extending the entire length of the pinna in two rows parallel to the pinna midvein; indusium round and umbrella-like, attached in the center and covering the spore sacs
- fronds shed copious spores as clouds of dust in late July and August

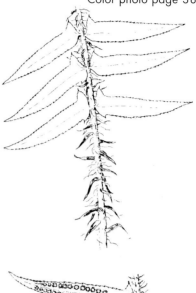

Habitat: Wetlands, forested transition zones, and uplands; most often occurs on hummocks, downed logs, or other places where it is not subjected to extremely wet conditions. Associates include salal *(Gaultheria shallon)*.

The once-pinnately compound fronds of sword fern have pinnae with continuous spore sacs.

Range: Native to western North America and Eurasia; interruptedly circumboreal. Sword fern is common in the Pacific Northwest from Alaska south to California. From near sea level to midmontane. Occurs in all counties in our area.

Similar Species: Of the ferns described in this book, sword fern is the only truly once-pinnately compound fern in our area. Licorice fern *(Polypodium glycyrrhiza)* and deer fern *(Blechnum spicant)* have pinnatifid fronds and are much smaller and the pinnae are attached to the frond stem along a broad base.

Sword fern fronds are erect to ascending and evergreen.

Ethnobotanical Use: The young rhizomes have been roasted and used to stave off starvation in the spring. (As cautioned in the introduction, some species of ferns are carcinogenic, so the rhizomes of this fern should not be eaten unless identification is certain and carcinogenic properties known.)

FERNS

Pteridium aquilinum var. *pubescens*
bracken fern

Family: Dennstaedtiaceae (Pteridaceae)
Status: FACU
Color photo page 385

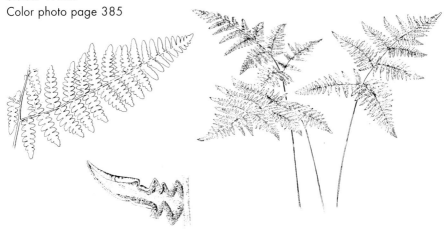

Bracken fern fronds are twice-to thrice-pinnately compound with pinnae that curl over the spore sacs to form a false indusium.

Bracken fern is the most common fern in the world. Large erect fronds emerge singly from thick, branching, woody rhizomes. The fronds are generally 0.5-2 m long, but reputedly up to 5 m tall, thick, wiry, yellow-green, and appear woody. Fronds and rhizomes have hairs, but no scales.

- fronds deciduous, triangular in outline, twice-to thrice-pinnately compound with the ultimate pinnae pinnatifid, appearing as three compound leaves
- pinnae generally hairless above and densely woolly below
- pinnae of terminal segments in 10-20 opposite pairs
- spore sacs continuous along the margins of the outer pinnae; leaf edges curl over them, acting as the indusium

Habitat: All habitats from moist to dry woods, in woodland clearings, along roadsides and open slopes. This is a weedy species preferring disturbed habitats such as avalanche tracks, fire scars, and ski slopes. From low elevations to subalpine. Often found associated with salal *(Gaultheria shallon)* and red huckleberry *(Vaccinium parvifolium)*.

Range: Circumboreal and widely distributed; occurs in North America and Eurasia. Common on both sides of the Cascades. The variety *pubescens* is found in the western United States and Canada.

Similar Species: Spreading wood fern *(Dryopteris expansa)* or oak fern *(Gymnocarpium dryopteris)* also have triangular-shaped fronds. However, spreading wood fern is smaller, nonwoody, tufted, often epiphytic on mossy logs and tree stumps, thrice-pinnately compound, with the last pinnae toothed giving it a 4-pinnate look, and has horseshoe-shaped indusia. Oak fern is also rhizomatous, but fronds rarely exceed 40 cm tall, frond stalks are thin, nonwoody, and black-wiry, and plants tend to form a continuous, herbaceous carpet of even-sized, delicate fronds in deep, midelevation coniferous forests.

Functional Value: Because of its rhizomatous and coarse nature, it can form a dense, almost thicketlike cover for songbirds and small mammals.

Ethnobotanical Uses: The rhizomes, when roasted and peeled, were a source of starch for Native Americans. The fronds were used to wrap fish and as camp bedding. The fronds contain thiaminase, and although the fiddleheads are considered a delicacy in Asia, the raw plants have been known to poison livestock, and are connected with stomach cancer.

Introduction to the Horsetails (genus: *Equisetum*)

Family: Equisetaceae

The horsetails are herbs that grow from underground stems, and have aerial stems that are erect, hollow, segmented, and interlocking. Like ferns, they produce spores, but with the horsetails spores are contained in cones at the tips of the stems. Some species have only one type of stem and are ***monomorphic***, in which case the fertile portion of the stem is located above a sterile stalk. Other species have separate fertile and sterile or vegetative stems, and are called ***dimorphic***. In most dimorphic species, the fertile stems are flesh-colored and branchless, and are produced early in the spring prior to the sterile stems. Horsetail stems often have branches that are whorled, leafless, thin, and jointed, and appear at the nodes between stem segments. Leaves are reduced, darkened, bract-like ***teeth*** atop a ***sheath*** that is also whorled around each joint. Stems are usually impregnated with silicate crystals, which makes them unpalatable to wildlife, but excellent as a scouring implement and was often used as such by the Native Northwest peoples. Most species, unless otherwise noted, occur in all counties throughout our area.

Chart for the Comparison of the Horsetail Species					
species	field horsetail (*E. arvense*)	water horsetail (*E. fluviatale*)	scouring rush (*E. hyemale*)	shady horsetail (*E. pratense*)	giant horsetail (*E. telmateia*)
stem type	dimorphic	monomorphic dimorphic	monomorphic	dimorphic	dimorphic
sterile stem height	15-60 cm	to 100 cm	20-150 cm	20-50 cm	to 300 cm
# ridges per sterile stem	10-12	4-25	15-50	10-18	14-40
stem diameter	1.5-6 mm	1.5-6 mm	4-14 mm	1-3 mm	15-20 mm
sterile sheath length	5-10 mm	4-9 mm	5-15 mm	2-6 mm	10-25 mm
sterile sheath teeth length	1-3 mm	1.5-3 mm	2-4 mm	1-2 mm	3-8 mm
central stem cavity (sterile)	1/2 stem diameter	1/2-4/5 stem diameter	3/4 stem diameter	1/3-1/2 stem diameter	1/3-2/3 stem diameter
fertile stem branched	no	yes	no	yes	no
cone	blunt, hollow, less than 4 cm long	blunt, less than 2 cm long	sharp-pointed, 2.5 cm long	blunt, less than 3 cm long	blunt, hollow, 4-10 cm long
special characters	annual	annual	evergreen, unbranched perennial	annual	annual

FERNS

Equisetum arvense
field horsetail, common horsetail

Status: FAC

Color photo page 385

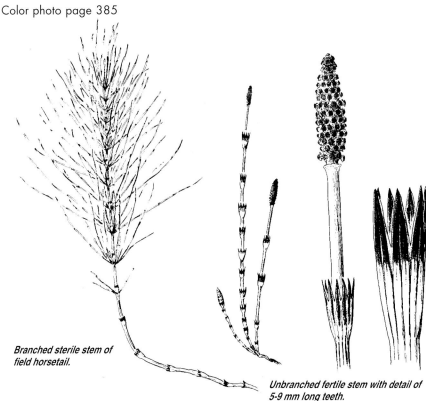

Branched sterile stem of field horsetail.

Unbranched fertile stem with detail of 5-9 mm long teeth.

Field horsetail is the most common of horsetails and can be one of the smallest of the dimorphic species. The size of the sterile stems varies with nutrient availability, but they can grow to 80 cm tall. Colorless fertile stems emerge in the spring, usually as large populations sprouting from damp banks. Rhizomes are creeping, branched, covered with a dark felt-like pubescence, and have tubers at the joints.

- sterile stems green, 15-60 cm, usually narrow, 10- to 12-ridged, with numerous whorled branches at most nodes; central cavity 1/2 diameter of stem (often 0.5-1 cm thick)
- sterile sheath with fewer than 20 (usually 10-12), brown to brownish green teeth
- fertile stems thick, 30 cm tall, tan to white with brown teeth, lacking branches; sheaths 15-20 mm long with teeth 5-9 mm long; cones solid, less than 4 cm long

Habitat: Prefers disturbed areas, such as along roadsides and in sandy, filled lots, but also grows in moist forests to wet meadows from the lowlands to alpine areas.

Similar Species: Shady horsetail *(Equisetum pratense)* has similar, small sterile stems with whorled branches, but fertile stems are persistent, green, and branched, and it is far less common in our area. Giant horsetail *(Equisetum telmateia)* also has colorless, branchless fertile stems that emerge in the spring, but these stems are much thicker and more robust; the sterile stems are 14- to 40-ridged with 20-40 teeth, a hollow, 4-10 cm long cone, and also more robust.

Equisetum fluviatile
water horsetail

Status: OBL
Color photo page 386

Water horsetail is either unbranched, or has a few irregularly branched, monomorphic stems that are weak and easily broken. Rhizomes are creeping, shiny, and reddish to brown.

- stems to 100 cm tall, with 4-25 shallow ridges; central cavity 1/2 to 4/5 diameter of stem
- sheaths green; teeth 1.5-3 mm long, dark brown to black, not transparent-edged
- cones deciduous, blunt

Habitat: Sedge meadows, occurring from the meadow to the edge of water. It is often found in ditches and other shallow water systems from low to moderate elevations.

Similar Species: Marsh horsetail *(Equisetum palustre)*, an uncommon horsetail in our area, also has narrow monomorphic stems, but has a central cavity that is less than 1/3 the diameter of the stem and fewer than 5-10 ridges on the stem. A hybrid of water horsetail and field horsetail *(Equisetum arvense)* is very similar to water horsetail, but has poorly developed cones and a smaller central cavity.

Unbranched and branched dimorphic stems of water horsetail.

Fertile stem topped with a blunt cone.

FERNS

Equisetum hyemale var. affine
scouring-rush, rough horsetail

Status: FACW

Color photo page 386

This is the only common, perennial, evergreen, unbranched species that is monomorphic. Plants occasionally branch at the top node, but only if the cone is broken off. Teeth can be deciduous or persistent. Rhizomes are creeping, slender, dark brown to black, and found deep in the soil.

- stems dark olive green, typically branchless, 20-150 cm tall, 4-14 mm thick, 15- to 50-ridged; central cavity 3/4 diameter of stem
- sheaths ash gray with black bands around the tip and either in the middle or at the base; teeth dark brown to black
- cones sharp-pointed, 2.5 cm long

Habitat: Forested wetlands in large communities, and also along road edges. It is often planted in created wetlands or along drainage swales.

Center, unbranched, evergreen stems of scouring rush, left; fertile cone; right, sheaths with black band and dark teeth.

Similar Species: None.

Equisetum pratense
shady horsetail, meadow horsetail

Status: FACW

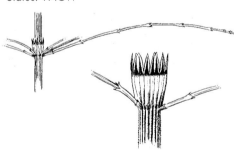

- fertile and sterile stems green to 50 cm tall, 10- to 18-ridged, with side branches ascending, spreading, and 3-angled; central cavity 1/3 to 1/2 diameter of stem
- sterile stem sheaths 2-6 mm long, green, with teeth 1-2 mm long

Habitat: Less disturbed habitats, such as stream banks and moist woods.

Branched sterile stems and toothed sheath of shady horsetail.

Similar Species: Field horsetail *(Equisetum arvense)* has similar sterile stems, but is more common, and has deciduous fertile stems that are tan to white and lack branches.

Shady horsetail is the least common of the dimorphic horsetails. The fertile stems are pale green when new, and later become dark green with whorled branches.

Equisetum telmateia var. *braunii*
giant horsetail
Status: FACW
Color photo page 386

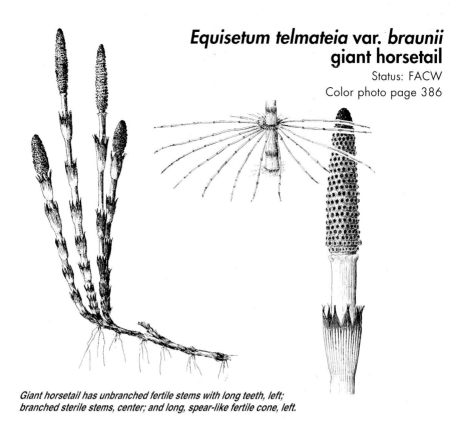

Giant horsetail has unbranched fertile stems with long teeth, left; branched sterile stems, center; and long, spear-like fertile cone, left.

This is the largest of the common dimorphic horsetails. Finger-like fertile stems appear in the spring, usually in large populations on moist banks. Rhizomes are black, covered with felt-like hairs, and may have pear-shaped tubers at the joints.

- sterile stems to 3 m tall, 2 cm thick, 14- to 40-ridged, with side branches horizontal to descending, 4-6 angled; central cavity 2/3 to 3/4 the diameter of the stem
- sterile sheaths 1-2.5 cm long with 14-40 teeth 3-8 mm long, pale below, dark above
- fertile stems 25-60 cm tall, branchless, light yellow, with hollow cones 4-10 cm long
- fertile sheaths 2-5 cm long with 20-30 teeth in groups of 2-4

Habitat: Prefers disturbed areas, such as along roadsides and in sandy, filled lots, but also grows in moist forests to wet meadows from the lowlands to alpine areas.

Similar Species: Field horsetail *(Equisetum arvense)* also has pale, branchless fertile stems but they are much narrower; sterile stems are 10- to 12-ridged, also narrower, and with fewer (less than 20) teeth.

Caution: This horsetail has been known to be poisonous to livestock and humans.

FERNS

383

Azolla filiculoides (Pacific water-fern)
Photo by Sarah Spear Cooke

Adiantum aleuticum (maidenhair fern)
Photo by Clayton Antieau

Blechnum spicant (deer fern)
Photo by Clayton Antieau

Blechnum spicant (deer fern)
Photo by Sarah Spear Cooke

Dryopteris expansa (spreading wood fern)
Photo by Clayton Antieau

Gymnocarpium dryopteris (oak fern)
Photo by Sarah Spear Cooke

Polypodium glycyrrhiza (licorice fern)
Photo by Clayton Antieau

Polystichum munitum (sword fern)
Photo by Sarah Spear Cooke

Pteridium aquilinum (bracken fern)
Photo by Sarah Spear Cooke

Equisetum arvense (field horsetail)
Photo by Sarah Spear Cooke

Equisetum arvense (field horsetail)
Photo by Sarah Spear Cooke

Selected References

Bigley, R.E., And S.W. Hull. 1993. Recognizing Wetlands and Wetland Indicator Plants on Forest Lands. Washington State DNR Forest Land Management Division, Contribution No. 500.

Biotic Consultants. 1992. Western Wetland Flora. Field Office Guide to Plant Species. USDA, Soil Conservation Service. Portland, Oregon.

Brayshaw, T.C. Catkin Bearing Plants of British Columbia. Occasional Paper No. 18, Royal British Columbia Museum, Victoria, British Columbia.

Brayshaw, T.C. 1985. Pondweeds and Bur-reeds, and Their Relatives, of British Columbia. Occasional Paper No. 26, Royal British Columbia Museum, Victoria, British Columbia.

Brayshaw, T.C. 1989. Buttercups, Waterlilies and Their Relatives in British Columbia. Royal British Columbia Museum Memoir No. 1. Royal British Columbia Museum, Victoria, British Columbia.

Buckingham, N.M. 1994. Plant Catalogue Review. in: Anderson, A.R. Plant Life of Washington Territory. Douglasia lOccasional Papers, Vol 5. Washington Native Plant Society, Seattle, Washington.

Christy, J.A. 1993. Classification and Catalogue of Native Wetland Plant Communities in Oregon. Oregon Natural Heritage Program, Portland, Oregon.

Clark, L.J. 1974. Lewis Clark's Field Guide to Wildflowers of Marsh and Waterway. Gray's Publishing Limited, Sidney, British Columbia.

Cowardin, L. M. V. Carter, F. C. Golet, and E. T. LaRue. 1979. Classification of Wetlands and Deepwater Habitats of the United States. FWS/OBS-79/31. U. S. Fish and Wildlife Service.

Creso, I. 1984. Vascular Plants of Western Washington. Irene Creso, Tacoma, Washington.

Davis, R.J. 1952. Flora of Idaho. W.C. Brown Company, Publishers, Dubuque, Iowa.

Douglas, G.W. 1982. The Sunflower Family (Asteraceae) of British Columbia. Volume I - Senecioneae. Occasional paper No. 23, Royal British Columbia Museum, Victoria, British Columbia.

Environmental Laboratory, US Army Corps of Engineers. 1987. Corps of Engineers Wetlands Delineation Manual. U. S. Army Corps of Engineers, Department of the Army, WES, Vicksburg, Mississippi. Technical Report Y-87-1.

Fitter, R., A. Fitter, and A. Farrer. 1984. Collins Pocket Guide to the Grasses, Sedges, Rushes and Ferns of Britain and Northern Europe. Collins. London.

Franklin, J.F., and C.T. Dyrness. 1973. Natural Vegetation of Oregon and Washington. Oregon State University Press. Corvalis, Oregon.

Gunther, E. 1973. Ethnobotany of Western Washington. University of Washington Press, Seattle, Washington.

Hermann, F.J. 1970. Manual of the Carices (sedges) of the Rocky Mountains and Colorado Basin. Agriculture Handbook #374, United States Department of Agriculture.

Hermann, F. J. 1975. Manual of the Rushes (*Juncus* spp.) of the Rocky Mountains and Colorado Basin. United States Department of Agriculture. Forest Service General Technical Report Rm-18.

Hickman, J.C., ed. 1993. The Jepson Manual Higher Plants of California. University of California Press, Berkeley, California.

Hitchcock, C. L., and A. Cronquist. 1973. Flora of the Pacific Northwest. University of Washington Press, Seattle, Washington.

Hitchcock, C. L., A. Cronquist, M. Ownbey, and J. W. Thompson. 1955-69. Vascular Plants of the pacific Northwest. 5 vols. University of Washington Press, Seattle, Washington.

Howell, J.T. 1970. Carex. In P. Munz and D. Keck (eds.) A California Flora. University of California Press, Berkeley.

Hurd, E.G., S. Goodrich, and N.L. Shaw. 1994. Field Guide to Intermountain Rushes. Intermountain Research Station General Technical Report INT-306. United States Forest Service.

Kartesz J. T. 1994. A synonymized checklist of the vascular flora of the United States, Canada, and Greenland. 2nd Ed. 2 Vols. (Checklist and Thesaurus). Timber Press, Portland, Orgon.

Klinka, K., V.J. Krajina, A. Ceska, and A.M. Scagel. 1989. Indicator Plants of Coastal British Columbia. University of British Columbia Press, Vancouver, British Columbia.

Kuhnlein, H.V., and N.J. Turner. 1991. Traditional Plant Foods of Canadian Indigenous Peoples. Nutrition, Botany and Use. Volume 8. In: Food and Nutrition in History and Anthropology, edited by S. Katz. Gordon and Breach Science Publishers, Philadelphia, Pennsylvania.

Kunze, L.M. 1994. Preliminary Classification of Native, Low Elevation, Freshwater Wetland Vegetation in Western Washington. Washington Natural Heritage Program, Washington State DNR, Olympia, Washington.

Lackschewitz, K. 1991. Vascular Plants of West-Central Montana Identification Guidebook. Intermountain Research Station, U.S. Forest Service, U.S.D.A., General Technical Report INT-277.

Larrison, E.J. , G.W. Patrick, W.H. Baker, and J.A. Yaitch. 1974. Washington Wildflowers. Seattle Audubon Society, Seattle, Washington.

Lellinger, David B. and Murray Evans. 1985. A Field Manual of the Ferns and Fern Allies of the United States and Canada. Smithsonian Institution Press, Washington D.C.

Leonard, W.P., H.A. Brown, L.C. Jones, K.R. McAllister, and R.M. Storm. 1993. Amphibians of Washington and Oregon. Seattle Audubon Society, Seattle, Washington.

Lyons, C.P. 1974. Trees, Shrubs, and Flowers to Know in British Columbia. J.M. Dent and Sons, Tornoto, Ontario.

Mason, H. L. 1957. A Flora of the Marshes of California. University of California Press, Berkeley, California.

Mathews, D. 1988. Cascade-Olympic Natural History. Raven Editors and Portland Audubon Society, Portland, Oregon.

Mitsch, W. J. and J. G. Gosselink. 1986 Wetlands. Van Nostrand Reinhold, New York.

Moore, M. 1993. Medicinal Plants of the Pacific Northwest. Red Crane Books, Sante Fe New Mexico.

Munz, P. A. 1964. Shore Wildflowers of California, Oregon and Washington. University of California Press, Berkeley.

Oregon natural heritage Data Base. 1987. Rare, Threatened and Endangered Plants and Animals of Oregon. Portland, Oregon.

Pojar, J, and A. McKinnon. 1994. Plants of the Pacific Northwest Coast: Washington, Oregon, British Columbia and Alaska. B.C. Ministry of Forests and Lone Pine Publishing.

Pritchard, K. 1991. A Field Guide to Wetland Characterization. Washington State University Extension, Seattle, Washington.

Reed, P. 1988. National List of Plant Species that Occur in Wetlands: Northwest Region 9. U.S. Fish and Wildlife Service, Biological Report 88(26.9).

Reed, P. 1993. Addendum to the National List of Plant Species that Occur in Wetlands: Northwest Region 9.

Reese, P.P. and W. Z. Ziegler.1995. Grounds for Gathering. Basketry plants west of the Cascades. Maverick Publications, Inc. Bend. Or.

Robinson, P. 1979. Profiles of Northwest Plants. Food Uses- Medicinal Uses, Legends. Far West Book Service, Portland Oregon.

Sweet, M. 1962. Common Edible and Useful Plants of the West. Naturegraph Company, Healdsburg, CA.

Vitt, D.H., J.E. Marsh, and R.B. Bovey. 1988. Mosses Lichens and Ferns of Northwest North America Lone Pine Publishing, Edmonton, Alberta.

Washington State Natural HeritageProgram. 1993. Endangered, Threatened & Sensitive Vascular Plants of Washington. Washington State Department of Natural Resources. Olympia, Washington.

Glossary

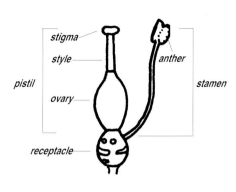

Flower parts

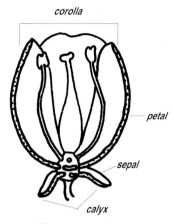

Inflorescence parts

achene: Dry, 1-seeded fruit from a 1-chambered ovary; often appearing to be a naked seed.

aggressive: Growing or spreading rapidly, outcompeting other plants; often difficult to control.

alternate: Arranged singly, often spirally, along an axis (*e.g.*, 1 leaf per node).

annual: A plant that lives for one year or growing season; essentially nonwoody.

anther: Pollen-forming portion of stamen, usually located at the tip of the anther.

asymmetric: An object not divisible into identical or mirror-image halves.

awl-like: Broad-based and tapered to a sharp tip.

alternate

awn: Bristle-like appendage or elongation, usually at tip (see grasses); in the composite family, stiff needle-like pappus element.

axillary: Pertaining to the upper angle (i.e. axil) between axis and branch or appendage (*e.g.*, between stem and leaf, or leaf midrib and secondary veins), or to structures occurring there (*e.g.*, buds, branches, flowers).

basal: At or near base of plant or plant part; especially pertaining to leaves clustered near ground, or to the nutritive tissue at base of an ovary.

berry: Fleshy fruit in which seeds are more than 1 and not encased in a stone.

biennial: A plant that lives for two years or growing seasons; essentially nonwoody, at least above ground.

blade: Flat, expanded portion of a leaf, petal, or other structure.

brackish: Somewhat salty; usually a mixture of marine and fresh water.

bract: Usually small, leaf- or scale-like structure located beneath a branch or stalk; generally associated with an inflorescence.

bristle: Relatively large, usually stiff, more or less straight hair; in the composite family, a fine, usually cylindrical pappus element.

bud: An incompletely developed, unelongated, unexpanded shoot, often over-wintering and protected by bud scales, either at a stem tip or axillary; an unopened flower.

bulb: Short underground stem and the fleshy leaves or leaf bases attached to and surrounding it (*e.g.*, an onion).

calyx (calyces): Outermost or lowermost whorl of flower parts (the sepals collectively); usually green and enclosing the remainder of the flower in the bud; sometimes indistinguishable from the corolla.

capsule: Dry, usually many-seeded fruit from a compound pistil, nearly always dry and irregularly open by pores, slits, or lines of separation.

catkin: Spike of flowers with inconspicuous petals, usually drooping and often with conspicuous bracts.

compound leaf

cyme

ray flower

disk flower

involucre

composite flower head

elliptic leaf

leaf with entire margins

ciliate: With a fringe of marginal hairs.

compound leaf: A leaf divided into distinct parts; in a *simple compound leaf* the blade is divided into first degree leaflets connected by an axis but no blade material (if there is connecting blade material, the leaf is lobed), in a *2-compound leaf* the first degree leaflets are divided again into second degree leaflets (if connecting blade material is present, the first degree leaflets are lobed).

cone: Reproductive structure composed of an axis, scales, and sometimes bracts; nonwoody and producing spores (*e.g.*, clubmosses, horsetails) or pollen (*e.g.*, conifers), usually woody and producing seeds (*e.g.*, most conifers, alders).

corolla: Whorl of flower parts immediately inside or above the calyx (the petals collectively); often large and brightly colored; sometimes indistinguishable from calyx.

cyme: Branched inflorescence in which the central or uppermost flower opens before the peripheral or lowermost on any particular axis.

deciduous: Falling off inherently; usually pertaining to leaves that fall seasonally and all together, or to plants that are seasonally leafless.

disk flower: In the composite family, a flower usually with both male and female part (occasionally all male or sterile), radial (occasionally with left right symmetry but always liguleless) flower with a 5- (rarely 4-) lobed corolla; appearing alone, all disc flowers in a composite head, or with marginal pistillate or ray flowers.

dissected: Irregularly, often sharply, and deeply cut but not necessarily compound; usually pertaining to leaves.

drupe: Fleshy or pulpy, berry-like fruit from the outside wall of a pistil of 1 or more ovary bearing structures in which a single seed is encased in a stone (as in cherries), or more than 1 seed is encased in an equal number of free or fused stones; the tissue is sometimes edible but the stone and contents are usually inedible.

elliptic: In the shape of a flattened circle or ellipse, broadest at the middle and thinning equally in both directions.

emersed: Plant normally rooted underwater and extending above surface, or part of such a plant normally held above surface.

ephemeral: A plant that lives for much less than one year or growing season; essentially nonwoody; pertaining to plant parts that are functional for a short time or fall early.

epidermis: Outermost cell layer (or, rarely, layers) of nonwoody plant parts.

evergreen: Pertaining to leaves that remain green and on the plant for more than one season, and that do not fall all together, or to plants that are never leafless.

exotic: Not native to, but occurring in, an area; introduced plant.

fleshy: Thick and juicy; succulent.

floret: In the grass family, one flower and subtending bracts (in general, palea and subtending lemma).

follicle: Dry, usually many-seeded fruit from a simple pistil, opens by drying on only one side, along a single suture.

fringed: Pertaining to parts with ragged or finely cut margins.

fused: United, as the petals together into a corolla tube or stamens onto petals; not free.

gland: A small, normally spheric body on the epidermis or at the tip of a hair that secretes a usually sticky substance.

habit: Characteristic mode of growth.

head: Dense, often spheric infloresence of flowers attached directly to a base (stalkless).

herb: A plant that, at least above ground, is essentially nonwoody and normally lives less than one year.

hypanthium: A tube, cup, or plate-like structure around the ovary; derived from the fused lower portions of sepals, petals, and stamens and which sits above the ovary, and below the petals.

indusium (indusia): In many ferns, a veil- or scale-like outgrowth of the leaf that covers a sorus.

inflorescence: An entire cluster of flowers and associated structures.

involucre: Groups of bracts more or less held together as a unit, beneath a flower or fruit; any group of structures which surrounds the base of another structure. (See illustration on facing page.)

leaflet: One leaf-like unit of a compound leaf, may be primary, secondary, tertiary *etc.*

legume: Pertaining to the pea family.

lemma: In the grass family, the lower, usually larger of two sheathing bracts beneath a flower, at the base of a floret.

opposite and alternate leaflets

ligulate flower: In the composite family, a flower with right/left symmetry and male and female parts, with the long, outer portion of the corolla (*i.e.*, the ligule) 5-lobed; appears only with other ligulate flowers, in a ligulate head.

ligule: In the composite family, strap-like outer portion of corolla in ligulate and ray flowers; in the grass family and some other grass-like plants, appendage at juncture of leaf sheath and blade, usually with a membranous or fringed margin.

linear: Very narrowly elongate and with nearly parallel sides.

margin: Edge, usually of a leaf or sepals or petals part.

membranous: Thin, pliable, and often somewhat translucent.

native: Occurring naturally in an area, as neither a direct nor indirect consequence of human activity; indigenous; not exotic.

naturalized: Not native (exotic) but now well established with human assistance.

node: Position on an axis (usually a stem) from which one or more structures (especially leaves) arise (see grasses).

oblique: With unequal sides or asymmetrical base.

opposite leaves

obtuse: With a short-tapered, blunt base or tip, the sides converge at greater than 90 degrees.

opposite: Two structures (usually leaves) per node.

ovary: The structure which encloses the eggs of flowering plants; the expanded bottom part of a pistil which contains the eggs (ovules).

ovate: Egg-shaped in outline and for leaves widest below the middle

palea: In the grass family, the upper, usually smaller of two sheathing bracts beneath a flower.

palmate: Radiating from a common point; usually pertaining to veins, lobes, or leaflets of a leaf.

panicle: Branched inflorescence in which the basal or lateral flowers open before the terminal or central flowers on any particular axis.

pappus: In the composite family, structures (*e.g.*, awns, bristles, scales) arising from the top of an inferior ovary, in place of sepals.

palmate

perennial: A plant that lives for more than 2 years.

perigynium: Variously shaped, sac-like structure enclosing the ovary and achene in *Carex.*

persistent: Not falling off; remaining attached.

petal: Individual member of the corolla, whether fused or not; often conspicuously colored.

raceme

rhizome

sheath

spike

pinnate: Usually pertaining to veins, lobes, or leaflets arranged in 2 dimensions along either side of an axis, as the segments along the shaft of a feather; a leaf is odd-pinnate if there is a terminal leaflet or even-pinnate if there is not.

pistil: Female reproductive structure of a flower, composed of an egg containing ovary at the base, one or more pollen-receiving stigmas at the tip, and often one or more styles between.

pistillate: Pertaining to flowers, inflorescences, or plants with fertile pistils but sterile or missing stamens.

prostrate: Lying flat on the ground.

raceme: Unbranched inflorescence in which the flowers are borne on stalks and nearly always open from bottom to top.

rachilla: The axis of a spikelet in the grasses and sedges.

rank: A column of parts of the same orientation along an axis (*e.g.*, leaves on an erect stem that are arranged in four vertical columns are 4-ranked).

ray flower: In the composite family, a flower with right/left symmetry which is generally pistillate or sterile, with the long, outer portion of the corolla (*i.e.* the ligule) often 3-lobed; appearing marginally and only with disk flowers.

receptacle: In individual flowers, the structure to which flower parts are attached; in heads or head-like inflorescences, especially in the composite family, the structure to which flowers or sometimes flowering heads are attached as well.

rhizome: Underground, often elongate, more or less horizontal stem; distinguished from roots by the presence of leaves, leaf scars, scales, buds, *etc.*

rosette: A radiating cluster of leaves usually at or near ground level.

scabrous: rough to the touch, usually due to short stiff hairs.

scale: Broad, flat lying, membranous outgrowth of the outer surface of a leaf, stem or flowering part; structure partially or entirely covering an over-wintering bud (*i.e.*, bud scale).

scar: Mark left by the natural separation of 2 structures, as a leaf scar on a stem.

sepal: An single usually leaf-like structure of the outermost set of leaves, whether fused or not, usually green; member of the calyx

sheath: A often tubular structure which partially or wholly surrounds another structure, such as the leaf blade bases in the grass family.

simple: Composed of a single part; undivided; unbranched.

sorus (sori): In many ferns, a distinct class of sporangia.

spike: Unbranched inflorescence in which the flowers are attached directly to the flower stalk and nearly always open from bottom to the top.

spine: Any sharp-pointed projection, including an outgrowth of the outer covering of a leaf, stem of flowering part ("prickle"), modified leaf or leaf part ("spine"), or modified branch ("thorn").

sporangium (sporangia): In nonseed plants (fern-allies and ferns), a case or container for spores.

stamen: The basic male structure of flowering plants; typically composed of a stalk-like filament and a terminal, pollen-producing anther, but sometimes partially fused to the corolla or to other stamens forming a tube.

stellate: Star-like; pertaining to a hair with 3 or more branches radiating from a common point.

sterile: Pertaining to plants or plant parts that do not produce or are not associated with the production of functional spores, pollen, eggs, or seeds.

stigma: The terminal part of the pistil on which pollen normally germi-nates; usually elevated above the ovary on a style, often lobed, usually sticky or hairy.

Stipules: A pair of basal appendages found on many leaves.

style: The slender stalk that typically connects the stigma(s) and the ovary.

submersed: Plant normally rooted and standing underwater, or part of a plant normally held underwater.

subshrub: A plant with lower stems woody, upper stems less woody and dying back seasonally.

subtend: To occur immediately below, as sepals subtend petals.

superior: An ovary that is attached to the top or center of a receptacle and free of all other floral parts.

tuber: A short, thickened, fleshy, underground stem for storage and sometimes propagation.

compound umbel

umbel: An inflorescence in which 3 to many slender flowering stalks, and, if compound, branches, radiate from a common point, characteristic of but not confined to the umbeliferae family.

unisexual: Pertaining to flowers in which either stamens or pistils, but not both, are fertile.

vernal: Pertaining to springtime; an area inundated only during the early growing season.

weed: A plant that is usually exotic, usually undesired, often aggressive, and often adapted to disturbed places.

whorl: A group of 3 or more structures of the same kind (usually leaves or flower parts) attached at 1 node.

whorl

Index

A

Abies 201
Abies amabilis 104
Acer circinatum 1, 10, 13, 18, 36, 57, 75, 138. *See also* vine maple
Acer glabrum 18
Acer macrophyllum 1, 14, 18. *See also* big-leaf maple
Aceraceae 18, 1
Adiantum aleuticum 384
Agropyron 306
Agropyron repens 328. *See also Elytrigia repens*
Agrostis 199, 306, 308, 315, 338.
Agrostis alba var. *alba* 310. *See also* redtop
Agrostis alba vars. *palustris* 313. *See also* creeping bentgrass
Agrostis capillaris 173, 309, 362. *See also Agrostis tenuis*; slender bentgrass
Agrostis gigantea 310, 362. *See also Agrostis alba* var. *alba*
Agrostis oregonensis 311. *See also* Oregon bentgrass
Agrostis scabra 312. *See also* rough bluegrass
Agrostis stolonifera 308, 313. *See also Agrostis alba* var. *major; Agrostis alba* var. *palustris*
Agrostis tenuis 309. *See also Agrostis capillaris*
Aira 338
Aira caryophyllea 314. *See also* silver European hairgrass
airplanes 4
Alaska blueberry 55. *See also Vaccinium alaskaense*
Alisma 183
Alisma plantago-aquatica 184, 224. *See also* broadleaf water-plaintain
Alisma plantago-aquatica var. *americanum* 184
Alismataceae 183
alkali grass 244. *See also Puccinellia pauciflora; Torreyochloa pauciflora*
Alnus rubra 2, 3, 8, 10, 14, 19, 22, 23, 48, 87, 138. *See also* red alder
Alnus sinuata 2
Alopecurus 247, 306, 315
Alopecurus aequalis 308, 363. *See also* short-awn foxtail
Alopecurus aequalis var. *aequalis* 315
Alopecurus geniculatus 183, 308, 363. *See also* water foxtail
Alopecurus geniculatus var. *geniculatus* 316
Alopecurus pratensis 317, 328, 344, 363. *See also* meadow foxtail

ambiguous owl clover 152. *See also Orthocarpus castillejoides*
Amelanchier alnifolia 19, 34, 48, 75. *See also Elymus mollis*
American beachgrass 318. *See also Elymus mollis*
American brooklime 145, 216, 238, 242, 298. *See also Veronica americana*
American bugleweed 136, 230. *See also Lycopus americanus*
American dunegrass 250, 318, 327, 364. *See also Elymus mollis*
American mountain ash 52. *See also Sorbus americana*
American searocket 96, 123, 225. *See also Cakile edentula*
American sloughgrass 320, 326, 363. *See also Beckmannia syzigachne*
American speedwell 216. *See also Veronica americana*
American tapegrass 215. *See also Vallisneria americana*
American threesquare 297. *See also Scirpus americanus*
American water-plantain 184. *See also Alisma plantago-aquatica*
American wild-celery 215. *See also Vallisneria americana*
Ammophila 306
Ammophila arenaria 318, 327
Ammophila breviligulata 318. *See also* American beachgrass
amphibians *175*
Andromeda polifolia 20, 27, 37. *See also* bog rosemary
Angelica 102, 105, 151
Angelica arguta 87. *See also* sharptooth angelica
Angelica genuflexa 87, 88, 224. *See also* sharptooth angelica
Angelica hendersonii 88. *See also* Henderson's angelica
Angelica lucida 87, 88. *See also* seawatch angelica
annual bluegrass 346, 347. *See also Poa annua*
Anthoxanthum 306
Anthoxanthum odoratum 319, 363. *See also* sweet vernalgrass
Apiaceae 87, 88, 102, 105, 124, 133, 151, 189
aquatic insects 175

curly dock 177. *See also Rumex crispus*

currant 6, 49

curvepod yellow cress 176. *See also Rorippa curvisiliqua*

Cuscuta salina 185, 226. *See also* salt-marsh dodder

Cuscuta salina var. *major* 109

Cuscutaceae 109

cut-leaf blackberry 46. *See also Rubus laciniatus*

cutleaved water horehound 136. *See also Lycopus americanus*

Cyanophyta 182

Cynodon dactylon 325, 342. *See also* Bermuda grass

Cyperus strigosus 288. *See also* strawcolor flatsedge

D

Dactylis glomerata 323, 343, 364. *See also* orchardgrass

daggerleaf rush 241, 247, 248, 251, 253, 356. *See also Juncus ensifolius*

Dallis grass 342

dandelion 128

Daucus carota 105

death camas 99. *See also Zigadenus venenosus*

deer 18, 21, 23, 25, 28, 29, 54, 57, 58, 60, 149

deer fern 259, 384. *See also Blechnum spicant*

deer-cabbage 98, 113. *See also Fauria cristagalli*

dense sedge 262, 271, 287. *See also Carex densa*

Deschampsia 338

Deschampsia cespitosa 88, 121, 152, 168, 199, 244, 246, 271, 324, 332, 350, 351. *See also* tufted hairgrass

Deschampsia elongata 324

devil's club 12, 35, 41, 78. *See also Oplopanax horridus*

dewberry 50. *See also Rubus ursinus*

Dewey sedge 263, 272, 273. *See also Carex deweyana*

diapers 12

Dicentra formosa 107. *See also* bleeding heart

different leaved water-chickweed 97

different leaved water-starwort 97, 132, 196, 225. *See also Callitriche heterophylla*

different-leaved wort 97. *See also Callitriche heterophylla*

Digitaria 320, 342. *See also* crabgrass

Disporum 201

Distichlis 185, 307

Distichlis spicata 91, 96, 121, 131, 157, 244, 246, 322, 333, 350, 364. *See also* seashore saltgrass

Distichlis spicata var. *spicata* 325

ditch-grass 182. *See also Ruppia maritima*

docks 177

door frames 6

doorweed 160. *See also Polygonum aviculare*

Douglas aster 90, 224. *See also Aster subspicatus*

Douglas fir 6, 29. *See also Pseudotsuga menziesii*

Douglas' hawthorn 24. *See also Crataegus douglasii*

Douglas' maple 18. *See also Acer glabrum*

Douglas spirea 8, 33, 49, 54, 82, 189. *See also Spiraea douglasii*

Douglas' squirrels 1

Douglas' water hemlock 102. *See also Cicuta douglasii*

Douglas-fir 1, 13, 140. *See also Pseudotsuga menziesii*

Draba 175

Drosera anglica 110

Drosera rotundifolia 227

Drosera rotundifolia var. *rotundifolia* 110. *See also* sundew

Droseraceae 110

Dryopteris expansa 259, 384. *See also* spreading wood fern

duckmeat 196

ducks 95, 342

duckweed 97, 290. *See also Lemna minor*

Dulichium arundinaceum 289, 360. *See also* dulichium

dune willow 70. *See also Salix piperi*

dusky willow 65. *See also Salix exigua*

dwarf dogwood 106. *See also Cornus unalaschkensis*

dwarf eelgrass 222, 238. *See also Zostera nana*

dwarf mistletoe 5. *See also Arceuthobium americanum*

dwarf Oregon grape 29. *See also Mahonia nervosa*

dwarf tundra birch 21. *See also Betula glandulosa*

dye 2, 19, 23, 29, 35, 55, 58, 152

eelgrass 182, 222, 238. *See also Zostera marina*

E

Echinochloa crusgalli 320, 326. *See also* large barnyard grass

Eleocharis 290, 298. *See also* spikerushes

Eleocharis acicularis 360

Contributors

Sarah Spear Cooke

Nancy Pascoe

Tom Duebendorfer

Scott Clay-Poole

Fred Weinmann

Rick Pratt

Jon and Priscilla Titus

Scott Moore

Ron Vanbianchi

Mary Fries

Scot Sundberg

Dyanne Sheldon

Richard Robohm

Binda Colebrook

Clayton Antieau

Catherine Conolly

Marty Chaney

Ken Brunner

Laura Potash

Jamie Hartley

Camera Shy:
Kathleen Sayce
Sharon Walton
Stacey Wenger
Sharon Rodman
Peter Zika

417